Macmillan/McGraw-Hill Reading

Students with print disabilities may be eligible to obtain an accessible, audio version of the pupil edition of this textbook. Please call Recording for the Blind & Dyslexic at 1-800-221-4792 for complete information.

Macmillan/McGraw-Hill

A Division of The ***McGraw·Hill*** *Companies*

Published by Macmillan/McGraw-Hill, a division of The McGraw-Hill Companies, Inc., Two Penn Plaza, NY, NY 10121

Printed in the United States of America

ISBN 0-02-190166-X/K-1

2 3 4 5 6 7 8 9 073/043 05 04 03 02

Table of Contents

Rhyming

OBJECTIVES

Identify children's knowledge of recognizing rhyming words.

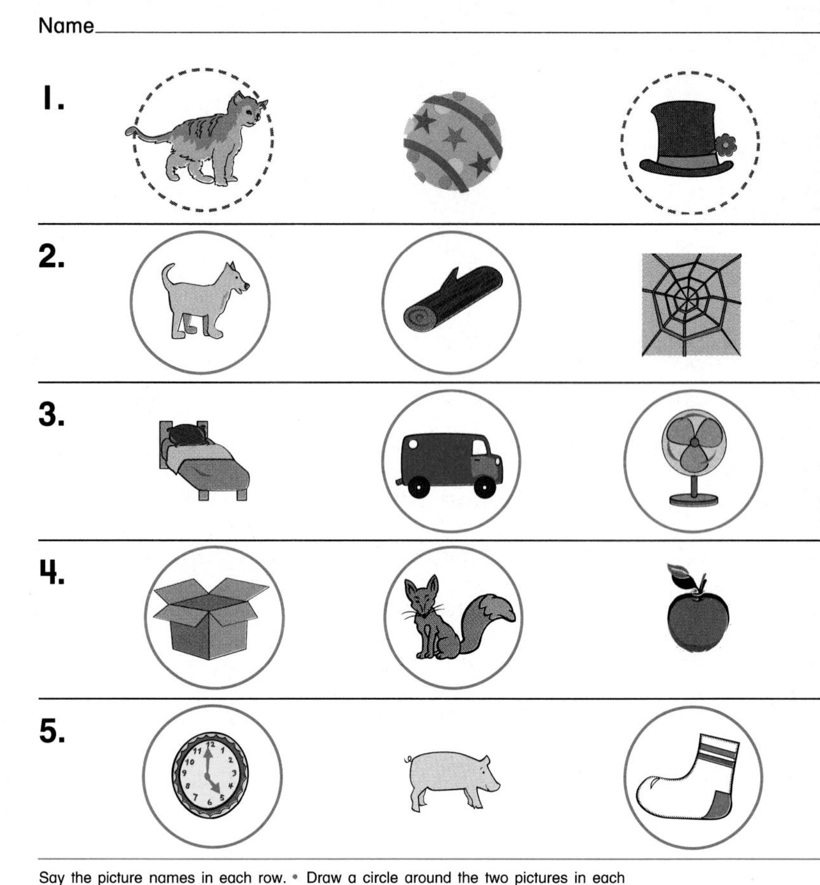
Name

1.

2.

3.

4.

5.

Say the picture names in each row. • Draw a circle around the two pictures in each row that rhyme.

PRETEST Phonological Awareness 5

PREPARE

RECOGNIZE RHYMING WORDS Use this page diagnostically to determine which children need instruction in identifying words that rhyme. You can also use the page as a review at the end of the program to determine what children have learned.

WARM UP Tell children that rhyming words have the same ending sounds. Have children repeat these rhyming words after you: *new, shoe.* Then play a guessing game using rhyming words. Say, for example, *Listen to these words:* cat, log, bat. *Which two words rhyme?* After children guess the correct answer, have children say the words *bat* and *cat* with you.

ASSESS

COMPLETE THE PUPIL PAGE Before children begin the page, read the directions aloud. Complete the first item together, guiding children through the steps and identifying the pictures. Have children do the remaining items on their own but identify the pictures for them as they work.

CLOSE

IDENTIFY RHYMING WORDS Use page 5 to assess children's knowledge of rhyming words. Use the results to determine which lessons to teach.

Name

1.

2.

3.

4.

5.

6.

Say the picture name slowly. • Say the word again and count the number of word parts or syllables. • Draw the number of lines to show the number of word parts.

6 PRETEST Phonological Awareness

Syllables

OBJECTIVES

Identify children's knowledge of identifying syllables.

PREPARE

IDENTIFYING SYLLABLES This page is useful as a diagnostic tool to determine which children need instruction in how to identify word parts or syllables. At the end of the program, you may want to use the page as a review to determine what children have learned.

WARM UP Hold up a classroom object and have children clap the number of word parts in the name of the object. Objects might include a pencil, eraser, book, marker, or block. Slowly name the object and clap to emphasize the word parts. For example, say *pen-cil* and clap two times. Then say the word slowly again and invite the class to clap for each word part they hear.

ASSESS

COMPLETE THE PUPIL PAGE Read the directions aloud and guide children through the first item. Identify the picture for children. Then tell children to make the number of marks that match the number of parts in the word. Name the remaining pictures, having children complete the items independently.

CLOSE

IDENTIFY SYLLABLES Use page 6 to assess children's ability to identify syllables. Use the results to determine which lessons to teach.

LANGUAGE SUPPORT

Children may need additional support while counting word parts. Have children practice identifying word parts by giving them blocks for each word part. For example, say: *The word* rainbow *has two word parts. Rain is the first part.* Display one block. *Bow is the second part.* Place a second block next to the first block. Explain that there are two word parts in the word *rainbow.* Repeat with other two-syllable words.

Beginning Sounds

OBJECTIVES

Identify children's knowledge of identifying initial sounds.

PREPARE

IDENTIFYING BEGINNING SOUNDS Use this page diagnostically to determine which children need instruction in beginning sounds. To determine what children have learned, you may want to have children complete the page again at the end of the program.

WARM UP Give children riddles to answer that require identifying beginning sounds. Use the name of a child in a sentence such as: *What does Matt like?* Challenge children to name an object that begins with the same sound as the child's name and use the answer in a sentence such as: *Matt likes monkeys.*

ASSESS

COMPLETE THE PUPIL PAGE After reading the directions aloud, help children identify the beginning sounds of the first three pictures. Help children decide which two pictures begin with the same sound. Have children complete the remaining items on their own, identifying the pictures for them as they work.

CLOSE

IDENTIFYING BEGINNING SOUNDS Use page 7 to assess children's knowledge of identifying beginning sounds. Use the results to determine which lessons to teach.

Name____________________

1.

2.

3.

4.

5.

Say the picture names in each row. • Draw a circle around the two pictures in each row that have the same beginning sound.

PRETEST Phonological Awareness 7

LANGUAGE SUPPORT

Hold up the following Phonics Picture Posters one at a time: *nest, dog, seal, monkey, turtle, cat*. Say the initial sound and then the picture name. For example, say /n/: *nest*. Have children repeat after you. Show children how to form their mouth for each sound.

Name________________________

1.

2.

3.

4.

5.

6.

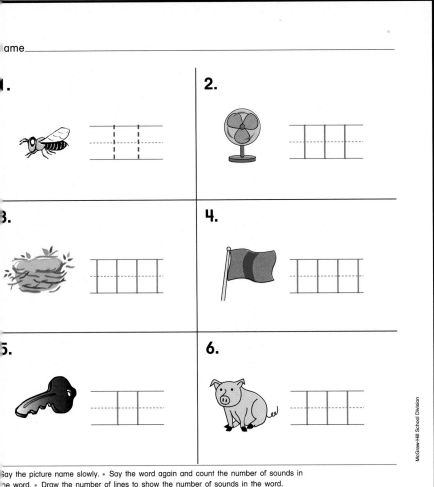

Say the picture name slowly. • Say the word again and count the number of sounds in the word. • Draw the number of lines to show the number of sounds in the word.

Counting Sounds

Identify children's knowledge of counting the number of sounds in one- to four-sound words.

PREPARE

COUNTING SOUNDS This page can help you determine which children need instruction in identifying sounds in a word. You may wish to use the page as a post-test at the end of the program.

WARM UP Say aloud a child's name with three sounds. Then, say the name again slowly emphasizing each separate sound. For example, say *Pat, /p/ /a/ /t/.* Invite children to echo the sounds of the name. Tell children the name *Pat* has three sounds. Have children count the sounds on their fingers as they say them with you.

ASSESS

COMPLETE THE PUPIL PAGE Read the directions aloud and identify the picture in the first item. Then, say the word again slowly, emphasizing each separate sound. Guide children in counting the number of sounds they hear and making that number of marks on the line. Name each of the remaining pictures.

CLOSE

IDENTIFY SOUNDS Use page 8 to assess children's ability to recognize separate sounds in words. Use the results to determine which lessons to teach.

Sound/Symbol Relationships

Identify children's knowledge of sound/symbol relationships for initial consonants and vowels.

PREPARE

BEGINNING SOUNDS AND LETTERS Use this page diagnostically to determine which beginning sounds and letters to focus on in this program and which children need instruction in these skills. You can also use the page as a review at the end of the program to determine what children have learned.

WARM UP Play a guessing game with children, using beginning consonant and vowel sounds. Say, for example: *I'm thinking of a fruit whose name begins with /b/. What am I thinking of?* (banana) After children guess the correct answer, write the letters *b* and *m* on the chalkboard and have a volunteer circle the letter that stands for /b/. Repeat with other words and sounds.

ASSESS

COMPLETE THE PUPIL PAGE Before children begin the page, read the directions aloud. Complete the first item together, guiding children through the steps and identifying the pictures. Have children do the remaining items on their own but identify the pictures for them as they work.

CLOSE

IDENTIFY SOUND/SYMBOL RELATIONSHIPS Use page 9 to assess with which initial sounds and letters children may be having difficulty. Use the results to determine which pupil pages to teach.

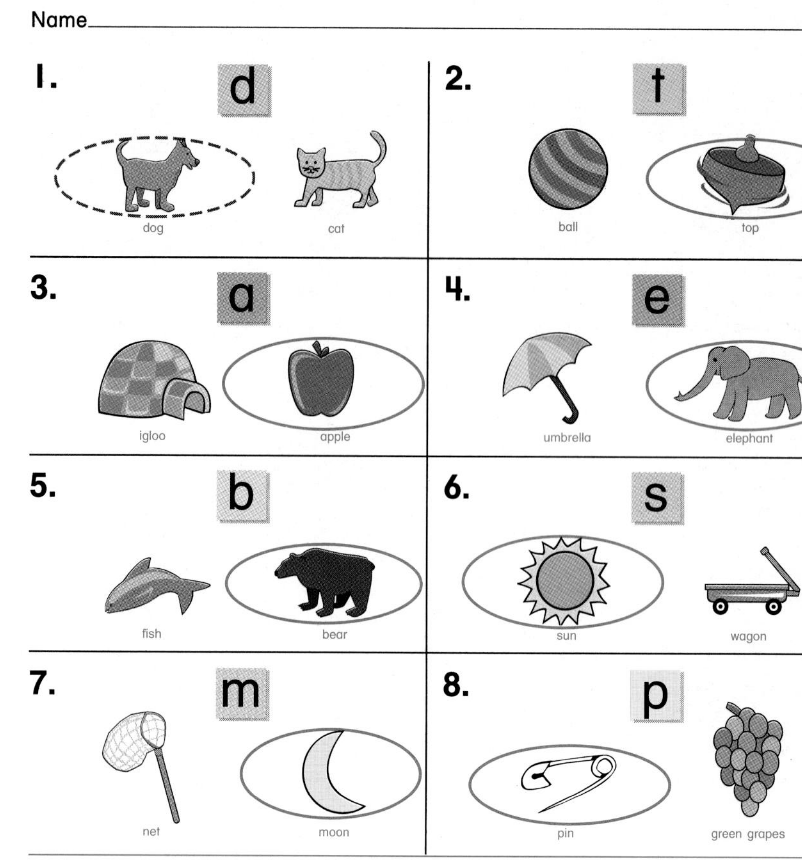

Name__________

1. d — dog, cat
2. t — ball, top
3. a — igloo, apple
4. e — umbrella, elephant
5. b — fish, bear
6. s — sun, wagon
7. m — net, moon
8. p — pin, green grapes

Look at the letter. • Say the sound it stands for. • Say the picture names. • Circle the picture whose name begins with the sound that letter stands for.

PRETEST Phonics: Sound/Symbol Relationships 9

Name

1. fan n	2. bed d	3. ham m
4. hat t	5. cap p	6. sock ck
7. log g	8. web b	9. six x

Say each picture name. • What sound does each picture name end with? • Write the letters that stand for the sound.

Sound/Symbol Relationships

Identify children's knowledge of sound/symbol relationships of final consonants.

PREPARE

ENDING SOUNDS AND LETTERS This page is useful as a diagnostic tool to determine which ending sounds and letters to focus on in this program and which children need instruction in these skills. At the end of the program, you may want to use the page as a review to determine what children have learned.

WARM UP Hold up two classroom objects that end with different consonant sounds and have children identify the object that ends with the sound you say. Choose from these sounds: /n/, /d/, /m/, /t/, /p/, /k/, /g/, /b/, /ks/. Objects might include a *pen*, *bead*, *drum*, *coat*, *soap*, *tack*, *peg*, *toy bear cub*, and *box*. Name each object. For example, hold up the pen and bead and ask: *Which ends with /d/, pen or bead?* Then invite a volunteer to write the letter that stands for /d/ on the chalkboard.

ASSESS

COMPLETE THE PUPIL PAGE Read the directions aloud and guide children through the first item. Identify the picture for children. Name the remaining pictures, having children complete the items independently.

CLOSE

IDENTIFY SOUND/SYMBOL RELATIONSHIPS Use page 10 to assess with which ending consonant sounds and letters children may be having difficulty. Use the results to determine which pupil pages to teach.

LANGUAGE SUPPORT

Write the letters *d*, *t*, *a*, *e*, *b*, *s*, *m* and *p* on the chalkboard. Have each letter identified. Then point to a letter in random order and say a word that begins with that sound/letter. Invite volunteers to think of other words that begin with that letter and sound. Continue with all the letters.

Then invite children to name words that rhyme with *fan*, *bed*, *hat*, *ham*, *cap*, *sock*, *log*, *web*, and *six*.

Blending

OBJECTIVES

Identify children's knowledge of blending and reading CVC words.

PREPARE

BLENDING TO READ WORDS Use this page diagnostically to determine which children need instruction in short vowels and blending and which vowel sounds and letters to focus on in this program. To determine what children have learned, you may want to have children complete the page again at the end of the program.

WARM UP Give children riddles to answer that require blending consonant sounds with short vowel sounds. When children say the correct answer, write the word on the chalkboard and read it aloud. For example: *You wear me on your head. I'm a /h/-/a/-/t/. What am I?* (hat) *I'm not cold. I'm /h/-/o/-/t/. What am I?* (hot) *I do this with a baseball bat. I /h/-/i/-/t/. What do I do?* (hit) *I'm a house made of grass. I'm a /h/-/u/-/t/. What am I?* (hut)

ASSESS

COMPLETE THE PUPIL PAGE After reading the directions aloud, help children blend the sounds of the first word, /k/-/a/-/t/, *cat*. Identify the pictures, *gift* and *cat*, for children. Have children complete the remaining items on their own, identifying the pictures for them as they work.

CLOSE

IDENTIFY BLENDING SOUNDS Use page 11 to assess children's knowledge of short vowel sounds and children's ability to read words by blending sounds. Use the results to determine which pupil pages to focus on.

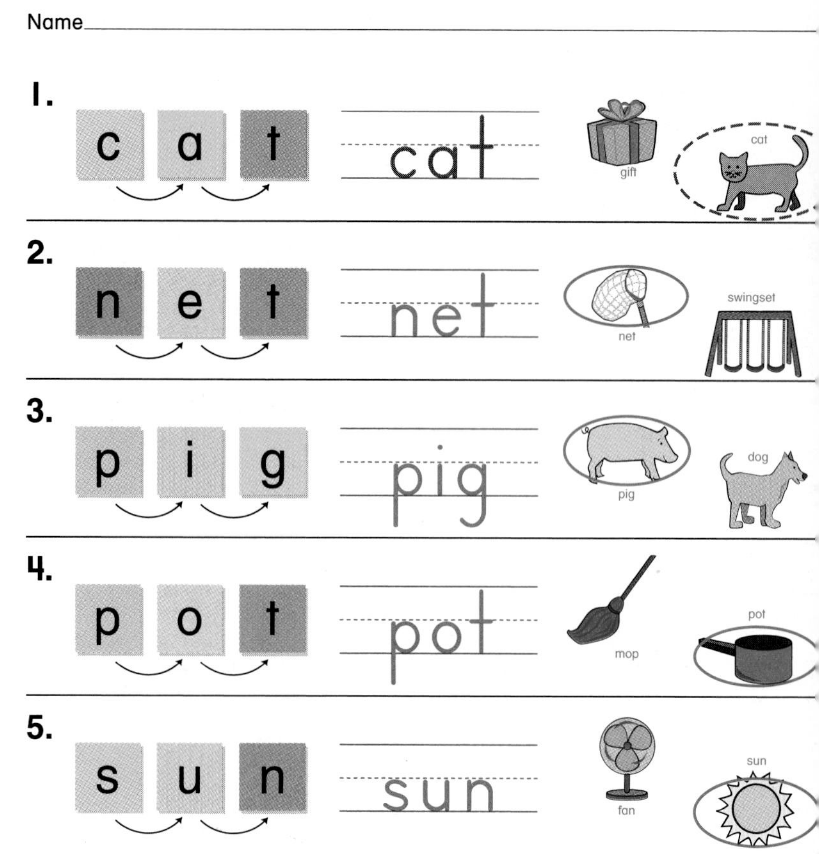

Name__________

1. c a t — cat — gift, cat
2. n e t — net — net, swingset
3. p i g — pig — pig, dog
4. p o t — pot — mop, pot
5. s u n — sun — fan, sun

Blend the sounds the letters stand for to read the word. • Then write the word.
• Circle the picture that goes with the word.

PRETEST Phonics: Blending 11

Name____________________

1. cap — c / g — c ap

2. box — p / b — b ox

3. lock — i / o — l o ck

4. rug — e / u — r u g

5. six — x / j — si x

6. van — m / n — va n

McGraw-Hill School Division

Say the picture name. • Circle the missing letter. • Then write the letter. • Read the word.

12 PRETEST Phonics: Blending

LANGUAGE SUPPORT

Write pairs of words that begin with the same letter on word cards, one word on a card. Use words such as: *cat, cup; pig, pet; sun, six; rug, rim; van, vet; lock, lip; box, bat*. Display the cards in random order on the chalkboard ledge. Have children repeat each word as you read it aloud. Ask children to first sort by beginning sound, then middle sound, and finally ending sound.

Blending

Identify children's knowledge of the letters that stand for sounds in initial, medial, and final positions in CVC words.

PREPARE

ISOLATING AND BLENDING SOUNDS This page can help you determine which children need instruction in recognizing the letters that stand for consonant and vowel sounds and how to blend these sounds. You may wish to use the page as a post-test at the end of the program.

WARM UP Display letter cards *a*, *g*, *p* from the Word Building Manipulative Cards. Write the following sentences on the chalkboard and read them aloud. Ask children to fill in the missing letters.

- *Please put peas in the __ot. The word begins with /p/. What is the word?* (pot) *Point to the letter* pot *begins with.*
- *That big, black bu__ is a spider. The word ends with /g/. What is the word?* (bug) *Point to the letter* bug *ends with.*
- *Six sisters s__t on a sofa. The word has /a/ in the middle. What is the word?* (sat) *Point to the letter in the middle of* sat.

ASSESS

COMPLETE THE PUPIL PAGE Read the directions aloud and identify the picture in the first item. Point out that the beginning letter is missing. Guide children through the steps of circling and writing the letter, then reading the word. Name each of the remaining pictures and point out which letter is missing.

CLOSE

IDENTIFY BLENDING SOUNDS Use page 12 to assess children's ability to recognize the letters that stand for sounds in all positions and to blend these sounds to read words. Use the results to determine which pupil pages to focus on.

High-Frequency Words

BJECTIVES

Identify children's knowledge of high-frequency words.

PREPARE

HIGH-FREQUENCY WORDS You can use this page diagnostically to identify which of the high-frequency words are familiar and which are unfamiliar to children. After completing the pages in this program that focus on the unfamiliar words, you may want to use this page as a post-test.

WARM UP Write the following rows of words on the chalkboard:

1.	he	is	the
2.	see	a	you
3.	we	have	are
4.	my	and	had

Invite volunteers to circle the words you say. Say these words: *is*, *you*, *we*, *and*.

ASSESS

COMPLETE THE PUPIL PAGE Read the directions aloud. Then tell children to listen to each word you say, find it in the row, and circle it. Read aloud: Row 1-*the*, Row 2-*see*, Row 3-*and*, Row 4-*do*, Row 5-*have*, Row 6-*my*.

CLOSE

IDENTIFY HIGH-FREQUENCY WORDS Use page 13 to assess children's knowledge of the high-frequency words *the*, *see*, *and*, *do*, *have*, *my*. Use the results to determine which pupil pages to teach.

Name________________

1.	has	is	with	the
2.	he	see	go	a
3.	you	that	for	and
4.	to	are	do	I
5.	of	have	was	said
6.	we	my	me	she

Listen to the word. • Circle the word you hear.

High-Frequency Words

OBJECTIVES

Identify children's knowledge of high-frequency words.

PREPARE

HIGH-FREQUENCY WORDS This page can help you identify which children need to work on high-frequency words and which pages to teach in the program. You may want to use this page as a post-test at the end of the program to determine which words children have learned.

WARM UP Display the High-Frequency Word Cards from the back of the Pupil's Edition on the chalkboard ledge: *he*, *my*, *with*, *said*, *that*, *we*. Then say the words, one at a time, and invite volunteers to find the words and take them from the chalkboard ledge.

ASSESS

COMPLETE THE PUPIL PAGE Read the directions aloud. Then tell children to listen to each word you say, find it in the row, circle it, and then write it. Read aloud: Row 1-*said*, Row 2-*we*, Row 3-*my*, Row 4-*he*, Row 5-*that*, Row 6-*with*.

CLOSE

IDENTIFY HIGH-FREQUENCY WORDS Use page 14 to assess children's knowledge of the high-frequency words *said*, *we*, *my*, *he*, *that*, *with*. Use the results to determine which pupil pages to teach.

Name____________________

1.	have	(said)	said
2.	(we)	me	we
3.	(my)	she	my
4.	has	(he)	he
5.	the	(that)	that
6.	(with)	was	with

Listen to the word. • Circle the word you hear. • Write the word.

LANGUAGE SUPPORT

Distribute word cards for *he*, *my*, *said*, *that*, *we*, *the*, *see*, *and*, *do*, *have*, and *my*, one card per child. Say a word and ask children who have that word to stand up and show their word. Invite volunteers to use the word in their own sentences. Repeat until all the words have been identified. You may wish to repeat by having children exchange their cards.

Develop

Phonological Awareness

Recognize Rhyming Words

Teach Explain that words with the same ending sounds, such as *can* and *tan* rhyme. Have children listen for rhyming words as you read the poem "*Nan and the Ant.*" Say: *Does knee rhyme with me?* (Yes.) *Does ant rhyme with me?* (No.)

Practice Say the words: *sleep*, *knee* and *creep*. Have a volunteer say the two words that rhyme. (sleep, creep) Then have the class repeat the two rhyming words. Continue with the following sets of words: *bat*, ***ball, fall; sock,*** *say*, ***rock;*** *bit*, ***big, fig.***

Nan and the Ant

Nan saw an ant
Creeping, crawling up her knee.
She gave it a crumb
And said, "Come and play with me."
Together they sat
Beneath a shady tree,
Nan and the ant,
Just as happy as can be!

Identify Beginning and Ending Sounds

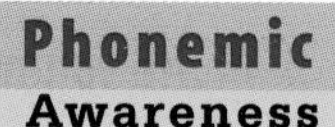

MATERIALS

- Phonics Picture Posters

  nest, apple, dog, seal, cat, hen, duck

Teach **FOCUS ON BEGINNING SOUNDS**

Say the words *nest* and *nap* slowly. Ask children if the two words begin with the same sound. (Yes) Tell children the words *nest* and *nap* begin with the /n/ sound. Have children say the /n/ sound with you. Repeat with the words *ant* and *apple* and the /a/ sound.

Practice Display the Phonics Picture Posters (picture side only) for *nest*, *apple*, *dog* and *seal*. Play the game I Spy. Say: *I spy a card that begins with /n/.* (nest) Have all children say the /n/ sound. Continue with the remaining posters.

FOCUS ON ENDING SOUNDS

Play another version of I Spy. Display the posters for *dog*, *duck*, *cat* and *hen*. Say: *I spy a card that ends with the /k/ sound.* (duck) Have all children say the ending sound /k/. Continue with the remaining posters.

Identify Middle Sounds

Phonemic Awareness

MATERIALS

- Phonics Picture Posters

  cat, van, pig

Teach Hold up the Phonics Picture Poster (picture side only) for *cat* and tell children the middle sound of the word *cat* is /a/. Have children repeat the /a/ sound with you. Then ask the children if the words *cat* and *map* have the same middle sound. (Yes)

Practice Play the I Spy game with middle sounds. Display the Phonics Picture Posters (picture side only) for *cat*, *van* and *pig*. Say: *I spy two cards that have the middle sound /a/.* (cat, van) Have children say the words *cat*, and *van* with you. Continue by saying the words in the box below. Have children identify the two words that have the same middle sound.

cap	lip	has	tap
box	win	wag	tub
tan	not	net	run

Blend Sounds

Phonemic Awareness

MATERIALS

- Yarn or string with 3 moveable beads

Teach Display the string with the beads separated. Point to each bead as you say /l/-/o/-/k/. Stretch out the sounds, moving the beads closer, blending *lock*. Demonstrate with other three-sound words such as: *pen*, *bag*, *nap*.

Practice Say the sounds for the following words with the beads separated: *bad*, *tap*, *not*, *pan*, *tan*, *nod*. Have volunteers push the beads together and say the word. Have the rest of the class repeat the word. Continue until all children have had a chance.

Introduce

Initial /n/Nn

OBJECTIVES

Children will identify initial /n/*Nn* and form the letters *Nn*.

PREPARE

PHONOLOGICAL AWARENESS As you sing the Phonics Song "Nancy's Nest," hold up the Phonics Picture Card for *nest*. Then have children clap and count the words in each line of the song.

Say the following words and ask children to nod when they hear /n/ at the beginning of a word: *nest, apple, nice, vet, neat. Phonemic Awareness*

TEACH

IDENTIFY INITIAL /n/*Nn* Write the letters *Nn* on the chalkboard. Explain that the letters *Nn* stand for the sound /n/. Have children point to the letters *Nn* on the chalkboard and say /n/. Then write: *Nick is our new neighbor.* Invite volunteers to circle the letters *Nn* in the words as they say /n/.

FORM *Nn* Review how to form the *N* and *n*. Have children use the Handwriting Models at the back of the Pupil's Edition to trace the letters.

PRACTICE

COMPLETE THE PUPIL PAGE Have children name the key picture *nest* at the top of the page and listen to the beginning sound /n/. Read the directions aloud and help children identify the pictures.

ASSESS/CLOSE

IDENTIFY AND USE INITIAL /n/*Nn* Use page 15 to assess children's knowledge of initial /n/*Nn*. Have children say a word that begins with /n/.

Name____________________

Nn

1. 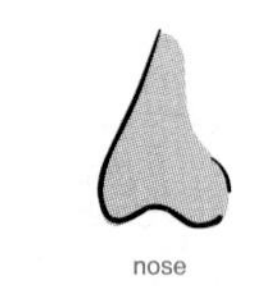
nose
Nn

2. necklace
Nn

3. 
ball

4. 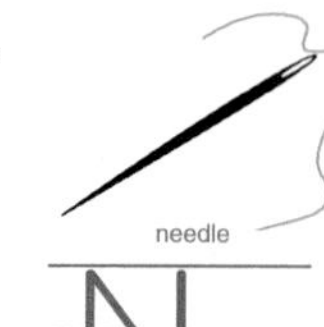
needle
Nn

5. 
cat

6. 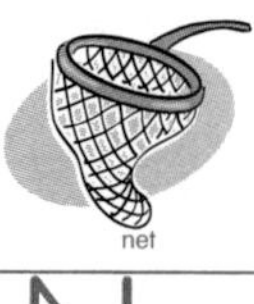
net
Nn

7. 

newspaper
Nn

8. 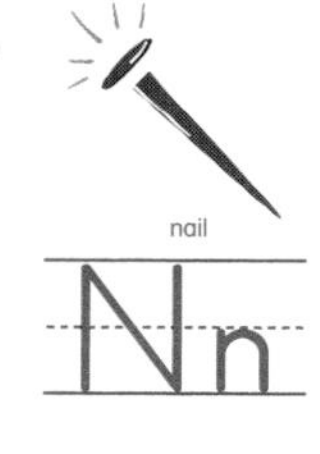
nail
Nn

Say the name of each picture. • If the name begins with the same sound as *nest*, write *Nn* on the line.

Listen

Nancy's Nest

Nancy has a nest.
Her nest is just the best.
Nancy eats nuts in her nest.
Her nest is just the best!

Sung to the tune of
"The Farmer in the Dell"
From **Songs from A to Z**

Phonics Picture Posters and Cards

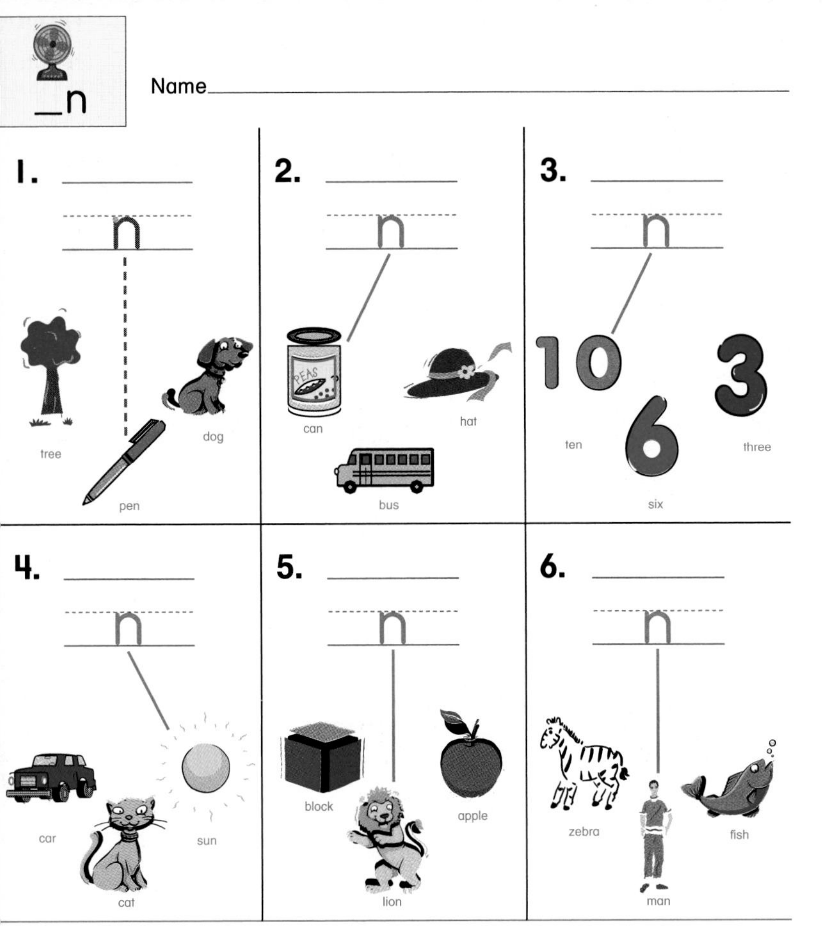
_n Name

1. ___ n

2. ___ n

3. ___ n

4. ___ n

5. ___ n

6. ___ n

Write the letter *n*. • Say the name of each picture. • Draw a line from the *n* to the picture whose name has the same ending sound as *fan*.

Introduce

Final /n/*n*

TESTED OBJECTIVES

Children will identify final /n/*n*.

PREPARE

PHONOLOGICAL AWARENESS Say the words *fan* and *can*. Tell children these words rhyme because they have the same ending sound. Have children think of other words that rhyme with *fan*.

Have children say /n/ when they hear you say a word that ends with the /n/ sound. Say these words: *run, walk, tan, pin, climb, pen, man.* *Phonemic Awareness*

TEACH

IDENTIFY FINAL /n/*n* Say *pan* and invite a volunteer to hold up a letter card, from the Word Building Manipulative Cards, for the ending sound. Remind children that the letter *n* stands for the sound /n/. Then write and say words ending with *n* and have volunteers circle the letter *n* and say /n/. For example: *fun, can, hen, sun, pan, win*.

PRACTICE

COMPLETE THE PUPIL PAGE Before children begin, read the directions aloud and help them identify the pictures.

ASSESS/CLOSE

IDENTIFY AND USE FINAL /n/*n* Use page 16 to assess children's knowledge of final /n/*n*. You may also wish to have children say a word that ends with /n/ and write *n*.

LANGUAGE SUPPORT

ESL The names of the key pictures will probably not be the same in some children's native languages. For non-English-speaking children, say the names of the key pictures aloud and have children repeat after you until they are able to recognize and pronounce the initial and final /n/.

ALTERNATE TEACHING STRATEGY

Have each child draw a picture of a word that begins or ends with *n*. When children finish their drawings, have them give their pictures to a partner. The partner names the picture, identifies whether the /n/ sound is at the beginning or ending of the word, and then prints *n* under it.

▶ **Kinesthetic/ Spatial**

Introduce

Initial /a/*Aa*

Children will identify initial /a/*Aa* and form the letters *Aa*.

PREPARE

PHONOLOGICAL AWARENESS Say the following words and have children repeat after you and clap the syllables: *ant, alligator, apple, anteater*.

Listen

While holding up the Phonics Picture Poster for *apple*, sing the song "Anna's Apples," and have the children raise their hand when they hear /a/ at the beginning of the word. ***Phonemic Awareness***

TEACH

IDENTIFY INITIAL /a/*Aa* Hold up the letter card *Aa* from the Word Building Manipulative Cards. Tell children that the letters *Aa* stand for the sound /a/. Encourage children to say /a/ with you as they point to the letter on the card. On the chalkboard write: *Ann and Nan saw an ant at the park.* Have volunteers circle the letters *Aa* at the beginning of words and say /a/.

FORM *Aa* For children who need a review of letter formation, write *A* and *a* on the chalkboard. Have children trace the letters on the Word Building Manipulative Cards.

PRACTICE

COMPLETE THE PUPIL PAGE Before children begin, read the directions aloud. Help children identify the key picture *apple* and the other pictures on the page.

ASSESS/CLOSE

IDENTIFY AND USE INITIAL /a/*Aa* Use page 17 to assess children's knowledge of initial /a/*Aa*. Say the sentence *Ann told Andy the answer.* Ask children to name the words that begin with /a/.

Name________________________________

Aa	1. astronaut Aa	2. ax Aa
3. pig	4. net	5. ant Aa
6. six	7. alligator Aa	8. arrow Aa

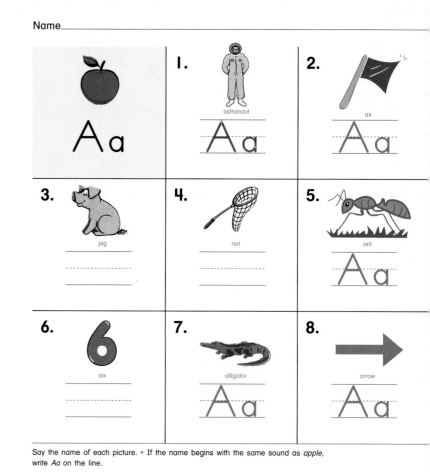

Say the name of each picture. • If the name begins with the same sound as *apple*, write *Aa* on the line.

Introduce Initial /a/*Aa* 17

Anna's Apples

Anna eats an apple a day,
Apple a day, apple a day.
Anna eats an apple a day.
Anna loves apples!

Sung to the tune of
"London Bridge"
From **Songs from A to Z**

Phonics Picture Posters and Cards

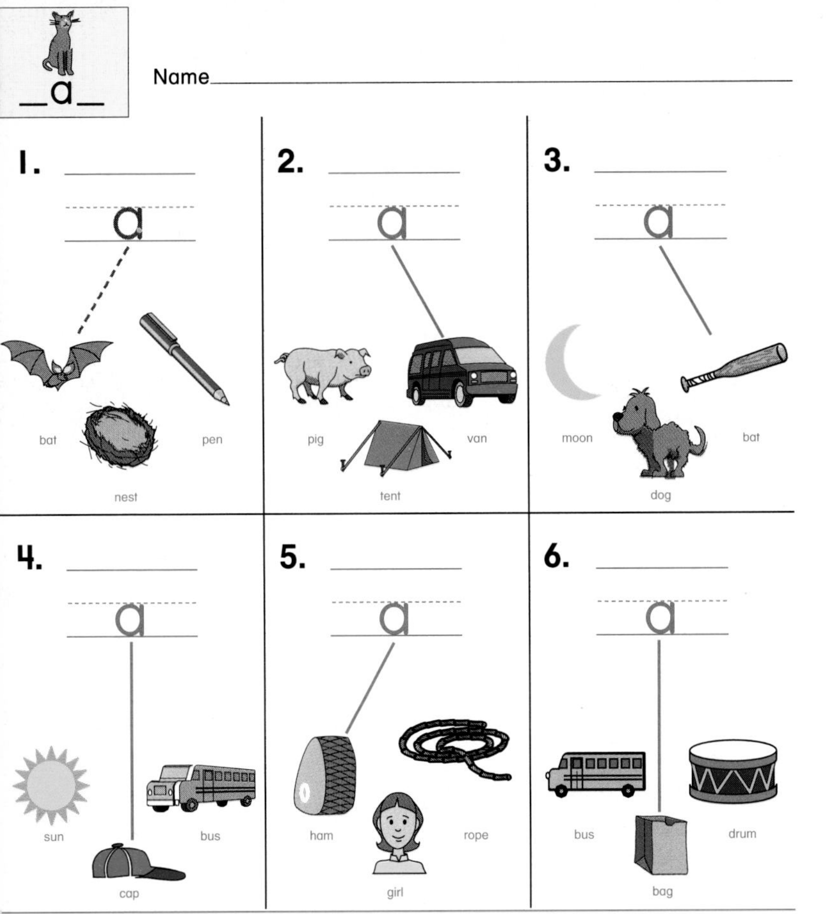

Write the letter. • Say the name of each picture. • Draw a line from the *a* to the picture whose name has the same middle sound as *cat*.

18 Introduce Medial /a/*a*

Introduce

Medial /a/*a*

OBJECTIVES

Children will identify medial /a/*a*.

PREPARE

PHONOLOGICAL AWARENESS Say the rhyming words *cat* and *bat*. Have children clap their hands when they hear you say a word that rhymes with *cat*. Say these words: *rat, sat, fly, man, flat, pat, dog, ball, that.*

Listen

Say the following sentence and have the children raise their hand when they hear /a/ in the middle of the word: "The fat cat chased a fast rat." *Phonemic Awareness*

TEACH

IDENTIFY MEDIAL /a/*a* Review that the letter *a* stands for the sound /a/. Say a child's name that has medial /a/, such as *Pat.* Ask a volunteer to write on the chalkboard the letter that stands for the middle sound. Then write other names with medial /a/, for example: *Dan, Pam, Matt, Jan, Sam, Cam*. Invite volunteers to circle the letter that stands for /a/ in each word.

PRACTICE

COMPLETE THE PUPIL PAGE Read the directions aloud and help children identify the pictures.

ASSESS/CLOSE

IDENTIFY AND USE MEDIAL /a/*a* Use page 18 for assessment. Ask children to write the letter that stands for /a/. Have them draw a picture of something that has /a/ in the middle of its name.

LANGUAGE SUPPORT

ESL Non-English-speaking children may not be familiar with the short *a* sound if there is no equivalent sound in their native languages. Record some one-syllable words with short *a* so that children can listen to them as needed. You may want to work with other teachers to group ESL students from different classrooms for a specific lesson on recognizing and pronouncing words with short *a*.

ALTERNATE TEACHING STRATEGY

Give children practice with short *a* rhyming words. Have them name words that rhyme with *cat* and name words that rhyme with *pan*. Then encourage children to complete sentences (real and nonsense) with rhyming words. For example:

The cat is on the ___. (mat)

▶ Linguistic/Auditory

Review

/n/*n*, /a/*a*

Children will identify /n/*n* and /a/*a* in words.

PREPARE

PHONOLOGICAL AWARENESS Have children name as many words as they can that rhyme with *man*.

Listen

Name a sound and specify its position. Read each sentence, having children raise a hand when they hear a word with the sound in that position.

initial /a/ *I watched the ants.* **medial /a/** *The ants were black.* **initial /n/** *They crawled on the napkin.* **final /n/** *I counted ten ants.*

Phonemic Awareness

TEACH

REVIEW /n/*n*, /a/*a* Distribute letter cards *n* and *a* from the Word Building Manipulative Cards. Draw three blank letter boxes on the chalkboard. Say the following words and ask children to show whether they hear /n/ or /a/ by holding up a letter card. Have volunteers place the letter card in the correct box to show where they hear the sound—at the beginning, middle, or end of a word. Say: *sat, act, fun, nod.*

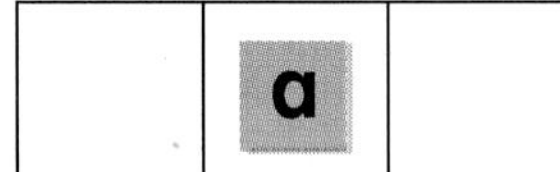

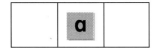

PRACTICE

COMPLETE THE PUPIL PAGE Read the directions aloud and guide children through each item on the page.

ASSESS/CLOSE

IDENTIFY AND USE /n/*n*, /a/*a* Use page 19 to assess children's progress with /n/*n*, /a/*a*.

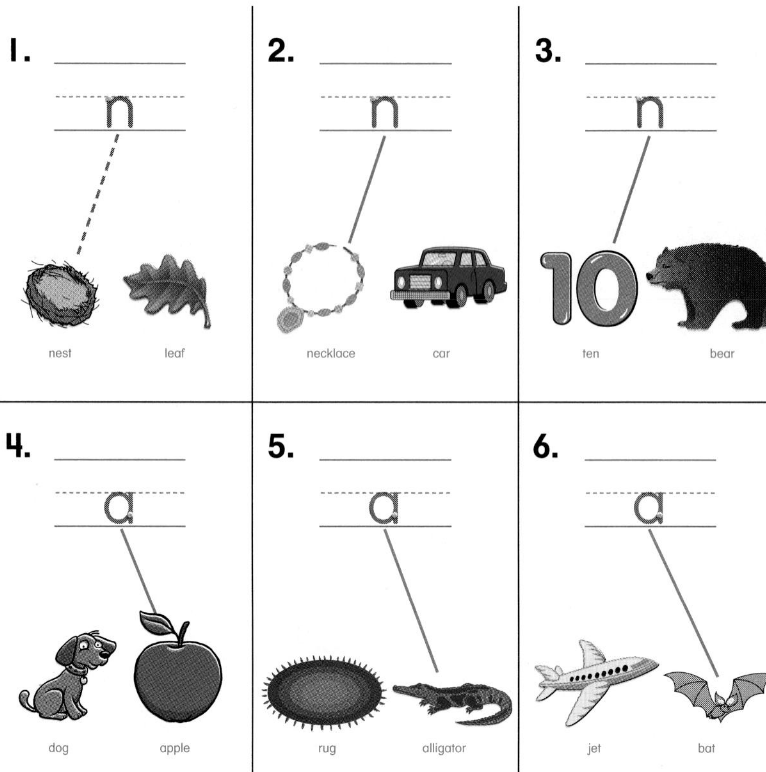

Name

1. n — nest, leaf
2. n — necklace, car
3. n — ten, bear
4. a — dog, apple
5. a — rug, alligator
6. a — jet, bat

Trace the letter. Say the sound it stands for. • Say the names of the pictures. • Draw a line from the letter to the picture whose name has the sound the letter stands for.

Review /n/n, /a/a 19

ALTERNATE TEACHING STRATEGY

Make a two-sided word card for each child, one side with the word *an* and the other side with the word *Nan*. Slowly say a sentence that uses *an* or *Nan*. Ask children to hold up their cards to show the word you used. Repeat the game several times with different sentences.

▶ **Auditory/Visual**

Name

1. N a n Nan

2. N a n Nan

3. N a n Nan

4. N a n Nan

5. N a n Nan

McGraw-Hill School Division

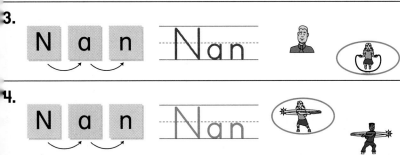

Blend the sounds the letters stand for to read the word. • Trace the letters. • Then write the word. • Circle the picture that goes with each word.

TEACHING TIP

DIRECTIONALITY Emphasize the directionality of left-to-right when writing a word. After blending the word *an*, ask children to name the letter that sits on the left. (a) Ask children to name the letter that sits to the right of *a*. (n) Next write the word *an* on chart paper, explaining that you start at the left and move to the right as you write each letter of the word. Ask children to write the word after you.

Blending with Short *a*

Children will blend and read short *a* CVC words.

PREPARE

Hold up the *n* letter card from the Word Building Manipulative Cards and say /n/. Have children repeat /n/. Then hold up the *a* letter card, say /a/, and have children say /a/. Tell children they will be learning to read words by blending the sounds for the letters *n* and *a*.

TEACH

MODEL AND GUIDE PRACTICE Place the *a* letter card on the chalkboard ledge, point to it, and say /a/. Ask children to repeat /a/ after you.

- Place the *n* letter card after the *a* letter card.
- Blend the sounds /a/ and /n/ together to read *an*. Have children repeat the word after you.

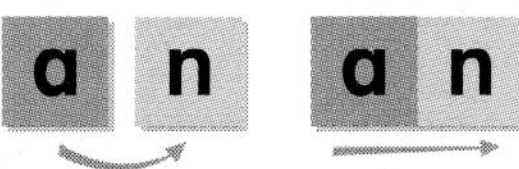

USE THE WORD IN CONTEXT Use *an* in a sentence to reinforce its meaning, for example: *The bird laid an egg.*

REPEAT THE PROCEDURE Use the word *Nan* to continue modeling and guided practice with short *a*.

PRACTICE

COMPLETE THE PUPIL PAGE Complete the page with children, reading the directions aloud and modeling the blending. Help children identify pictures and complete each step.

ASSESS/CLOSE

BLEND AND READ WORDS Use page 20 to assess children's skill in blending with short *a*.

Introduce

High-Frequency Words

Children will identify and read the high-frequency words *the* and *is*.

PREPARE

LISTEN TO WORDS Tell children that you will read a sentence with the word *the*. Have them raise a hand when they hear the word *the*: *I see* ***the*** *bird.* Repeat with *is* and the sentence *It* ***is*** *a jay.*

TEACH

IDENTIFY THE WORDS Write the words *the* and *is* on the chalkboard side by side and read each word aloud. Distribute the word cards *the* and *is* from the High-Frequency Word Cards in the back of the Pupil's Edition. Say a word and have children raise the appropriate card. Repeat a few times. Then write the sentences from the Prepare section on the chalkboard. Read them aloud, pointing to each word in each sentence. Ask children to hold up *the* or *is* when they hear each word read aloud.

PRACTICE

COMPLETE THE PUPIL PAGE Before children begin, read the directions aloud. Explain to children that they should circle more than one word in each row.

ASSESS/CLOSE

REVIEW THE PAGE Use page 21 to assess children's knowledge of the words *the* and *is*. Have children use the word *is* in an oral sentence.

Name____________________

1.	the	is	(the)	is	(the)
2.	is	(is)	the	the	(is)
3.	is	(is)	(is)	the	the
4.	the	(the)	is	is	(the)
5.	the	is	(the)	is	(the)

Read the first word in each row. • Circle the words in the row that are the same.

Introduce High-Frequency Words: *the, is* 21

ALTERNATE TEACHING STRATEGY

Have children work in pairs to find the words *the* and *is* on charts, signs, and pictures in the classroom. Call on pairs to point to and identify the words they have found.

▶ **Interpersonal/Visual**

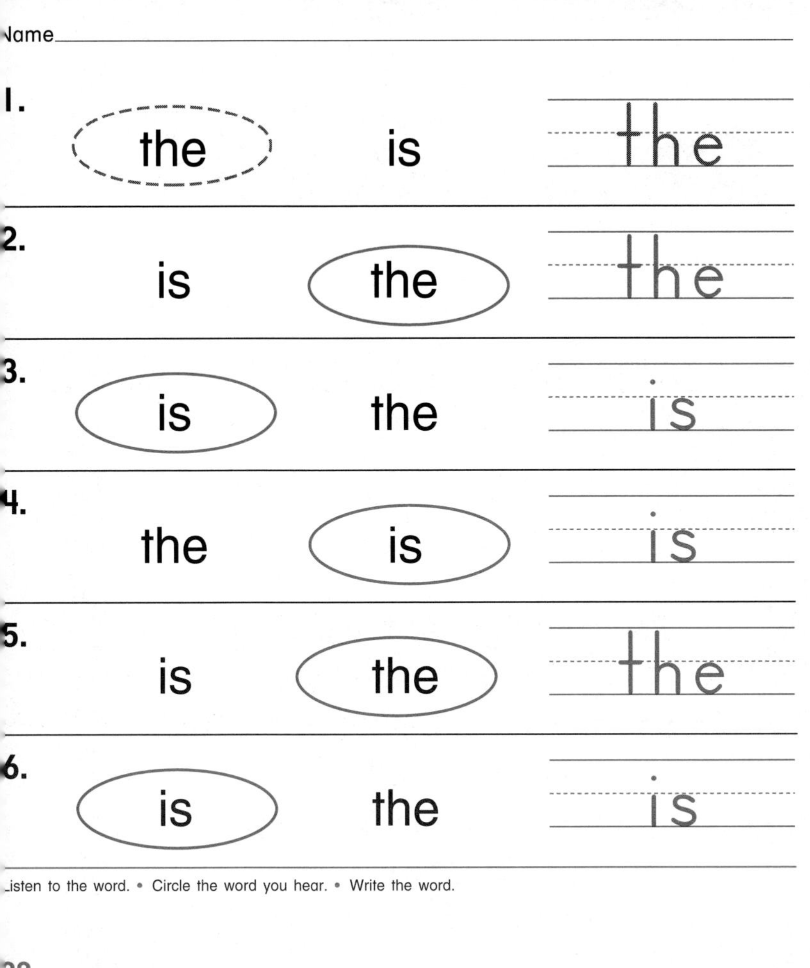
Name

1. the is the

2. is the the

3. is the is

4. the is is

5. is the the

6. is the is

Listen to the word. • Circle the word you hear. • Write the word.

McGraw-Hill School Division

22 Review High-Frequency Words

Review

High-Frequency Words

Children will identify and read the high-frequency words *the* and *is*.

PREPARE

LISTEN TO WORDS Read aloud the following sentences and have children listen for the words *the* and *is*: *The story about the puppy is funny. The puppy is black, and his name is Ink.* Invite children to raise a hand when they hear either word.

TEACH

IDENTIFY THE WORDS Distribute the word cards *the* and *is*. Say *the* and *is* as you write each word side by side on the chalkboard. Ask volunteers to match their cards to the words on the chalkboard. Then write the sentences from the Prepare section on the chalkboard. Read the sentences aloud and invite all children to hold up the word card for *the* or *is* each time they hear these words.

PRACTICE

COMPLETE THE PUPIL PAGE Before children begin, read the directions aloud. Tell children to listen as you say the words they are to circle and write: (1) *the*; (2) *the*; (3) *is*; (4) *is*; (5) *the*; (6) *is*.

ASSESS/CLOSE

REVIEW THE PAGE Use page 22 to assess children's progress with the words *the* and *is*. Challenge children to write the word *the* on an index card.

TEACHING TIP

DIRECTIONALITY Use the sentences from the Prepare activity to emphasize the directionality of left-to-right when writing a message. As you write the message on chart paper, model for children how to write the words in a sentence from left-to-right. Before writing the second line, explain that you will write the second line under the first. Read the message, pointing to each word as you read. Emphasize the directionality of left-to-right and top-to-bottom.

Ask children to write the same message. Remind them to write left-to-right and top-to-bottom.

Develop

Phonological Awareness

Count Words

MATERIALS
- sticky notes
- blocks or counters (5 per child)

Teach Read "*A Pet for Sam and Sue*." Tell children you are going to count the number of words in a sentence. Repeat the second sentence and for every word place a sticky note on the chalkboard. Tell children there are five words in the sentence.

A Pet for Sam and Sue

Sam and Sue are feeling sad,
Sam and Sue are blue.
Some sort of pet is what they want,
Any kind will do.
Along comes Sis, who says,
"Surprise!"
"Here is a pup with soft brown eyes."

Practice Distribute five blocks or counters to each child. Say a sentence with three words, such as *Sam is happy*. Have children count the words by placing a block or counter in front of them as you say each word. Then have children count the blocks/counters. Repeat with three to five-word sentences.

Identify Beginning Sounds

Phonemic Awareness

MATERIALS
- Phonics Picture Posters

  dog, seal

Teach Display the Phonics Picture Poster (picture side only) for *dog*. Say the word *dog*, emphasizing /d/. Have children repeat the word and beginning /d/ of other words: *dinosaur, dig, dad*. Ask children to listen to pairs of words and say "*dog*" if both words start with /d/: *desk/dog*; *dot/not*; *done/down*. Repeat with the Phonics Picture Poster for *seal*. Have children listen for the /s/ sound and say "seal" if both words begin with /s/. Use these words: *Sam/Sue*, *sad/happy*, *some/size*, *if/sit*, *sick/silly*.

Practice Have each child think of a word beginning with /d/. The group whispers "*dog*" whenever a word with initial /d/ is said. Repeat the activity for the initial sound /s/ using the picture card for *seal*.

Identify Ending Sounds

Phonemic Awareness

MATERIALS
- Word Building Manipulative Card
  sled

Teach Display the Word Building Manipulative Card for *sled* (picture side only). Say the word, emphasizing the final /d/. Say other words ending in /d/, having children repeat the words and ending sound: *had, sad, mud, bed*. Have children clap once when a word ends with /d/: *ham, bead, bread, get, mad*.

Practice Ask such questions as these: *Does weed end in /d/? Does win end in /d/? Do head and feed both end with /d/?* Then say the following pairs of words and have children say *sled* if both words end with the /d/ sound.

bread	fed	said	sad
would	run	had	man

Blend Sounds

Phonemic Awareness

Teach Say the sounds /p/-/e/-/t/ and ask children to repeat the sounds with you. Then blend the sounds together to say the word: *pet*. Repeat with other words that have three sounds such as: *Sam, sad, some, pup*.

Practice Organize children in three groups. Give each group a sound; then use a ruler to 'conduct' the groups to say the sounds separately. Then have children blend the sound to say each word. Use three sound words such as: *den, sad, sat, dan, pet, wet, nag*.

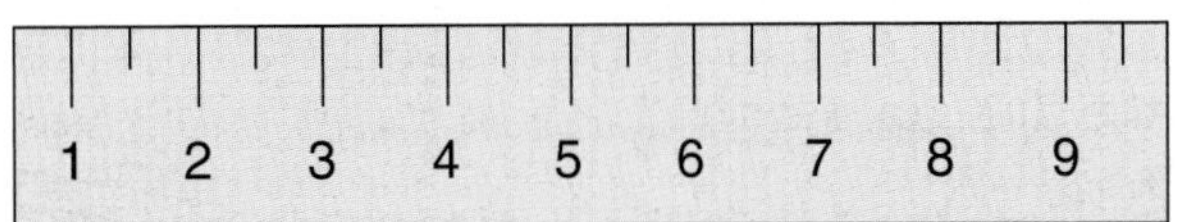

Introduce

Initial /d/*Dd*

Children will identify initial /d/*Dd* and form the letters *Dd*.

PREPARE

PHONOLOGICAL AWARENESS Say the words *dog*, *dinosaur*, *deer* and *duck*. Ask children to clap and count the syllables for these animal names.

Listen

Hold up the Phonics Picture Poster for *dog*. As you sing the Phonics Song "My Dog Dusty," have the children hold up their finger every time they hear a word that starts with the /d/ sound. *Phonemic Awareness*

TEACH

IDENTIFY INITIAL /d/*Dd* Hold up the *Dd* letter card from the Word Building Manipulative Cards. Explain that the letters *Dd* stand for the sound /d/. Write the following question on the chalkboard: *Dan, how do you do?* Read the question aloud. Have children hold up their *Dd* letter card when they hear a word beginning with /d/.

FORM *Dd* Have children write the letters on paper folded into fourths, using the Handwriting Models at the back of the Pupil's Edition, as a reference.

PRACTICE

COMPLETE THE PUPIL PAGE Read the directions with children and help them identify each picture.

ASSESS/CLOSE

IDENTIFY AND USE INITIAL /d/*Dd* Use page 23 to assess children's knowledge of initial /d/*Dd*. Have children draw the answer to this riddle and write its beginning letter: *My name begins with /d/. I'm found in a room. You can open and close me. What am I?* (door)

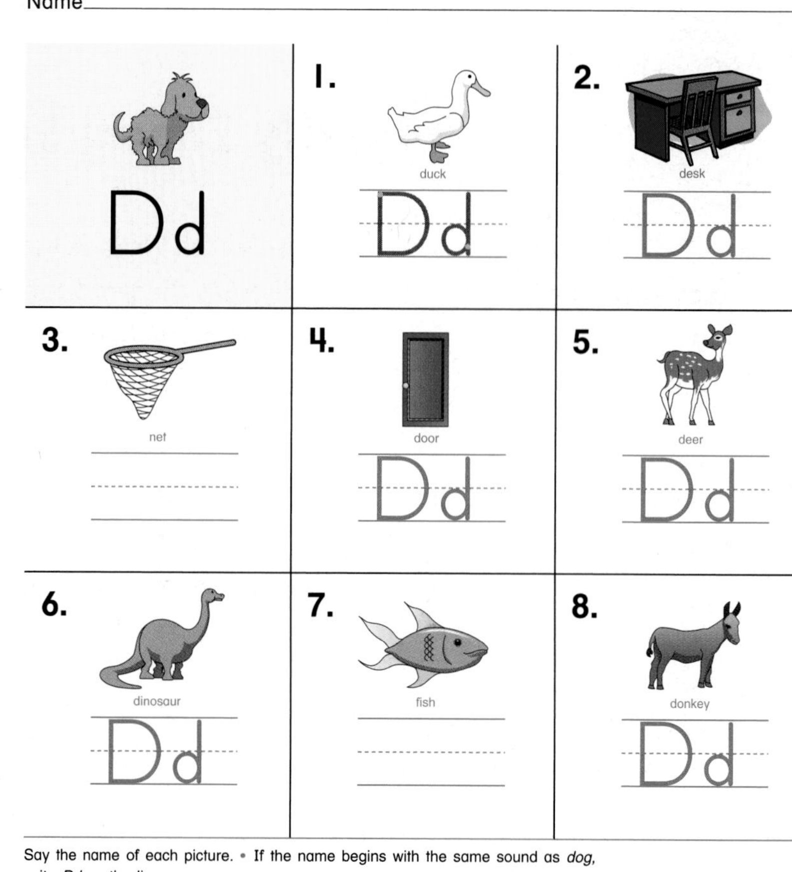

Name

Dd

1. duck Dd
2. desk Dd
3. net
4. door Dd
5. deer Dd
6. dinosaur Dd
7. fish
8. donkey Dd

Say the name of each picture. • If the name begins with the same sound as *dog*, write *Dd* on the line.

Introduce Initial /d/*Dd* 23

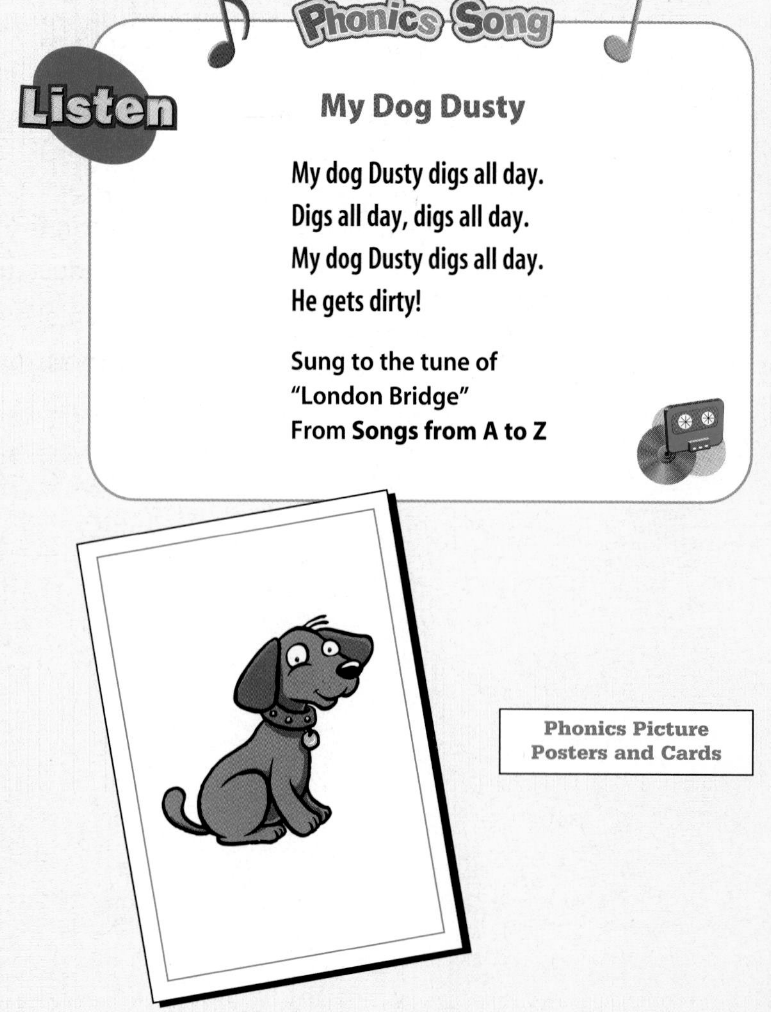

Phonics Song
Listen
My Dog Dusty
My dog Dusty digs all day.
Digs all day, digs all day.
My dog Dusty digs all day.
He gets dirty!
Sung to the tune of
"London Bridge"
From Songs from A to Z

Phonics Picture Posters and Cards

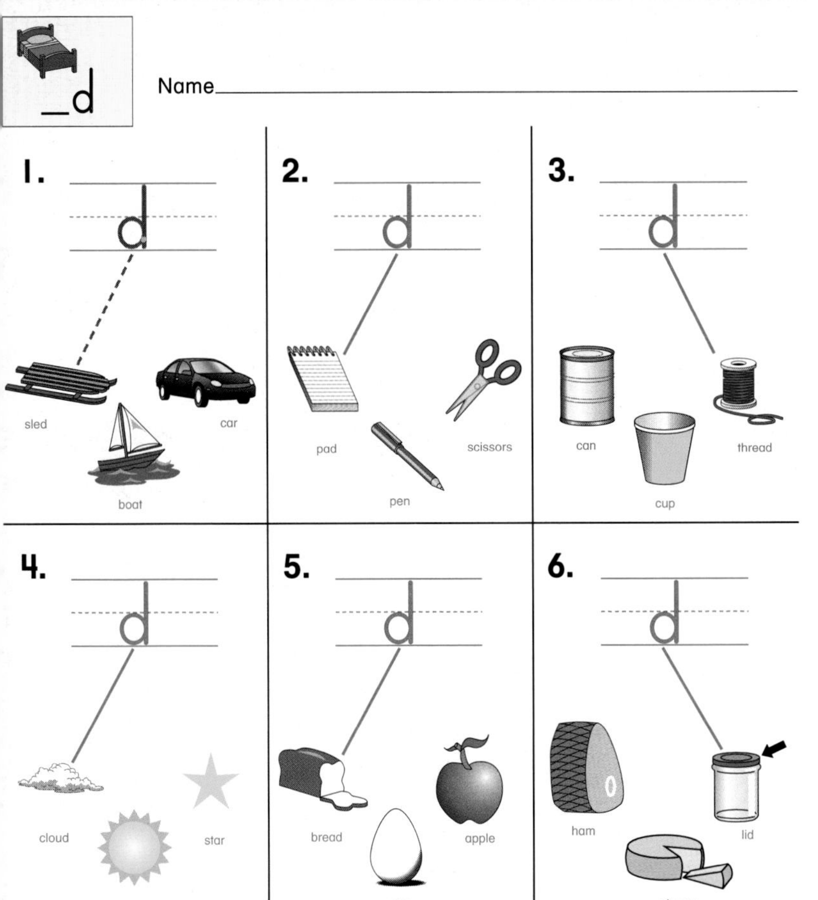
_d Name

1. d sled car boat

2. d pad scissors pen

3. d can thread cup

4. d cloud star sun

5. d bread apple egg

6. d ham lid cheese

McGraw-Hill School Division

Write the letter *d*. • Say the name of each picture. • Draw a line from the *d* to each picture whose name has the same ending sound as *bed*.

24 Introduce Final /d/d

Introduce

Final /d/d

Children will identify final /d/*d*.

PREPARE

PHONOLOGICAL AWARENESS Have children

brainstorm words that rhyme with *bed*, such as *red, lead, said, Fred, wed, Ned, head*.

Have children say /d/ sound when they hear you say words that end with the same sound. Say these words: *bed, rid, tall, sock, Ted, odd, tan, rod*. *Phonemic Awareness*

TEACH

IDENTIFY FINAL /d/*d* Remind children that the letter *d* stands for the sound /d/. Say the word *bad*. Invite a volunteer to write the letter that stands for the ending sound of this word on the chalkboard. Write *bad, had, mad, sad* on the chalkboard. Have volunteers say the ending sound /d/ and circle the letter *d* in each word.

PRACTICE

COMPLETE THE PUPIL PAGE After reading the directions aloud, encourage children to identify the key picture and its ending sound. Help children identify the other pictures.

ASSESS/CLOSE

IDENTIFY AND USE FINAL /d/*d* Use page 24 to assess children's knowledge of final /d/*d*. Have children answer this riddle by drawing a picture and writing the letter *d* under it: *My name ends with /d/. I'm the top of a pot. What am I?* (lid)

TEACHING TIP

INSTRUCTIONAL Some children may mix up lowercase *d* with lowercase *b*. Give them the *d* letter card and ask them to trace over the letter *d* with their fingers while saying /d/.

ALTERNATE TEACHING STRATEGY

Invite a volunteer to the front of the room. Whisper a word to him or her that begins or ends with /d/. Then have the child pantomime the word while others guess. A child who guesses correctly is the next player to pantomime. Use words such as *duck, donkey, deer, dinosaur, door, bed, head*.

▶ Visual/Kinesthetic

Introduce

Initial /s/*Ss*

Children will identify initial /s/*Ss* and form the letters *Ss*.

PREPARE

PHONOLOGICAL AWARENESS While holding up the Phonics Picture Poster for *seal*, sing the song *"Sally Seal."* Then have children clap the number of words in each line.

Have the children say the /s/ sound with you. Tell them to repeat this sound each time they hear it in the song *"Sally Seal."* Sing the song again. *Phonemic Awareness*

TEACH

IDENTIFY INITIAL /s/*Ss* Display letter cards *n*, *a*, *d*, *s* from the Word Building Manipulative Cards on the chalkboard ledge. Ask a volunteer to hold up the letter that stands for the sound /s/. Tell children that the letters *Ss* stand for /s/. Have them say /s/ as they point to the *Ss* letter card. Have children brainstorm a list of words that begin with /s/*Ss*.

FORM *Ss* Review how to write *S* and *s*. Have children trace the letters in the Handwriting Models in the back of the Pupil's Edition.

PRACTICE

COMPLETE THE PUPIL PAGE Before children begin, read the directions aloud and identify the key picture *seal*. Have volunteers identify the other pictures on the page.

ASSESS/CLOSE

IDENTIFY AND USE INITIAL /s/*Ss* Use page 25 to assess children's knowledge of initial /s/*Ss*. Ask children to write the letter that stands for the sound they hear at the beginning of the word *sap*.

Name____________________

Ss	1. sandwich Ss	2. dish
3. sun Ss	4. seven Ss	5. suitcase Ss
6. saw Ss	7. sink Ss	8. fan

Say the name of each picture. • If the name begins with the same sound as *seal*, write *Ss* on the line.

Phonics Song

Sally Seal

I see Sally. I see Sally
She's a seal. She's a seal.
Sally sails her sailboat,
Sally sails her sailboat,
In the sea, in the sea.

Sung to the tune:
"Where is Thumbkin?"
From **Songs from A to Z**

Phonics Picture Posters and Cards

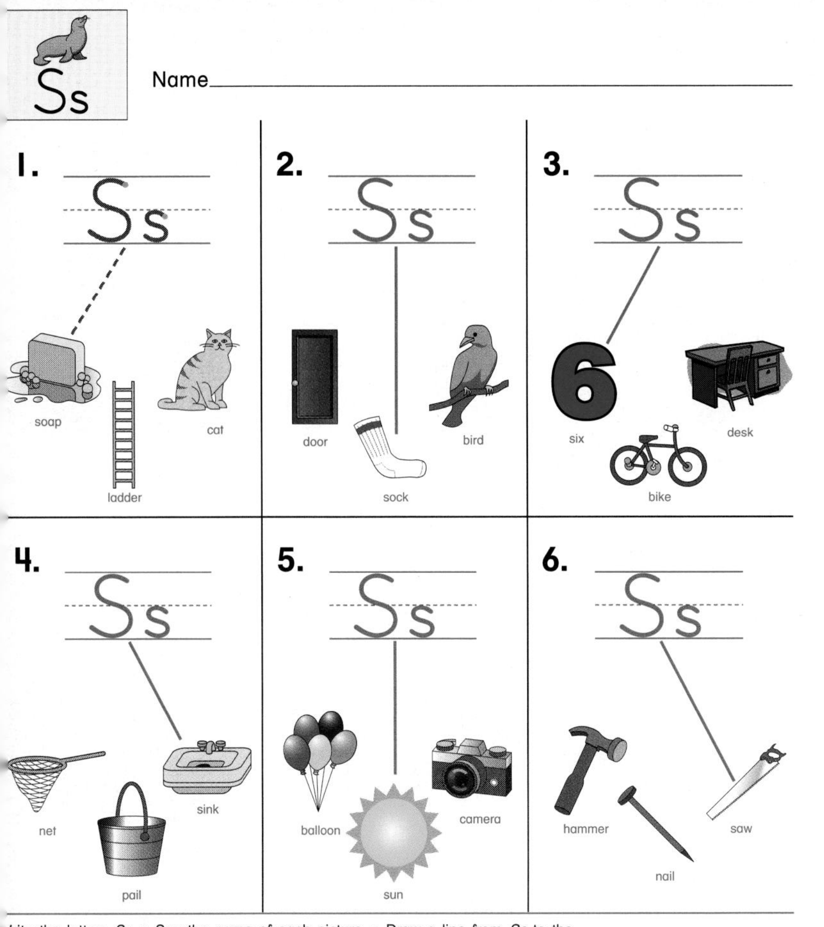

Write the letters *Ss*. • Say the name of each picture. • Draw a line from *Ss* to the picture whose name has the same beginning sound as *seal*.

26 Review Initial /s/*Ss*

Review

Initial /s/Ss

OBJECTIVES

Children will identify initial /s/*Ss*.

PREPARE

PHONOLOGICAL AWARENESS While holding up the Phonics Picture Poster for *seal*, review the song, "Sally Seal." Then have children think of words that rhyme with *seal*, such as *real, feel, teal, heal* and so on.

Put small objects in a box and invite children to take turns choosing one. Tell children to name the object and put it on the chalkboard ledge if it begins with /s/. Objects might include *sailboat, numerals six* and *seven, ball, salt in shaker, soap, pen, bead. Phonemic Awareness*

TEACH

IDENTIFY INITIAL /s/*Ss* Distribute the *s, d, n* and *a* cards from the Word Building Manipulative Cards. Say *soup* and ask a volunteer to hold up a letter card for the beginning sound. Review that the letters *Ss* stand for the sound /s/. Write and say the names of the objects that are on the chalkboard ledge and have volunteers circle initial *s* and say /s/.

PRACTICE

COMPLETE THE PUPIL PAGE Read the directions aloud and help children identify the pictures. Then complete the page together.

ASSESS/CLOSE

IDENTIFY AND USE INITIAL /s/*Ss* Use page 26 to assess children's progress. Say this sentence: *Ann drew six silver moons and seven suns.* Have children write the letters *Ss* each time they hear a word that begins with /s/.

LANGUAGE SUPPORT

ESL Some non-English-speaking children may not understand the use of the words *blue* and *soft* in the rhyme. Explain that in the rhyme, *blue* does not mean a color but means "unhappy." The word *soft* does not mean "fluffy" but is used to describe eyes that are a pretty, light brown.

ALTERNATE TEACHING STRATEGY

Have children make the letter *s* using different colored pipe cleaners. Children glue their pipe cleaner letters onto drawing paper. Have children share their letter *s* collages.

▶ **Kinesthetic/Interpersonal**

Review

/d/d, /s/s

Children will identify /d/*d* and /s/*s* in words.

PREPARE

PHONOLOGICAL AWARENESS Have children name as many words as they can that rhyme with *sad.*

Say a sound and its position. Read each sentence and ask children to raise a hand when they hear a word with the sound in that position.

initial /d/ *I have a doll with brown hair.*
initial /s/ *Her name is Sabrina.*
medial /a/ *She wears a red hat.*

Phonemic Awareness

TEACH

REVIEW /d/*d*, /s/*s* Distribute the *d* and *s* letter cards from the Word Building Manipulative Cards. Say a word and have children tell if they hear /d/ or /s/ in the word by holding up its letter card. Draw three blank letter boxes on the chalkboard and invite volunteers to place the letter in the correct box to show where they hear the sound—at the beginning, middle, or end of the word. Say: *sit, den, dig, saw.*

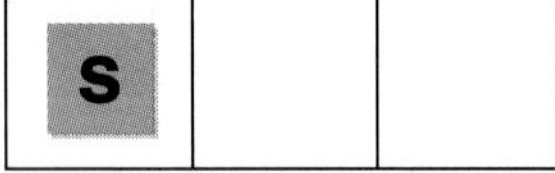

PRACTICE

COMPLETE THE PUPIL PAGE Before children begin, read the directions aloud and identify pictures with children.

ASSESS/CLOSE

IDENTIFY AND USE /d/*d*, /s/*s* Use page 27 to assess children's progress with /d/*d*, /s/*s*. Have children name words that begins with /d/ and /s/.

Name________________

1. s (seal, net)	2. s (deer, sink)	3. d (tree, bed)
4. d (dog, ax)	5. s (sun, doll)	6. d (dinosaur, van)

Trace the letter. • Say the sound it stands for. • Say the names of the pictures. • Draw a line from the letter to the picture whose name has the sound the letter stands for.

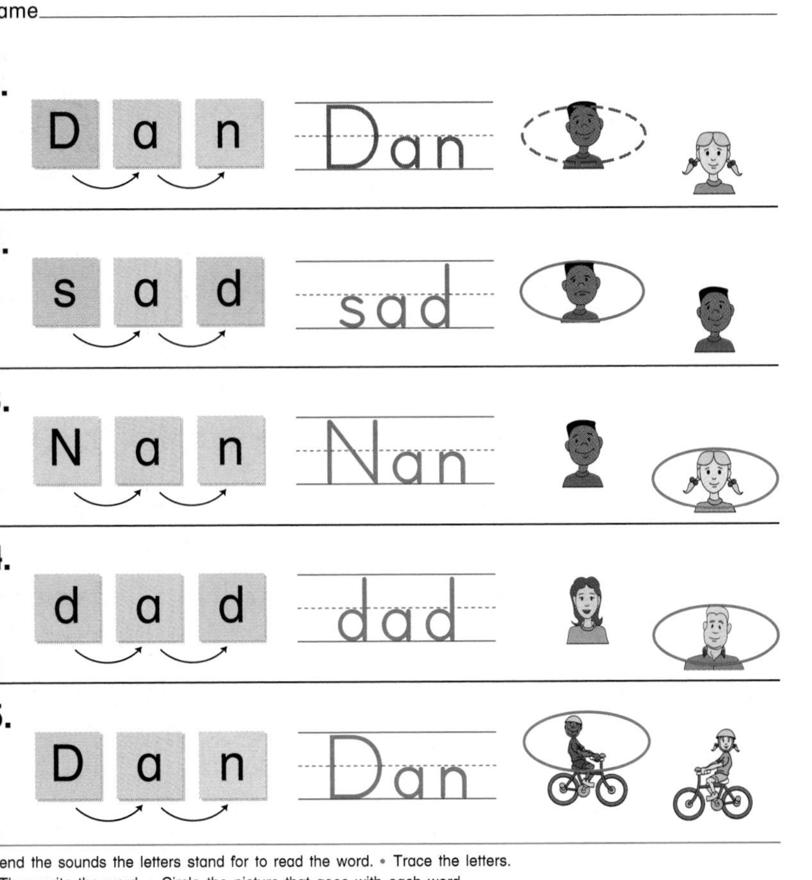
ame____________________

1. D a n — Dan

2. s a d — sad

3. N a n — Nan

4. d a d — dad

5. D a n — Dan

Blend the sounds the letters stand for to read the word. • Trace the letters. Then write the word. • Circle the picture that goes with each word.

McGraw-Hill School Division

28 Blending with Short *a*

Blending with Short *a*

Children will blend and read short *a* CVC words.

PREPARE

Display the *a*, *d*, *n*, *s* letter cards from the Word Building Manipulative Cards. Point to each letter and review the sound each stands for. Have children repeat the sounds after you.

TEACH

MODEL AND GUIDE PRACTICE Place the *a* letter card on the chalkboard ledge, point to it, and say /a/. Ask children to repeat /a/ after you.

- Place the *d* letter card next to the *a* letter card.
- Blend the sounds /a/ and /d/ together to read *ad* and have children repeat the word after you.
- Place the *s* letter card before the *a* letter card.
- Blend the sounds /s/, /a/, /d/ together to read *sad*. Have children repeat the word after you.

USE THE WORD IN CONTEXT Use *sad* in a sentence to reinforce its meaning, for example: *The sad boy was crying.*

REPEAT THE PROCEDURE Use the following words to continue modeling and guided practice: *dad, Dan, Nan.*

PRACTICE

COMPLETE THE PUPIL PAGE Read the directions aloud, model how to blend the sounds, and identify the pictures.

ASSESS/CLOSE

BLEND AND READ WORDS Use page 28 to assess children's skill in blending with short *a*.

ALTERNATE TEACHING STRATEGY

Write the word *Dan* on the chalkboard. Explain that *Dan* is a person's name, and that one way to tell is by the capital *D* at the beginning. Write the following words on the board in random order: *Dad, Dan, Nan, an, ad*. Have children identify the names by the capital letters. Read the names aloud.

▶ **Auditory/Visual**

Introduce

High-Frequency Words: *with, has*

OBJECTIVES

Children will identify and read the high-frequency words *with* and *has*.

PREPARE

LISTEN TO WORDS Ask children to clap when they hear the word *with* in this sentence: *The girl draws with a red crayon.* Then ask children to clap when they hear *has* in this sentence: *The boy has a green crayon.*

TEACH

IDENTIFY THE WORDS Distribute word cards *with* and *has* from the back of the Pupil's Edition. Write the sentences from the Prepare section on the chalkboard. Read the sentences aloud and have a volunteer circle the words *with* and *has*. Ask volunteers to match their cards to those words in the sentences. Then reread the sentences pointing to each word as you read, and have all children hold up *with* or *has* when they hear those words.

PRACTICE

COMPLETE THE PUPIL PAGE Before children begin, read the directions aloud. Remind children that they should circle more than one word in each row.

ASSESS/CLOSE

REVIEW THE PAGE Use page 29 to assess children's recognition of the words *with* and *has*. Place word cards *with* and *has* face down and ask children to flip over one card and read it aloud.

Name____________________

1. with	has	(with)	has	(with)
2. with	has	(with)	has	(with)
3. with	(with)	(with)	has	has
4. has	(has)	with	with	(has)
5. has	with	(has)	with	(has)

Read the first word in each row. • Circle the words in the row that are the same.

ALTERNATE TEACHING STRATEGY

Use two word cards for each high-frequency word: *the*, *with*, *is*, and *has*. Randomly place each set of cards in two columns on a bulletin board. After each word in the left column attach a piece of yarn long enough to reach the other column. Then have children, in turn, attach the yarn from a word in the left column to its matching word in the right column.

▶ **Visual/Kinesthetic**

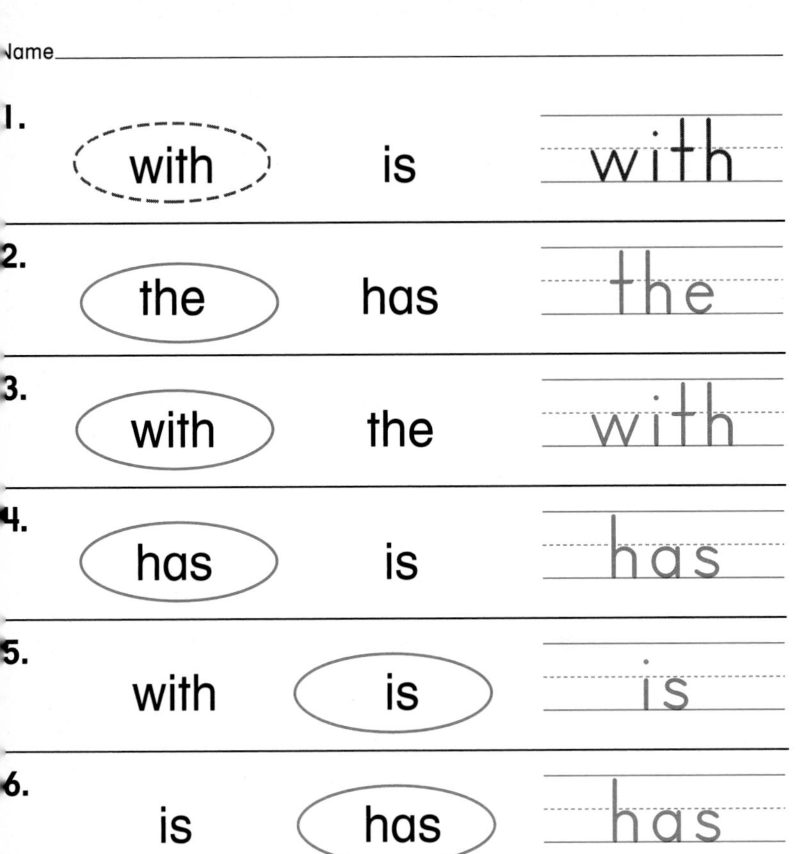

Name________________

1.	with	is	with
2.	the	has	the
3.	with	the	with
4.	has	is	has
5.	with	is	is
6.	is	has	has

Listen to the word. • Circle the word you hear. • Then write the word.

McGraw-Hill School Division

30 Review High-Frequency Words

Review

High-Frequency Words

Children will identify and read the high-frequency words *with, has, the, is.*

PREPARE

LISTEN TO WORDS Tell children that you will say a word and then read a sentence. Ask them to wave their right hand when they hear the word.

the	*Look at the cat.*	**is**	*The toy is a ball.*
with	*It plays with a toy.*	**has**	*The ball has a bell in it.*

TEACH

IDENTIFY THE WORDS Distribute High-Frequency Word Cards *the, with, is,* and *has* from the back of the Pupil's Edition. On the chalkboard, write *the, with, is, has.* Point to each word and read it aloud. Have children hold up the matching card as you reread the words. Then write the sentences from the Prepare section. As you read the sentences aloud, have children hold up the appropriate word card when they see and hear the word.

PRACTICE

COMPLETE THE PUPIL PAGE Read the directions aloud. Tell children to listen as you say the words they are to circle and write: (1) *with;* (2) *the;* (3) *with;* (4) *has;* (5) *is;* (6) *has.*

ASSESS/CLOSE

REVIEW THE PAGE Use page 30 to assess children's progress with the high-frequency words *with, has, the, is.* Say the following sentence and have children hold up the missing card: *The boy was_______his mom.*

TEACHING TIP

DIRECTIONALITY As you write the sentences from the Prepare activity on chart paper, explain to children that you start to write on the left and move to the right. Point out the spaces you leave between words. Emphasize the top-to-bottom directionality as you begin each new line. Reread the message, moving your finger underneath each word to emphasize directionality.

Have children write the message about the cat. Tell children to write the message from left-to-right and from top-to-bottom. You may wish to have children write a new message.

Develop

Phonological Awareness

Count Syllables

Teach Read the poem. Then clap and say the name *Max* and tell children the word *Max* has one word part. Then say the name *Pe-ter* and clap the two word parts. Have children clap and say the word parts with you.

Practice Play "Who's That?" The first child points to a classmate and asks: *"Who's that?"* The classmate responds by saying and clapping the word parts in his or her name. Then he or she points to another child and asks, *"Who's that?"* Continue until all children have had a turn.

Max the Clown

Max the Clown is a happy man,
He laughs the whole day through.
You won't feel glum,
you won't feel mad,
Should Max come to visit you.

Identify Beginning and Ending Sounds

Phonemic Awareness

MATERIALS

- **Phonics Picture Posters** *monkey, iguana*
- **Bean bag**

Teach **FOCUS ON BEGINNING SOUNDS**

Display the Phonics Picture Poster (picture side only) for *monkey*. Say the word *monkey*, emphasizing the initial /m/. Have children repeat the word and /m/ with you. Repeat using the Phonics Picture Poster for *iguana* and the beginning /i/ sound.

Practice Say the following words and have children point to the poster that shows the same beginning sound: *man, igloo, if, Max, money, itch, mad, ink, is.*

FOCUS ON ENDING SOUNDS

Tell children the /m/ sound can be heard at the end of a word, as in the word *ham*. Have children say *ham* and the ending /m/ sound. Then have children say "ham" when they hear you say a word ending with /m/. Use these words: *Sam, hum, jar, same, ball, Kim.*

Identify Middle Sounds

Phonemic Awareness

MATERIALS

- **Phonics Picture Posters**
  bib

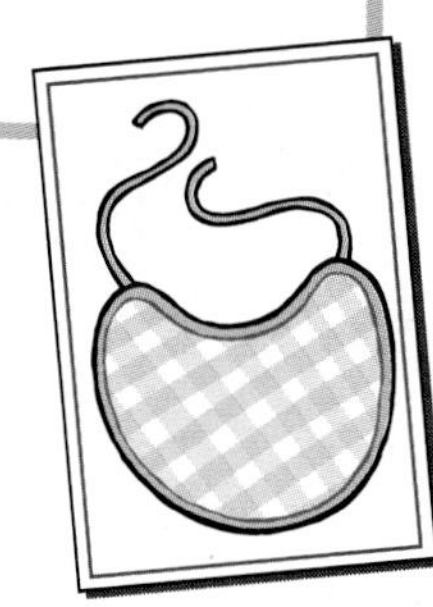

Teach Display the Phonics Picture Poster (picture side only) for *bib*. Say the word, elongating the middle /i/ sound. Have children repeat the word and the /i/ sound. Repeat with names from the poem: *Sid*, *Min*. Then say words with and without the middle /i/ sound, having children say /i/ when they hear that sound in a word: *big*, *bag*, *Tim*, *sit*, *bug*.

Practice Say the words *Min*, *Sid* and *Jan*. Tell children the words *Min* and *Sid* have the same middle sound. Then tell children you will say three words and they will say the two words that have the same middle sound. Use these words: *Bill*, *Pat*, *Min*; *Sid*, *Vin*, *Jack*; *Kim*, *John*, *Will*; *Jim*, *Tam*, *Kit*.

Blend Sounds

Phonemic Awareness

MATERIALS

- **Three sheets paper**

Teach Tape three pieces of paper to a wall. Have children listen as you say the following three sounds, while pointing to one piece of paper for each sound: /k/-/i/-/m/. Tell children you will put the sounds together to say a name. Say *Kim* as you quickly slide your finger across the three pieces of paper. Have children say the word *Kim* with you. Then have the rest of the children repeat the word.

Practice Then say the sounds for the following words: *din*, *Dad*, *Kim*, *Rat*, *mat*, *sit*, *bad*, and *bid*. Have volunteers blend the sounds to say the words.

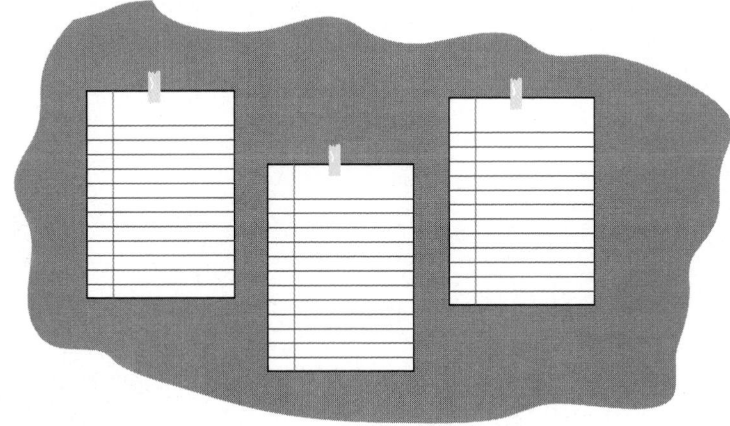

Introduce

Initial /m/*Mm*

OBJECTIVES

Children will identify initial /m/*Mm* and form the letters *Mm*.

PREPARE

PHONOLOGICAL AWARENESS Say the words *moon, man, fan* and have children identify the rhyming words. Repeat with the words *make, rake, map*.

Listen

As you sing the song, "Marco Monkey," hold up the Phonics Picture Poster for *monkey*. Have children clap each time they hear the /m/ sound at the beginning of a word. *Phonemic Awareness*

TEACH

IDENTIFY INITIAL /m/*Mm* Distribute the letter card *Mm* from the Word Building Manipulative Cards and display it on the chalkboard ledge. Explain that the letters *Mm* stand for the sound /m/. Write the sentence *Max makes a map* on the chalkboard and ask a volunteer to circle the letters *Mm*. Have all children say /m/.

FORM *Mm* Write the letters *M* and *m*, reviewing how to form these letters. Have children trace the Handwriting Models in the back of the Pupil's Edition. Then have them write the letters on paper.

PRACTICE

COMPLETE THE PUPIL PAGE After reading the directions aloud, have children name the key picture *monkey* and identify the other pictures.

ASSESS/CLOSE

IDENTIFY AND USE INITIAL /m/*Mm* Use page 31 to assess children's knowledge of initial /m/*Mm*. Have children say the sound /m/ and a word that begins with *M* or *m*.

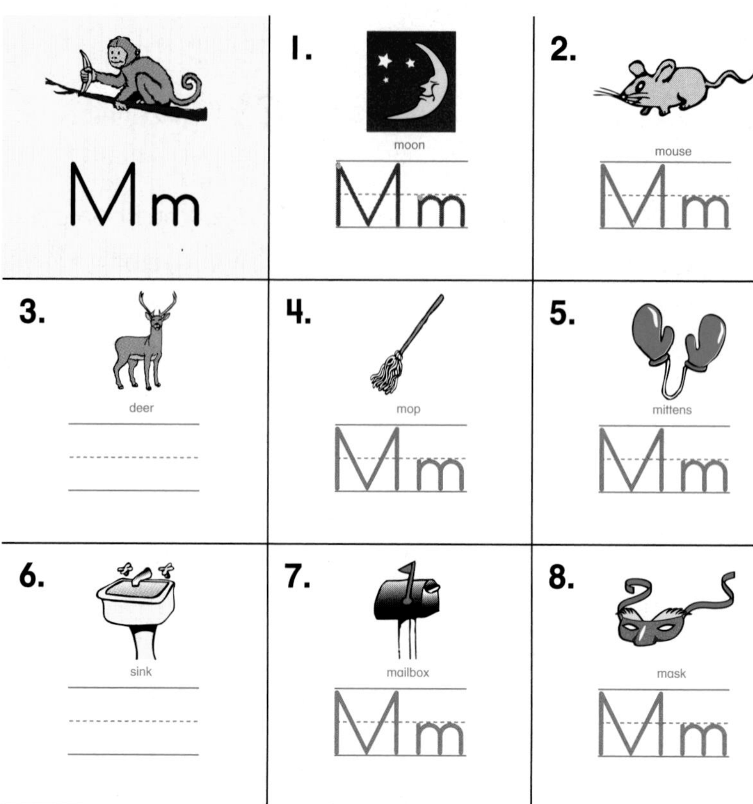

Name____________________

Mm	1. moon Mm	2. mouse Mm
3. deer	4. mop Mm	5. mittens Mm
6. sink	7. mailbox Mm	8. mask Mm

Say the name of each picture. • If the name begins with the same sound as *monkey*, write *Mm* on the line.

Introduce Initial /m/*Mm* 31

Listen

Marco Monkey

Marco the monkey likes to munch.
Marco the monkey likes to munch.
Marco the monkey likes to munch.
Marco munches on muffins!

Sung to the tune:
"Skip To My Lou"
From **Songs from A to Z**

Phonics Picture Posters and Cards

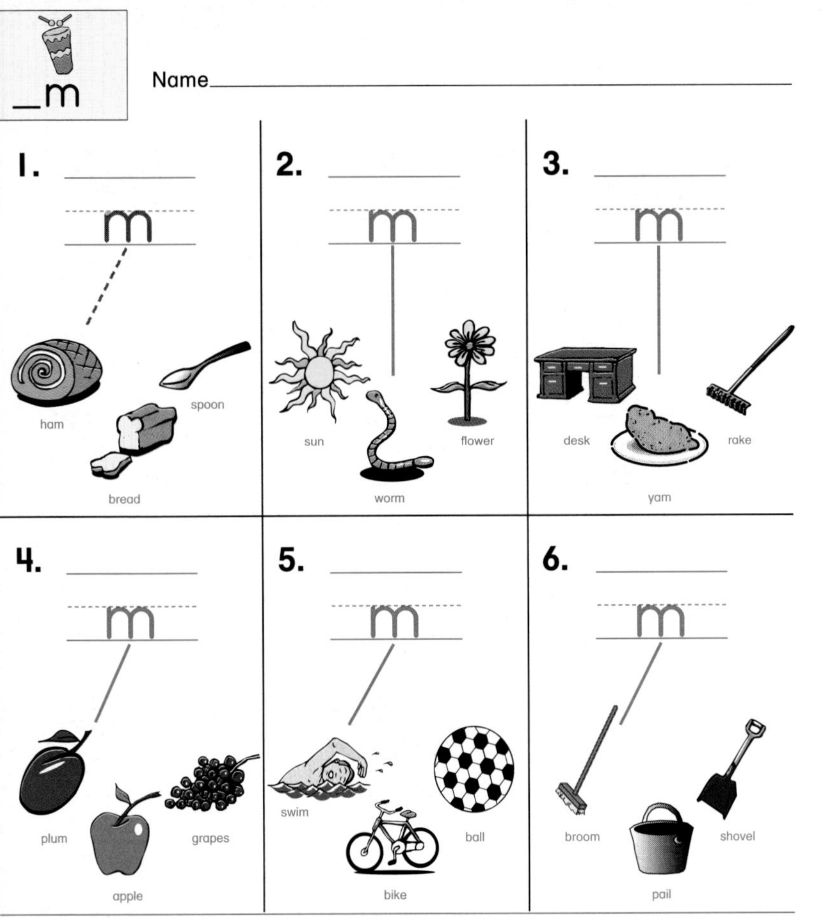
_m Name______________________

1. m
ham, spoon, bread

2. m
sun, flower, worm

3. m
desk, rake, yam

4. m
plum, grapes, apple

5. m
swim, ball, bike

6. m
broom, shovel, pail

McGraw-Hill School Division

Write the letter *m*. • Say the name of each picture. • Draw a line from the *m* to each picture whose name has the same ending sound as *drum*.

32 Introduce Final /m/m

Introduce

Final /m/*m*

Children will identify final /m/*m*.

PREPARE

PHONOLOGICAL AWARENESS Play a rhyming game with children. Say: *I say* ham, *you say* _____." *(rhyming word)* If children have difficulty review some words that rhyme with ham such as, *jam*, *Sam*, *lamb*, *Pam*, *Tam* and so on.

Listen

Say the following sentence: "*I like to* hum *when I play the* drum." Have the children clap each time they hear the /m/ sound at the end of a word. *Phonemic Awareness*

TEACH

IDENTIFY FINAL /m/*m* Display or draw pictures of a *broom* and a *drum* on the chalkboard. Have children say the name of each picture. Invite a volunteer to write the letter that stands for the sound they hear at the end. Then write *broom* and *drum* and ask volunteers to circle the letter *m* and say /m/.

PRACTICE

COMPLETE THE PUPIL PAGE Before children begin, read the directions aloud and help them identify the pictures on the page.

ASSESS/CLOSE

IDENTIFY AND USE FINAL /m/*m* Use page 32 to assess children's progress with final /m/*m*. Say the words *Kim* and *jam* and have children write the letter that stands for the final sound in both.

TEACHING TIP

INSTRUCTIONAL Because the letters *M*, *N* and *m*, *n* have similar shapes, some children may confuse these letters. You may need to review how to identify these letters and provide extra handwriting practice.

ALTERNATE TEACHING STRATEGY

Display the letter cards *n*, *a*, *d*, *s*, *m* along the chalkboard ledge in random order. Have children work in groups to think of how the letters can be arranged to form words. Call on a member of each group to rearrange the letters to form and say a word. Tell children that they can use names.

▶ **Linguistic/Kinesthetic**

Introduce

Initial /i/*Ii*

OBJECTIVES

Children will identify initial /i/*Ii* and form the letters *Ii*.

PREPARE

PHONOLOGICAL AWARENESS Read the song, "Izzy Iguana" to the children and have them clap the words while you count the words with your fingers.

While holding up the Phonics Picture Poster for *iguana*, sing the song, "Izzy Iguana." Have children raise their hand when they hear /i/ at the beginning of a word. *Phonemic Awareness*

TEACH

IDENTIFY INITIAL /i/*Ii* Say the words *if, it, is,* and *in*. Have volunteers write the letter that begins each word. Explain that the letters *Ii* stand for /i/. Then write these sentences: *A bird ___s ___n the snow. ___s ___t cold?* Read the sentences aloud. Invite volunteers to write the missing letters *Ii* while all children say /i/. Reread the sentences, emphasizing the short *i* sound.

FORM *Ii* Children may need to review how to write *I* and *i*. Have children use the letter cards from the Word Building Manipulative Cards to write *I* and *i* on paper folded into fourths.

PRACTICE

COMPLETE THE PUPIL PAGE Read the directions aloud and identify the key picture *iguana* for children. Complete the page together, helping children identify the pictures.

ASSESS/CLOSE

IDENTIFY AND USE INITIAL /i/*Ii* Use page 33 to assess children's progress. Write *a, d, i, s* on the chalkboard. Invite volunteers to circle the letter *i* and say the sound it stands for.

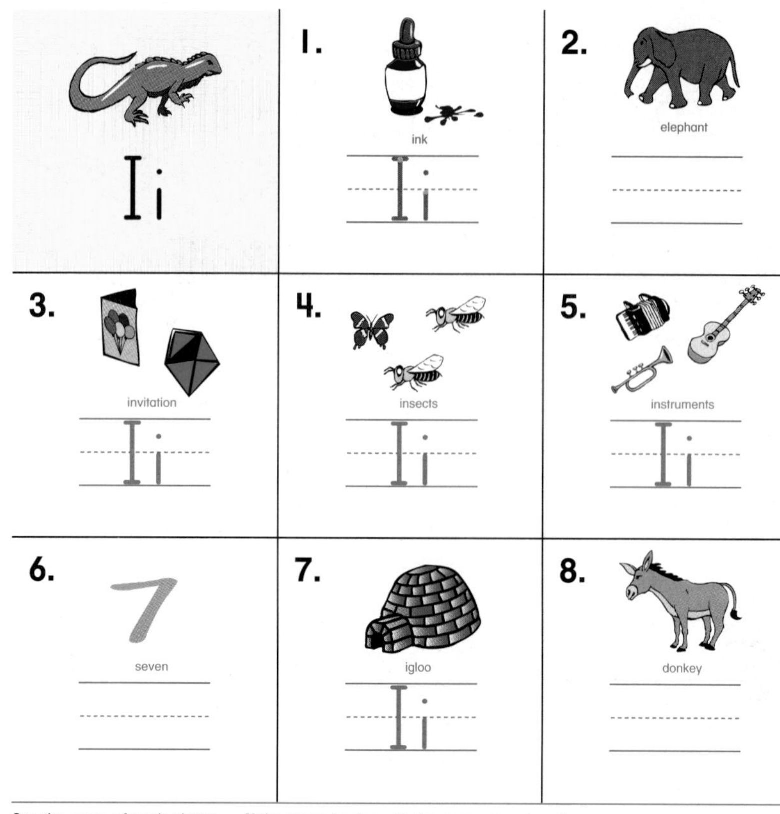

Ii

1. ink Ii
2. elephant
3. invitation Ii
4. insects Ii
5. instruments Ii
6. seven
7. igloo Ii
8. donkey

Say the name of each picture. • If the name begins with the same sound as *iguana*, write *Ii* on the line.

Introduce Initial /i/*Ii* 33

Izzy Iguana

Izzy Iguana is ill today,
Ill today, ill today.
He can't invite his friends to play,
Izzy is ill, indeed!

Tune: "Here We Go 'Round the Mulberry Bush"
From **Songs from A to Z**

Phonics Picture Posters and Cards

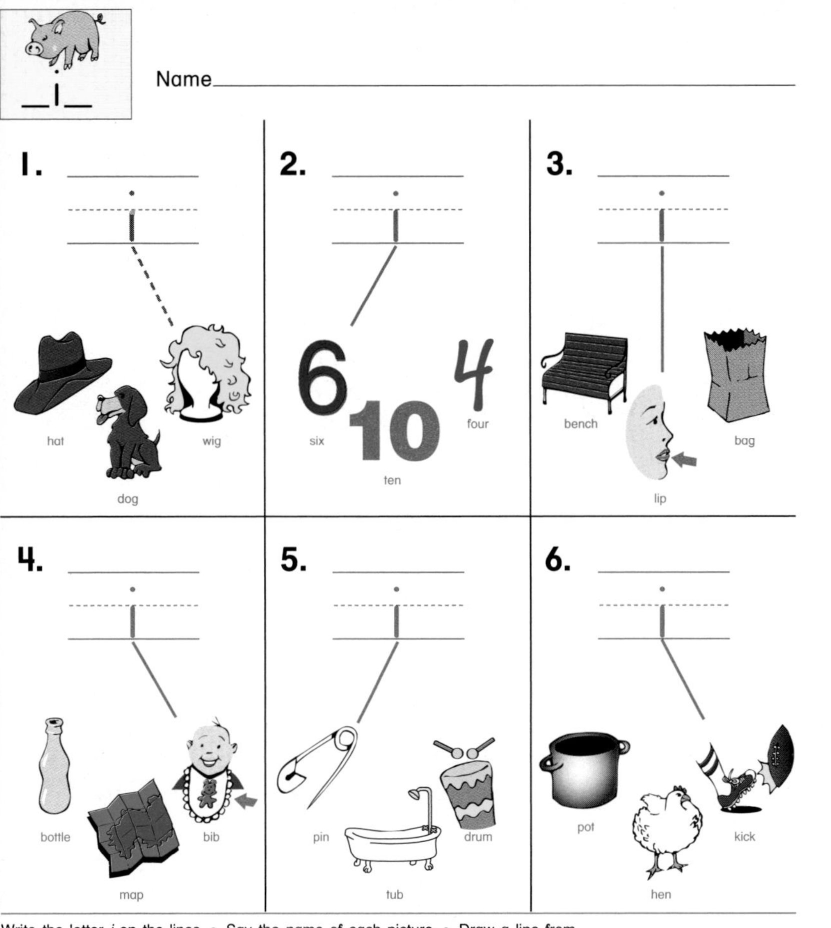
Name

1. i — hat, dog, wig
2. i — six, ten, four
3. i — bench, lip, bag
4. i — bottle, map, bib
5. i — pin, tub, drum
6. i — pot, hen, kick

McGraw-Hill School Division

Write the letter *i* on the lines. • Say the name of each picture. • Draw a line from the *i* to the picture whose name has the same middle sound as *pig*.

34 Introduce Medial /i/*i*

Introduce

Medial /i/*i*

Children will identify medial /i/*i*.

PREPARE

PHONOLOGICAL AWARENESS Brainstorm with children words that rhyme with *pig*, such as *wig*, *fig*, *big*, *dig* and so on. Remind children that the words must have the same ending sound *-ig*.

Say the following words and have children say /i/ when they hear a word with the middle /i/ sound: *pig*, *Nick*, *sat*, *bin*, *ten*, *will*, *bib*, *run*, *fin*. *Phonemic Awareness*

TEACH

IDENTIFY MEDIAL /i/*i* Remind children that the letter *i* stands for the sound /i/. Say the characters from the rhyme and have children identify the names that have medial /i/: *Sam*, *Sid*, *Min*, *Dan*. Then write *Sid* and *Min* on the chalkboard and invite volunteers to circle the letter that stands for /i/ in these words.

PRACTICE

COMPLETE THE PUPIL PAGE Before children begin the page, read the directions aloud and help them identify the pictures.

ASSESS/CLOSE

IDENTIFY AND USE MEDIAL /i/*i* Use page 34 to assess children's knowledge of medial /i/*i*. Encourage children to answer this riddle: *I am a number. I have /i/ in the middle of my name. What am I?* (six)

LANGUAGE SUPPORT

ESL In Spanish and in many other languages, there is no vowel sound /i/, and the vowel sound for the letter *i* is like the English long *e*. Pair a non-English-speaking child who needs extra practice pronouncing this sound with an English-speaking child. Have partners name pictures with initial /i/*i* and medial /i/*i* together.

ALTERNATE TEACHING STRATEGY

Organize children into small groups. Assign each group a word that contains short *i* in the middle: *hit*, *kiss*, *fix*, *mix*, *swim*, *kick*, or *rip*. Challenge groups to create riddles for their classmates using one clue. For example, *This is what Tom did to the ball.* (hit)

▶ **Logical/Auditory**

Review

/m/m, /i/i

Children will identify /m/*m* and /i/*i* in words.

PREPARE

PHONOLOGICAL AWARENESS Read the following sentences aloud. Have children repeat after you, whispering each sentence.

Read the sentences again and invite children to clap when they hear a word with the sound you say. ***Phonemic Awareness***

initial /i/ *Igloos are houses made of snow.*
medial /i/ *Some people live in these houses.*
initial /m/ *Why do people wear mittens?*
final /m/ *Tim and Sam have red mittens.*

TEACH

REVIEW /m/*m*, /i/*i* Write *m* and *i* on the chalkboard. Draw three blank letter boxes below the letters. Ask children to listen for /m/ and /i/ in the words you say. Say a word and have volunteers, in turn, write *m* or *i* in the appropriate letter box to indicate where they hear the sound in the word. Use these words: *map, hum, bit, inch.*

PRACTICE

COMPLETE THE PUPIL PAGE After reading the directions aloud, help children identify the pictures.

ASSESS/CLOSE

IDENTIFY AND USE /m/*m*, /i/*i* Use page 35 to assess children's progress with /m/*m*, /i/*i*.

Name__________

1. m	2. m	3. m
pig, man	mask, girl	broom, apple
4. i	**5. i**	**6. i**
igloo, cap	drum, iguana	pin, ball

Trace the letter. Say the sound it stands for. • Say the names of the pictures. • Draw a line from the letter to the picture whose name has the sound the letter stands for.

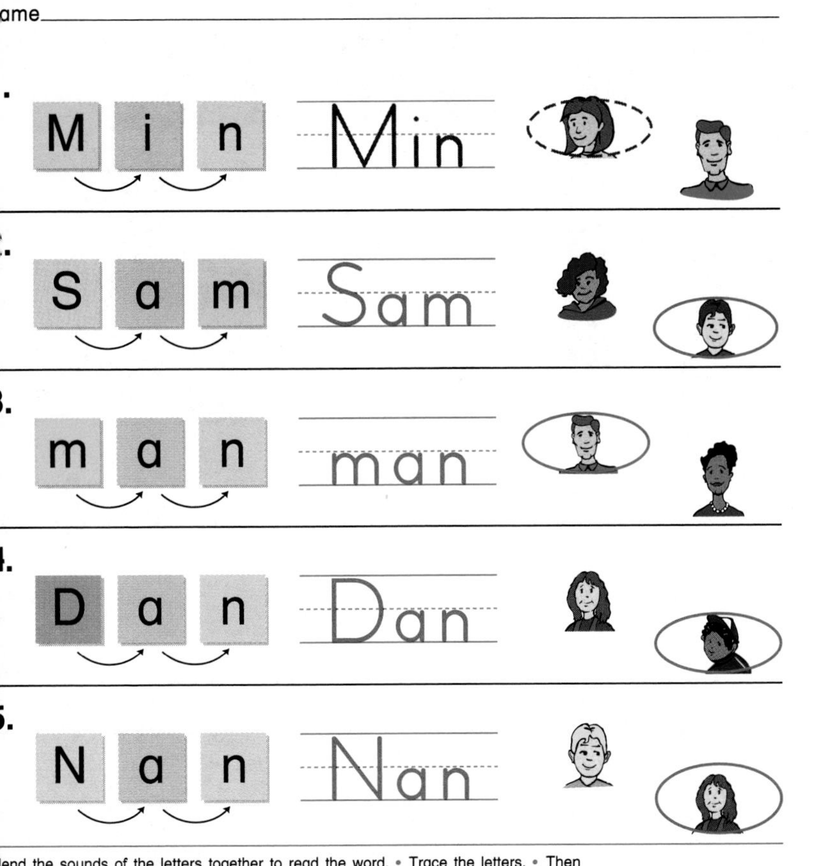
ame

1. M i n — Min
2. S a m — Sam
3. m a n — man
4. D a n — Dan
5. N a n — Nan

McGraw-Hill School Division

lend the sounds of the letters together to read the word. • Trace the letters. • Then rite the word. • Circle the picture that goes with each word.

36 Blending with Short *a* and *i*

Blending with

Short *a* and *i*

TESTED OBJECTIVES

Children will blend and read short *a* and *i* CVC words.

PREPARE

Place letter cards *a*, *d*, *i*, *m*, *n*, *s* from the Word Building Manipulative Cards on the chalkboard ledge. Hold up each card and review the sound for each letter. Ask children to say each sound after you.

TEACH

MODEL AND GUIDE PRACTICE Display the *i* letter card and point to it. Say /i/ and have children repeat /i/.

- Place the *m* letter card next to the *i* letter card.
- Blend the sounds /i /and /m/ together and have children repeat after you.
- Place the *d* letter card before the *i* letter card.
- Blend the sounds /d/, /i/, /m/ together to read *dim*.
- Have children repeat the word *dim* after you.

USE THE WORD IN CONTEXT Use *dim* in a sentence to reinforce its meaning, for example: *It's hard to see in dim light.*

REPEAT THE PROCEDURE Use the following to continue modeling and guided practice: *did, sad, mad, man.*

PRACTICE

COMPLETE THE PUPIL PAGE After reading the directions, model how to blend the sounds. Identify pictures with children.

ASSESS/CLOSE

BLEND AND READ WORDS Use page 36 to assess children's skill in blending with short *a* and *i*.

ALTERNATE TEACHING STRATEGY

Help children distinguish between the /a/ and /i/ sounds by having them repeat after you as you chant pairs of short *a* and *i* words that are similar, emphasizing the difference in the vowel sound. For example: *did, dad; sit, sat; Sid, sad; Min, man.*

▶ Auditory

Read the Story

Children will use their knowledge of phonics and decoding and high-frequency words to read.

Nan

BEFORE READING

PREVIEW Have children look at the picture on the cover of the story. Read the title, *Nan*, aloud and explain that the story is about a girl named Nan. Invite children to take a **picture walk** through pages 2, 3, and 4 to preview the story. Write the high-frequency words *is*, *the*, *with* and *has* on the chalkboard. Have the children find these words on pages 2 and 3. Invite volunteers to say the words as you point to them.

MAKE PREDICTIONS Ask children what they think will happen in the story. Ask: *What do you think Nan and her friends will do in this story?* Record children's predictions on the chalkboard.

DURING READING

READING SUGGESTIONS Encourage children to use the pictures to guide them through the story. On page 2, have the children find the high-frequency word, *the*. Explain to them that this is where they should begin reading. Encourage children to track print from left-to-right with their finger as they read the story.

The man has  .

2

Sam is with  .

3

Min has .

4

Dan has .

5

TEACHING TIP

MANAGEMENT Help children put together their own take-home story. Give the following directions to the children. Demonstrate as needed.

To put book together,
Tear out the story page.
Cut along the dotted line.
Fold each section on the fold line.

Nan is 6.

6

Dad has ___.

7

Nan is in ___.

8

Read the Story

AFTER READING

RETURN TO PREDICTIONS Read aloud children's predictions from the chalkboard. Discuss whether their predictions matched what happened in the story. Talk about whether or not the story ended as children thought it would end.

RETELL THE STORY Encourage children to retell the story in these two ways:

- Ask children to retell the story using the pictures. Have children tell what is happening on each page by looking at the picture.
- Have one child tell a sentence beginning the story. Then have another child add another sentence to continue the story. Continue until the end the story.

STORY QUESTIONS Ask the following questions about the story.

- *Who is Nan?* (Nan is the birthday girl.) ***Literal/Story Details***
- *On page 4, why is Min carrying party hats?* (To bring to the party for everyone to wear.) ***Inferential/Use Illustrations***
- *What other things could the guests bring to the party?* (Cake and decorations) ***Critical/Make Inferences***

Cross Curricular: Social Studies

BUILD A NEIGHBORHOOD Provide a set of building blocks. Let children work as partners to build a neighborhood together. Tell them to discuss what kinds of buildings they need, such as a library, school, post office and so on. Encourage them to share ideas with their partners and to listen to the ideas of each other as they work together.

▶ **Spatial/Interpersonal**

Introduce

Colors

Children will identify the colors *red*, *blue*, and *yellow*.

PREPARE

INTRODUCE COLORS Tell children that colors can be found everywhere. Invite children to point out colors they recognize around the room. Tell children that they will learn three colors today: *red*, *yellow* and *blue*.

TEACH

IDENTIFY COLORS Tell children that you will show them the colors *red*, *blue*, and *yellow*. Hold up a sheet of red construction paper, and say *This is red.* Repeat with sheets of *blue* and *yellow* paper. Give each child a *red*, a *blue*, and a *yellow* crayon or block. Show an object that is *red* and have children raise the appropriate crayon or block and say the color name. Repeat with other *red*, *blue*, and *yellow* objects.

PRACTICE

COMPLETE THE PUPIL PAGE Before children begin, read the directions aloud. Then name each object and color at the top of the pupil page. Explain to children that they should color the objects in the picture the same color as indicated at the top of the page.

ASSESS/CLOSE

REVIEW THE PAGE Use page 39 to assess children's knowledge of the colors *red*, *blue*, and *yellow*. Have children name other objects in the classroom that are the same colors.

Name____________________

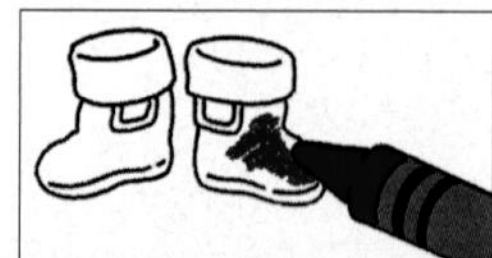

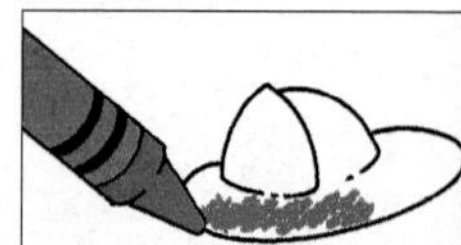

Name each color and object. • Then find and color the objects in the picture the same color.

Beginning Reading Concepts: *Colors* 39

ALTERNATE TEACHING STRATEGY

ESL APPROPRIATE Have children use *red*, *blue*, and *yellow* finger paint. As each child dips his or her finger into individual colors, remind them of the color name.

▶ Kinesthetic/Visual

Name

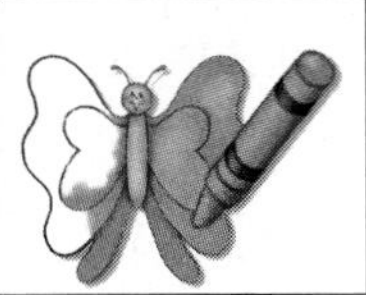

Name each color and object. • Then find and color the objects in the picture the same color.

40 Beginning Reading Concepts: *Colors*

TEACHING TIP

INSTRUCTIONAL Make a bar graph titled, "Our Favorite Colors." Place a paper square at the top of a piece of chart paper for the following colors: *red, blue, yellow, green, orange, purple*. Then help each child write their name below their favorite color. Count up the number of "votes" for each color. Have each child say all of the color names aloud.

Introduce

Colors

TESTED OBJECTIVES

Children will identify the colors *orange*, *green*, and *purple*.

PREPARE

INTRODUCE COLORS Review the colors *red*, *blue* and *yellow* with children. Have them point to something in the room that is *red*, *blue* or *yellow*. Tell children they will learn three new colors today: *orange*, *green* and *purple*.

TEACH

IDENTIFY COLORS Tell children that you will show them the colors *orange*, *green*, and *purple*. Hold up an orange marker and say *This is orange*. Repeat with a *green* and a *purple* marker. Then hold up an *orange* object. Tell children to name the color of the object. Show additional objects that are *orange*, *green*, and *purple*. Repeat, having children name each color.

PRACTICE

COMPLETE THE PUPIL PAGE Before children begin, read the directions aloud. Then name each object and color at the top of the pupil page. Tell children to color the objects in the picture the same color as indicated at the top of the page.

ASSESS/CLOSE

REVIEW THE PAGE Use page 40 to assess children's ability to identify the colors *orange*, *green*, and *purple*. Challenge children to name other objects in the classroom that are the same colors.

Develop

Phonological Awareness

Blend Onsets and Rimes

Teach Read the poem aloud. Have children listen as you say the sounds */c/-/at/.* Then blend the sounds to say the word *cat*. Have children blend the sounds with you. Repeat with other onsets and rimes such as: /m/-/at/; /s/-/it/; /f/-/at/; /t/-/im/.

Practice Read one line of the poem at a time. In each line, say the last word as an onset and rime. For example, Say: *Tim the Cat sits on a* /m/-/at/. Have children blend the sounds to say the word.

A Cat on a Mat

Tim the Cat sits on a mat.
The mat is big and tan.
Can Dan and Nat sit on the mat?
Tim Cat says they can.
Then Min and Sid come to the mat,
They ask if they can sit.
Tim Cat says, "You may sit down,
But only if you fit!"

Identify Beginning Sounds

Phonemic Awareness

MATERIALS
- Phonics Picture Posters
  turtle, cat
- Old magazines

Teach Display the Phonics Picture Poster (picture side only) for *turtle* and tell children the word *turtle* begins with the sound /t/. Say other words beginning with /t/ such as *top, tip, tap, tag,* having children repeat the word and the initial /t/ with you. Repeat with the Phonics Picture Poster for *cat* and the beginning /k/ sound. Have children repeat each of the following words and the /k/ sound: *cat, cap, can, cot.*

Practice Have children work with a partner to find pictures of items beginning with /t/ and /k/ in old magazines. Children may present their pictures to the class and say the word and the beginning sound. Repeat the Teach and Practice activities using the picture card for *cat* and such words as: *cat, come, call, cab, cut, cup, can, coat.*

Identify Ending Sounds

Phonemic Awareness

MATERIALS

- Word Building Manipulative Card
  foot

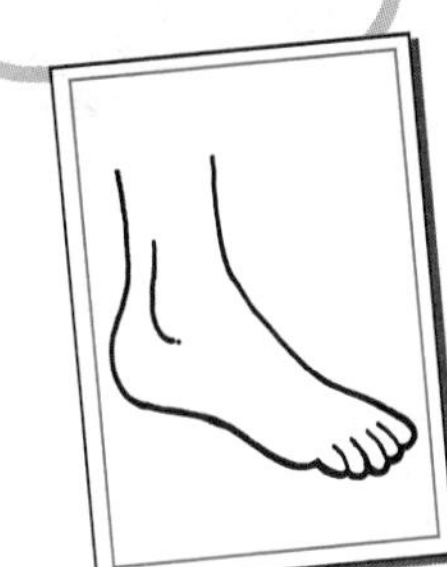

Teach Display the Word Building Manipulative Card for *foot* (picture side only). Say the word, emphasizing the final /t/. Tell children the word *foot* ends with the /t/ sound. Have children say *foot* and /t/. Say pairs of words, having children say the word that ends with /t/: *cab/cat*; *mat/mad*; *hot/hop*.

Practice Tell children the words *cat* and *hot* both end with the /t/ sound. Say the following pairs of words and have children say the sounds that each pair of words ends with: *tan/sun*; *bit/hut*; *had/did*; *cut/pat*; *win/fun*; *hot/pit*.

Segment Sounds

Phonemic Awareness

MATERIALS

- Blocks or snap cubes (one per child)

Teach Tell children they will break apart words into separate sounds. Say the word *man*. Then put three blocks on the table and demonstrate by moving a block forward for each separate sound: /m/-/a/-/n/. Tell children the word *man* has three sounds. Have children repeat the sounds with you. Repeat with other words such as: *sit*, *mad*, *fit*, *bag*, *bib*.

Practice Distribute three blocks to groups of three children. Circulate as children practice segmenting sounds you provide, using the blocks to indicate the three distinct sounds. Ask children to point to the block that shows the beginning, middle or ending sound in each word they have segmented. Use words such as *hot*, *ham*, *him*, *mug*, *cat*, *cab*, *win*, *ten*, *can*.

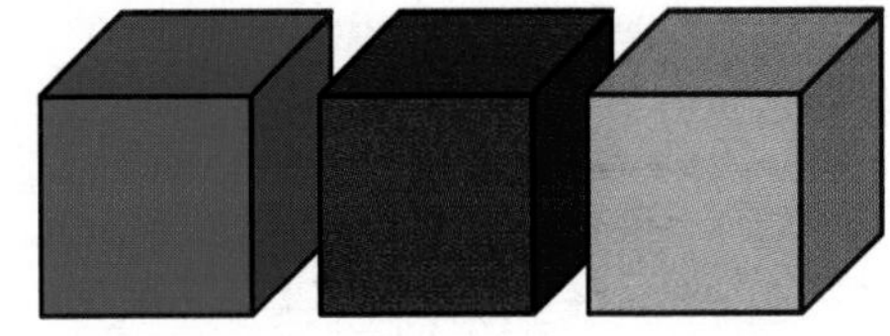

Introduce

Initial /t/*Tt*

Children will identify initial /t/*Tt* and form the letters *Tt*.

PREPARE

PHONOLOGICAL AWARENESS Say the following words and have children repeat after you and clap the syllables: *turtle, tap, toes, table.*

Listen

While holding up the Phonics Picture Poster for *turtle*, sing the song, "Teddy Turtle." Ask the children to tap their finger on their desk when they hear /t/ at the beginning of a word. *Phonemic Awareness*

TEACH

IDENTIFY INITIAL /t/*Tt* Write the word *too* on the chalkboard, and read it aloud. Explain that the letters *Tt* stand for the sound /t/. Have a volunteer circle the letters *Tt* as the class says /t/. Then write on the chalkboard: *Timmy the toad hopped by a tulip.* Read the sentence aloud and invite children to circle the letters *Tt* and say /t/.

FORM *Tt* Review how to write *T* and *t*. Have children write the letters on squares of paper. Children may use the Handwriting Models in the back of the Pupil's Edition for reference.

PRACTICE

COMPLETE THE PUPIL PAGE Have children name the key picture *turtle*. Then read the directions aloud and help children identify the other pictures.

ASSESS/CLOSE

IDENTIFY AND USE INITIAL /t/*Tt* Use page 41 to assess children's knowledge of initial /t/*Tt*. Also ask children to say a word or name that begins with /t/.

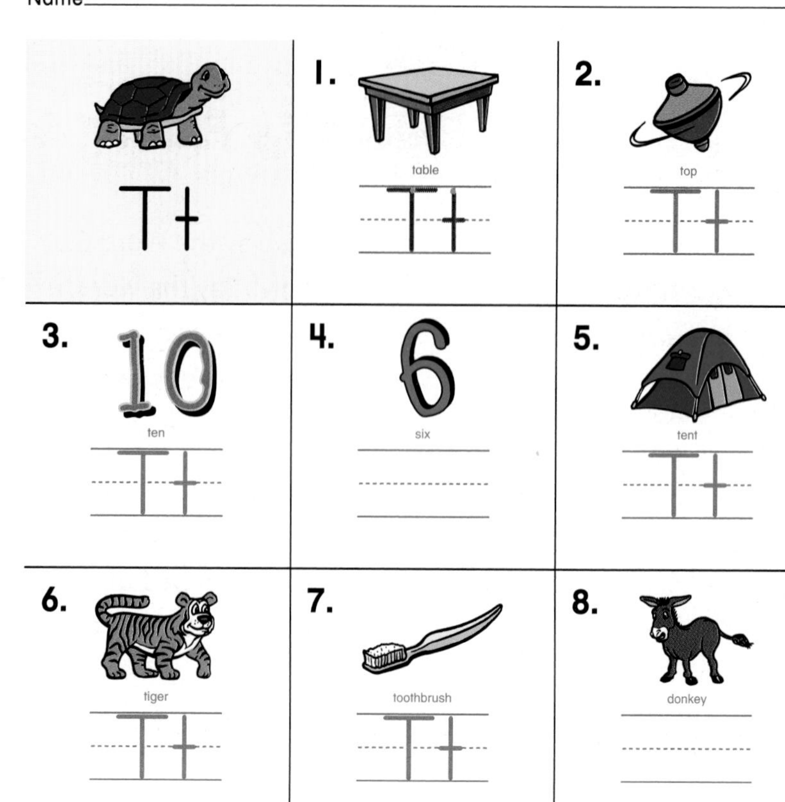
Name

Tt

1. table Tt
2. top Tt
3. ten Tt
4. six
5. tent Tt
6. tiger Tt
7. toothbrush Tt
8. donkey

Say the name of each picture. • If the name begins with the same sound as *turtle*, write *Tt* on the line.

Introduce Initial /t/*Tt* 41

Listen

Teddy Turtle

Teddy Turtle says, "Tickle your nose."
Teddy Turtle says, "Touch your clothes."
Teddy Turtle says, "Tap your toes."
"Tap your toes," says Teddy.

Sung to the tune:
"Skip To My Lou"
From **Songs from A to Z**

Phonics Picture Posters and Cards

Name ______________________

 _t_	1.  boot t	2.  pen
3. 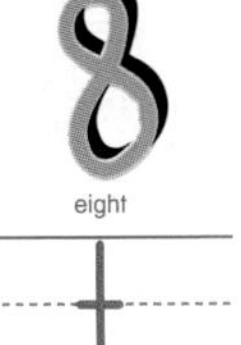 eight t	4.  jet t	5.  clock
6. 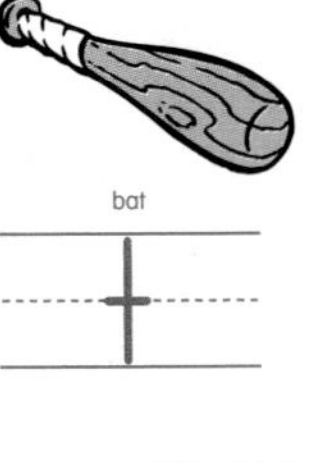 bat t	7. 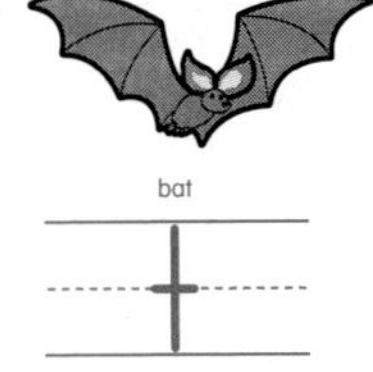 bat t	8. 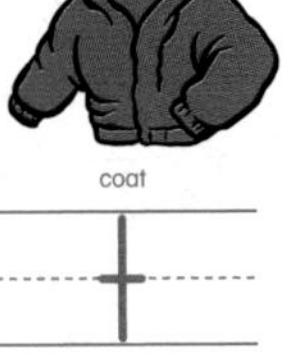 coat t

Say the name of each picture. • If the name has the same ending sound as *cat*, write *t* on the line.

42 Introduce Final /t/*t*

TEACHING TIP

MANAGEMENT You may wish to provide copies of the nine-box grid described in the Teach section for each pair of children. As each word is identified, children can place a marker on the word on their grid or color the appropriate word box with a yellow crayon.

ALTERNATE TEACHING STRATEGY

Have children print *t* in the middle of a page and around it draw pictures of things whose names begin or end with *t*. When they finish, invite children to share their pictures with classmates.

▶ Visual/Linguistic

Introduce

Final /t/*t*

Children will identify final /t/*t*.

PREPARE

PHONOLOGICAL AWARENESS Say each set of words and have children say the two words that rhyme: *cat, fat, pen; sit, sock, fit; up, cut, nut; hot, rock, cot.*

Listen

Say the following words and have children say /t/ when they hear that sound at the end of a word: *fit, nut, car, fan, cut, hot, then, that, sat, sap.* *Phonemic Awareness*

TEACH

IDENTIFY FINAL /t/*t* Say *Nat* and invite a volunteer to write the letter that stands for the ending sound. Then pass out *t* letter cards from the Word Building Manipulative Cards. Draw a large grid with nine boxes on a sheet of oaktag and write each of the following words in a box: *Nat, sad, mat, sat, him, sit, let, nut, hen.* Invite children to place letter cards on words with final /t/t.

PRACTICE

COMPLETE THE PUPIL PAGE Help children identify the key picture *cat*, and its ending sound /t/. Read the directions with children and identify the pictures.

ASSESS/CLOSE

IDENTIFY AND USE FINAL /t/*t* Use page 42 to assess children's skill with final /t/*t*. Have children supply the missing word in the following sentence and write its ending letter: *The ___ meowed.* (cat)

Introduce

Initial /k/*Cc*

OBJECTIVES

Children will identify initial /k/*Cc* and form the letters *Cc*.

PREPARE

PHONOLOGICAL AWARENESS Say the sentence Listen *Cassie Cat can count to ten.* Then say the sentence *Cassie cat can count to six* and have the children identify the word that was changed.

While holding up the Phonics Picture Poster for *cat*, sing the song, "Cassie Cat." Ask the children to clap when they hear the /k/ sound at the beginning of a word. *Phonemic Awareness*

TEACH

IDENTIFY INITIAL /k/*Cc* Write *Cc* on the chalkboard. Explain that the letters *Cc* can stand for the sound /k/. Write these words around the letter: *cat*, *Sid*, *come*, *can*, *dog*. Say each word and have children repeat after you and listen for /k/. Ask volunteers to draw a line from each word that begins with *c* to the letters *Cc* while the class says /k/.

FORM *Cc* Some children may need to review how to write *C* and *c*. Invite children to draw a cat on paper and write the letters *Cc* around it.

PRACTICE

COMPLETE THE PUPIL PAGE Guide children through the page by reading the directions aloud and identifying the pictures.

ASSESS/CLOSE

IDENTIFY AND USE INITIAL /k/*Cc* As well as using page 43 to assess children's knowledge of initial /k/*Cc*, have children draw a picture of an object whose name begins with /k/*Cc*.

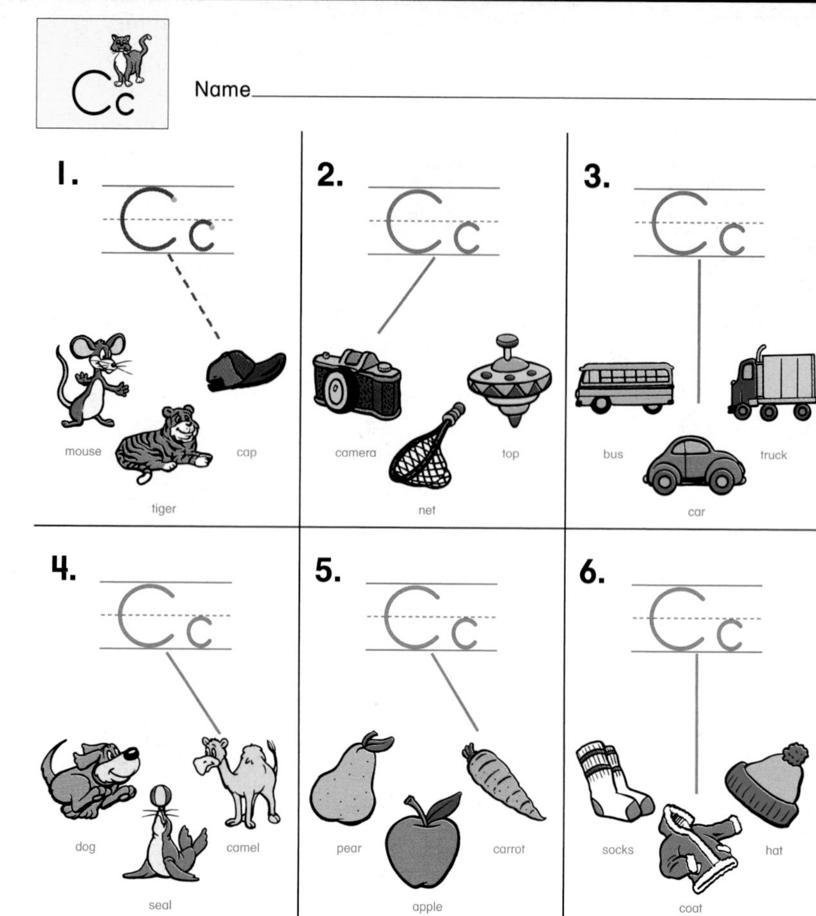

Cc Name__________

1. Cc — mouse, cap, tiger
2. Cc — camera, top, net
3. Cc — bus, truck, car
4. Cc — dog, camel, seal
5. Cc — pear, carrot, apple
6. Cc — socks, hat, coat

Write the letters *Cc*. • Say the name of each picture. • Draw a line from *Cc* to each picture whose name begins like *cat*.

Introduce Initial /k/*Cc* 43

Listen

Cassie Cat

Cassie Cat can count to ten.
Watch her count to ten again.
Cassie counts the things she sees
Like cows and cars and bumblebees!
Cassie Cat can count to ten.
Watch her count to ten again!

Tune:
"Twinkle, Twinkle Little Star"
From **Songs from A to Z**

Phonics Picture Posters and Cards

Name____________________

Cc

1. 

cap

Cc

2. 

camera

Cc

3. 

candle

Cc

4.

bear

5. 

turtle

6. 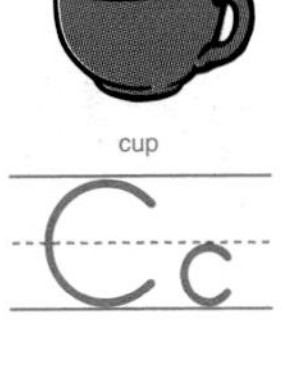

cup

Cc

7.

corn

Cc

8. 

cow

Cc

Say the name of each picture. • If the name begins with the same sound as *cat*, write *Cc* on the line.

44 Review Initial /k/*Cc*

Review

Initial /k/Cc

Children will identify initial /k/*Cc*.

PREPARE

PHONOLOGICAL AWARENESS Review the song "Cassie Cat" with children. Say the words *ten* and *again* and have children think of other words that rhyme with these words such as *when*, *hen*, *men*, and so on.

Listen

Say the following pairs of words and have children say the word that begins with the /k/ sound: *car/ten*; *can/tick*; *tulip/cat*; *line/cane*; *come/soft*. *Phonemic Awareness*

TEACH

IDENTIFY INITIAL /k/*Cc* Read aloud this sentence: *Tim Cat says they can.* Have children identify the words beginning with /k/. Remind children that the letters *Cc* can stand for /k/. Write the sentence on the chalkboard and invite volunteers to circle initial *Cc*.

PRACTICE

COMPLETE THE PUPIL PAGE Before children begin the page, read the directions aloud and help them identify the pictures.

ASSESS/CLOSE

IDENTIFY AND USE INITIAL /k/*Cc* Use page 44 to assess children's progress with initial /k/*Cc*. Say the word *camel* and have children identify the initial sound and write the letter that stands for it.

LANGUAGE SUPPORT

INSTRUCTIONAL Some languages do not have the consonant *c*. The equivalent letter is *k*. Non-English-speaking children whose native language has no *c* may need extra practice with /k/*c*. You may want to use words from the child's native language to introduce /k/.

ALTERNATE TEACHING STRATEGY

Have children draw and color a picture of an object that begins with /k/*c*, such as a car, cat, cup, cape, cow, coat. Help children label their pictures. Read the picture names aloud with children, emphasizing the initial /k/.

▶ Auditory/Visual

Review

/t/t, /k/c

Children will identify /t/*t* and /k/*c* in words.

PREPARE

PHONOLOGICAL AWARENESS Read the sentences below. Have children clap out the syllables in each word.

initial /k/ *I saw a camel on television.*
initial /t/ *It had two humps on its back.*
final /t/ *Camels live where it is hot.*

Reread the sentences. Have children wave when they hear a word with the sound you say. *Phonemic Awareness*

TEACH

REVIEW /t/*t*, /k/*c* Write the letters *t* and *c* on the chalkboard. Remind children that *t* stands for the sound /t/ and that *c* can stand for the sound /k/. Then draw three blank letter boxes. Have children listen for /t/ and /k/ in the words you say. Invite volunteers to write the letter in the correct box to show where they hear the sound—at the beginning, in the middle, or at the end of the word. Say: *can, pot, tub, hat*.

PRACTICE

COMPLETE THE PUPIL PAGE Help children complete the page. Read the directions aloud and help children name the pictures.

ASSESS/CLOSE

IDENTIFY AND USE /t/*t*, /k/*c* Use page 45 to assess children's progress with /t/*t*, /k/*c*. Have children write the letter that stands for the sound /k/. Repeat with /t/.

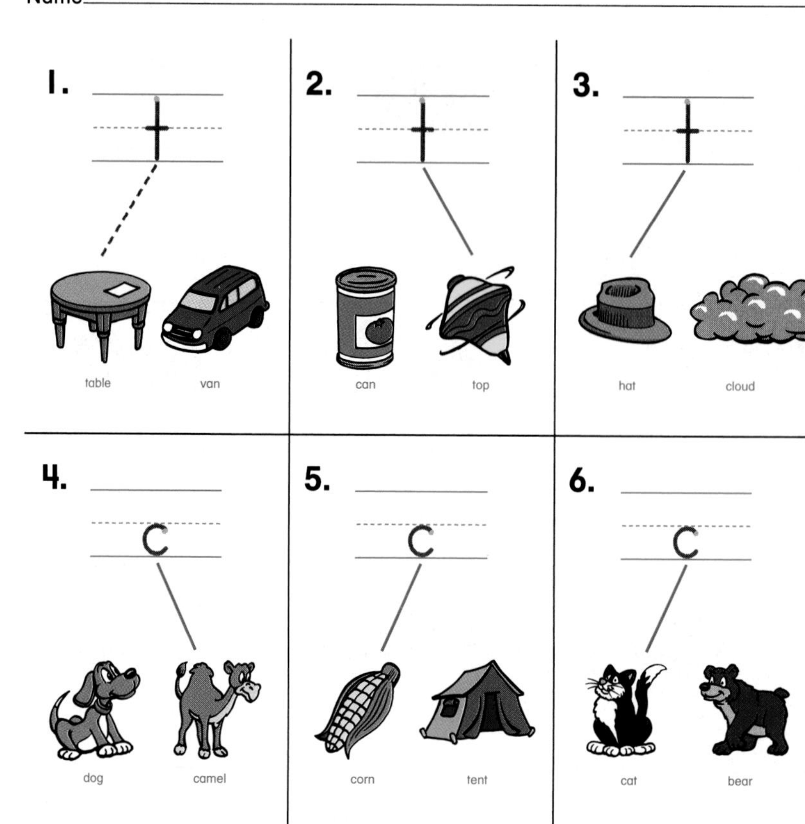

Name

1. cat / can — cat
2. Min / Sid — Min
3. cat / can — can
4. man / mat — mat
5. sad / sit — sit

McGraw-Hill School Division

Read the words. • Circle the word that names the picture. • Then write the word.

46 Blending with Short *a* and *i*

ALTERNATE TEACHING STRATEGY

Tell children that rhyming words have the same sounds at the end, for example: *tap* and *map*. Write the words *cat*, *man*, and *Dan* on the chalkboard. Invite volunteers to name the two words that rhyme. Have children name other words that rhyme with *man*. Write them on the chalkboard.

▶ **Auditory/Visual**

Blending with

Short *a* and *i*

TESTED OBJECTIVES

Children will blend and read short *a* and *i* CVC words.

PREPARE

Display the *a, c, d, i, m, n, s, t* letter cards from the Word Building Manipulative Cards. Point to each letter and say its sound. Have children repeat the sound.

TEACH

MODEL AND GUIDE PRACTICE Place the *i* letter card on the chalkboard ledge and say /i/. Have children repeat /i/.

- Place the *n* letter card next to the *i* letter card.
- Blend the sounds /i/ and /n/ together to read *in* and have children repeat the word after you.
- Place the t letter card before the *i* letter card.
- Blend the sounds /t/, /i/, /n/ together to read *tin*. Have children repeat the word *tin* after you.

USE THE WORD IN CONTEXT Use the word in a sentence to reinforce its meaning, for example: *Tin is a metal.*

REPEAT THE PROCEDURE Use the following words to continue modeling and guided practice: *Tim, Sid, tan, cat.*

PRACTICE

COMPLETE THE PUPIL PAGE Before children begin, read the directions aloud and help them identify the pictures.

ASSESS/CLOSE

BLEND AND READ WORDS Use page 46 to assess children's skill in blending with short *a* and *i*. Have children use letter cards to build and read a short *i* CVC word.

Introduce

High-Frequency Words: *he, see*

Children will identify and read the High-Frequency Words *he* and *see.*

PREPARE

LISTEN TO WORDS Read these sentences aloud and ask children to raise a hand when they hear the words *he* and *see*:
Tim can see a dog.
He is big.
He can see Tim.

TEACH

IDENTIFY THE WORDS Write the sentences from the Prepare section on the chalkboard. As you read the sentences aloud, invite volunteers to underline the words *he* and *see*. Give each child word cards for *he* and *not* from the High-Frequency Word Cards in the back of the Pupil's Edition. Have children play a matching game in small groups, turning their word cards face down. When a child turns up matching words, he or she reads the words aloud and keeps the cards.

PRACTICE

COMPLETE THE PUPIL PAGE Read the directions aloud before children begin the page. Point out to children that they should circle more than one word in each row.

ASSESS/CLOSE

REVIEW THE PAGE Use page 47 to assess children's recognition of the words *he* and *see*. Write the word *see* and ask children to read it aloud.

Name____________________

1.	he	see	(he)	see	(he)
2.	see	he	(see)	he	(see)
3.	see	(see)	he	(see)	he
4.	he	(he)	see	see	(he)
5.	he	see	(he)	see	(he)

Read the first word in each row. • Circle the words in the row that are the same.

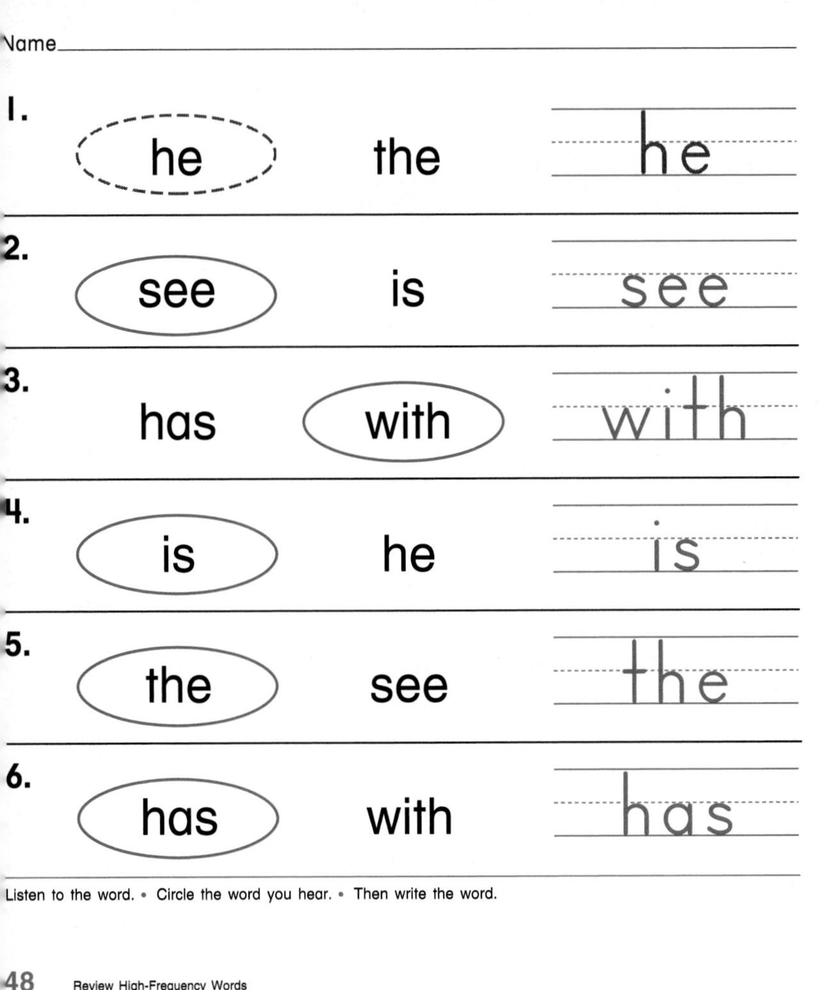

Name_______________

1.	he	the	he
2.	see	is	see
3.	has	with	with
4.	is	he	is
5.	the	see	the
6.	has	with	has

Listen to the word. • Circle the word you hear. • Then write the word.

48 Review High-Frequency Words

Review

High-Frequency Words

TESTED **OBJECTIVES**

Children will identify and read the high-frequency words *with, he, see, the, is, has*.

PREPARE

LISTEN TO WORDS Read aloud the word at the beginning of each sentence and ask children to listen for this word as you read the sentence. Invite children to raise a hand when they hear the word.

with	*My dog plays with me.*	**see**	*I see my dog.*
the	*We play in the yard.*	**is**	*He is a pup.*
he	*He likes to run.*	**has**	*He has big feet.*

TEACH

IDENTIFY THE WORDS Distribute these word cards from the High-Frequency Word Cards in the back of the Pupil's Edition: *with, he, see, the, is, has,* and display a set on the chalkboard ledge. Ask children to hold up the appropriate card as you point to and say each word. Write the sentences from the Prepare section on the chalkboard and read them aloud. Then name the high-frequency words and have volunteers find and match their cards to the words in the sentences.

PRACTICE

COMPLETE THE PUPIL PAGE Read the directions aloud. Then read these words for children to circle and write: (1) *he*; (2) *see*; (3) *with*; (4) *is*; (5) *the*; (6) *has*.

ASSESS/CLOSE

REVIEW THE PAGE Use page 48 to assess children's progress with the words *with, he, see, the, is, has*.

ALTERNATE TEACHING STRATEGY

Make a high-frequency word headband for each child. Write a high-frequency word on a sentence strip and fasten it around a child's head. Then have children walk around the room looking for others with the same word. Encourage children to use their word in an oral sentence.

▶ **Linguistic/Kinesthetic**

Develop

Phonological Awareness

Blend Onsets and Rimes

Teach Read aloud the poem *"Funny Animals."* Then tell children you will name an animal from the poem by saying the name in two parts: /f/-/ox/. Then blend the sounds into the word *fox*. Tell children they can put sounds together to say words. Repeat with /f/-/ish/ and /f/-/awn/.

Practice Present a rime such as /at/ and have children take turns blending various onsets with that rime: /c/-/at/, cat; /f/-/at/, fat; /m/-/at/, mat; etc.

Funny Animals

I've never seen a ferret with a mop,
Or a fish spin a top,
Or a fox on a cot,
Or a fawn paint a dot.
But that is not to say,
That I won't see these funny animals one day!

Identify Beginning and Ending Sounds

Phonemic Awareness

MATERIALS

- **Phonics Picture Posters**
  fish, octopus, dog, seal, nest, monkey, lion, cat, duck

Teach **FOCUS ON BEGINNING SOUNDS**
Display the Phonics Picture Poster (picture side only) for *fish*. Tell children the word *fish* begins with the sound /f/. Have children say the word and the sound with you: *fish*: /f/. Repeat for the initial sound /o/ using the poster for *octopus*. Have children say the beginning sound for these words: *otter, fan, on, Ollie, four, ox, fun, fur, Oliver.*

Practice Play *"I'm Thinking of a Word."* Display the Phonics Picture Poster for *fish*, *octopus*, *dog*, *seal*, *nest*, and *monkey*. The first child says *"I'm thinking of a word that has the beginning sound _."* The child who guesses correctly goes next.

FOCUS ON ENDING SOUNDS
Display the posters for *dog*, *seal*, *lion*, *cat* and *duck*. Play the same game having children focus on ending sounds: *"I'm thinking of a word that has the ending sound _."*

Identify Middle Sounds

Phonemic Awareness

MATERIALS

- **Phonics Picture Posters**

  pot, bib, cap

Teach Display the Phonics Picture Poster (picture side only) for *pot*. Tell children the middle sound for the word *pot* is /o/. Have children repeat the word and the sound /o/. Ask questions such as: *What sound do you hear in the middle of the word* mop? *Do* hot *and* cot *sound the same in the middle?*

Practice Display the posters for *pot*, *bib*, and *cat*. Say a word and have children point to the poster that has the same middle sound. Use these words: *tack, kid, sock, hop, cat, big, man.*

Segment Sounds

Phonemic Awareness

MATERIALS

- ***Word Building Boxes* from Word Building Manipulative Cards**
- **Paper clips**

Teach Display a Word Building Box with three sections. Segment the sounds in the word *top*: /t/-/o/-/p/, putting a self-stick note in each box as you say each sound. Remind children of the order of the sounds: the beginning sound is /t/; the middle sound is /o/; the ending sound is /p/. Have children say the sounds with you as you point to each box.

Then remove the middle self-stick note and ask *"What sound was here?"* (/o/) Repeat for other words such as: *cat, fox, fig, man, box, hot, sock.*

Practice Distribute Word Building Boxes and paper clips to each child. Each pair listens as you say a word and then segments the sounds. Have children place the paper clips in each box to mark each sound. Have volunteers identify the beginning, middle, and ending sounds in each word.

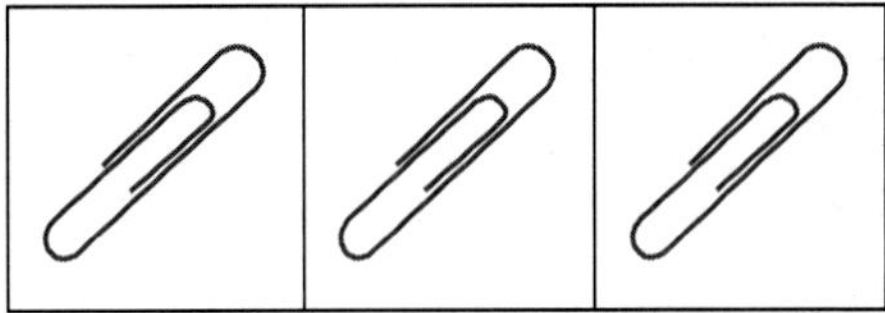

Introduce

Initial /o/*Oo*

Children will identify initial /o/*Oo* and form the letters *Oo*.

PREPARE

PHONOLOGICAL AWARENESS Read the first two lines of *Ollie Octopus* to the children. Then have them clap out the syllables in the words *Ollie* and *Octopus*. Ask the children which word is longer.

As you hold up the Phonics Picture Poster for *octopus*, sing the song, "Ollie Octopus." Have the children stand up each time they hear an /o/ sound at the beginning of the word. *Phonemic Awareness*

TEACH

IDENTIFY INITIAL /o/*Oo* Hold up the *Oo* letter card from the Word Building Manipulative Cards. Tell children that the letters *Oo* stand for the sound /o/. Then write these words on cards and have children say /o/ as you point to *o* in each word: *on, ox.* Write the sentences below on the chalkboard and read them aloud. Invite volunteers to use the word cards to complete the sentences. *I put a hat___the table.* (on) *An___is very strong.* (ox)

FORM *Oo* Remind children how to write *O* and *o*. Have children trace the letters on the letter cards.

PRACTICE

COMPLETE THE PUPIL PAGE Before children begin, read the directions aloud. Help children identify the key picture *octopus* and the other pictures on the page.

ASSESS/CLOSE

IDENTIFY AND USE INITIAL /o/*Oo* Use page 49 to assess children's knowledge of initial /o/*Oo*. Ask children to say a word that begins with /o/.

Name____________________

O o	1. otter O o	2. olive O o
3. apple	4. boat	5. ox O o
6. iguana	7. ostrich O o	8. horse

Say the name of each picture. • If the name begins with the same sound as *octopus*, write *Oo* on the line.

Ollie Octopus

Ollie Octopus likes to bake
Omelets, pies, and carrot cake.
Ollie bakes for Ozzie Ox,
Otto Otter and Oscar Fox.
Ollie Octopus likes to bake
Omelets, pies, and carrot cake.

Tune: "Twinkle, Twinkle Little Star"
From **Songs from A to Z**

Phonics Picture Posters and Cards

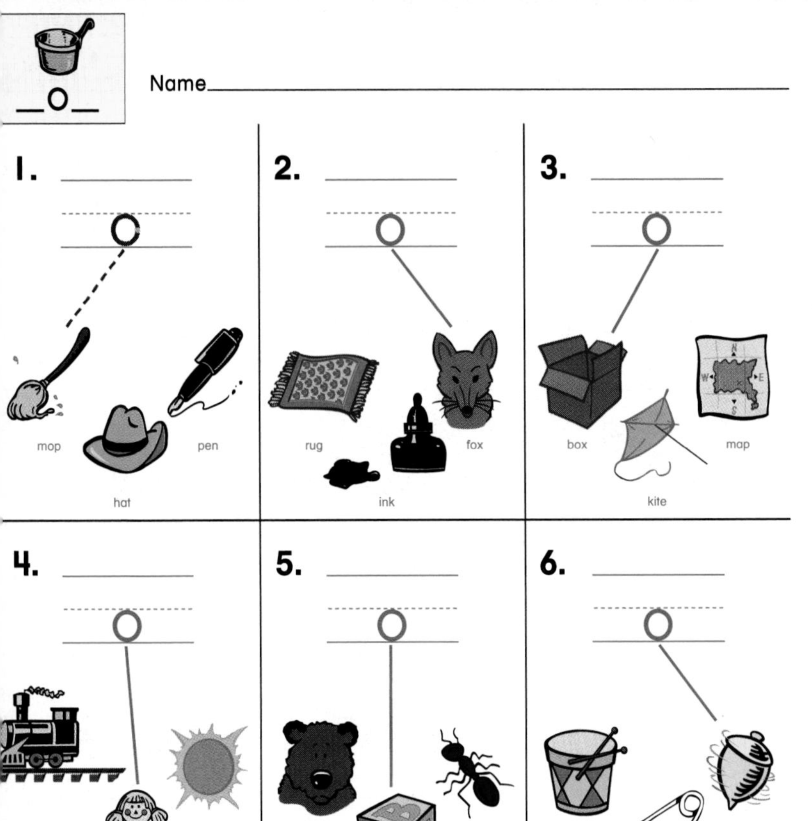
Name________________

_o_

1. 2. 3. 4. 5. 6.

mop hat pen rug ink fox box kite map train doll sun bear block ant drum safety pin top

Write the letter *o*. • Say the name of each picture. • Draw a line from the *o* to each picture whose name has the same middle sound as *pot*.

McGraw-Hill School Division

50 Introduce Medial /o/*o*

Introduce

Medial /o/*o*

Children will identify medial /o/*o*.

PREPARE

PHONOLOGICAL AWARENESS Tell children you will put some sounds together to say a word. Say: /p/-/ot/: *pot*. Then say the following sounds and have children blend them to say the words: /n/-/ot/; /k/-/ot/; /l/-/ot/; /g/-/ot/; /d/-/ot/.

Listen

Say the following words and have children say /o/ when they hear a word with the same middle sound: *hat*, *hot*, *Tom*, *pat*, *pot*, *sick*, *sock*, *rock*. *Phonemic Awareness*

TEACH

IDENTIFY MEDIAL /o/*o* Review that the letter *o* stands for the sound /o/. Say *got* and invite a volunteer to write the letter that stands for the middle sound. Then encourage children to suggest words that rhyme with *got*. Write the words and ask volunteers to circle the letter that stands for /o/.

PRACTICE

COMPLETE THE PUPIL PAGE Before children begin, read the directions aloud and help them identify the pictures. To help children compare middle sounds, have them say *dot* after they name each picture.

ASSESS/CLOSE

IDENTIFY AND USE MEDIAL /o/*o* Use page 50 to assess children's progress with medial /o/*o*. Have children tell you a word that rhymes with *hot* and then write the letter that stands for the medial sound.

TEACHING TIP

INSTRUCTIONAL When writing letters, some children may confuse lowercase *o* with lowercase *a* because of their similar shapes. Provide handwriting models and extra practice with both of these letters.

ALTERNATE TEACHING STRATEGY

Tell children that you are going to say some words. Have them make new words by changing the middle sound to the short o sound. Use these words: *hit*, *cat*, *fix*, *map*, *tip*, *pit*.

▶ **Linguistic/Auditory**

Introduce

Initial /f/*Ff*

OBJECTIVES

Children will identify initial /f/*Ff* and form the letters *Ff*.

PREPARE

PHONOLOGICAL AWARENESS Say the following words: *fish*, *food* and *mood*. Ask the children to name the two words that rhyme.

Listen

As you hold up the Phonics Picture Poster for *fish*, sing the song, "Finny the Fish." Have the children hold up a finger each time they hear a /f/ sound at the beginning of the word. *Phonemic Awareness*

TEACH

IDENTIFY INITIAL /f/*Ff* Hold up letter card *Ff* from the Word Building Manipulative Cards. Explain that the letters *Ff* stand for the sound /f/, and have children say /f/. Draw a fish on the chalkboard and tell children that the word *fish* begins with the letter *f*. Write *Ff* on the *fish*.

FORM *Ff* Some children may need extra practice with letter formation for *F* and *f*. Review on the chalkboard how to form the letters. Have children work together to draw a school of fish and write *f* or *F* inside each fish.

PRACTICE

COMPLETE THE PUPIL PAGE Have children name the key picture *fish* and listen to the beginning sound /f/. Then read the directions aloud and help children identify the pictures.

ASSESS/CLOSE

IDENTIFY AND USE INITIAL /f/*Ff* Use page 51 to assess children's knowledge of initial /f/*Ff*. Have children name a number that begins with /f/.

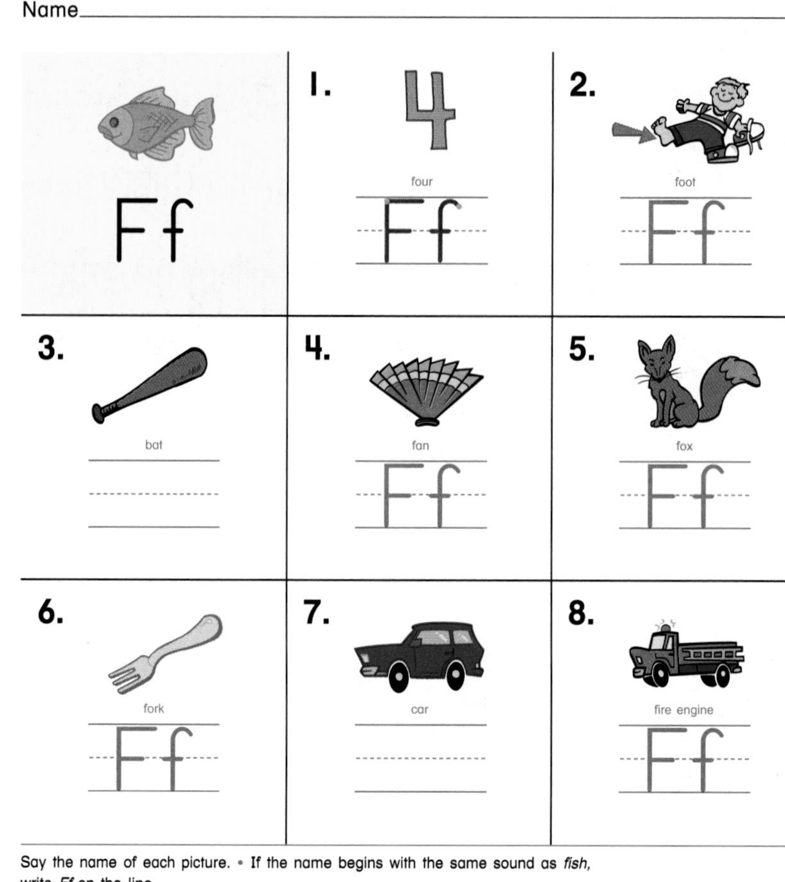
Name____________________

Ff	1. four Ff	2. foot Ff
3. bat	4. fan Ff	5. fox Ff
6. fork Ff	7. car	8. fire engine Ff

Say the name of each picture. • If the name begins with the same sound as *fish*, write *Ff* on the line.

Introduce Initial /f/*Ff* 51

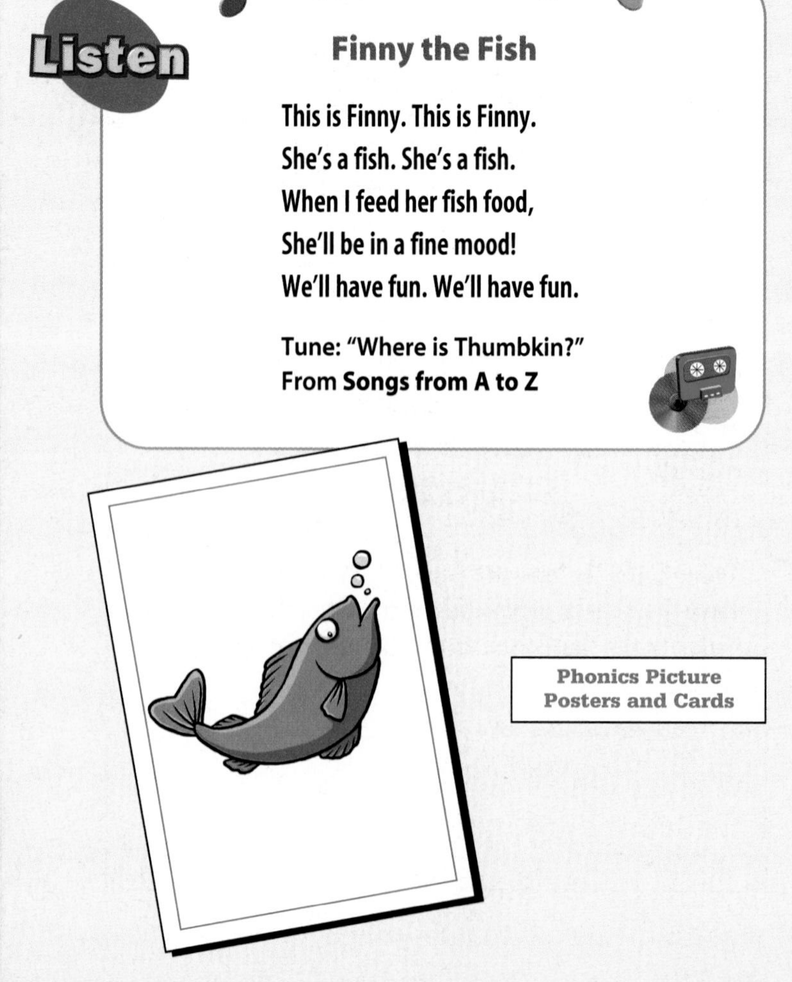

Phonics Song
Listen
Finny the Fish
This is Finny. This is Finny.
She's a fish. She's a fish.
When I feed her fish food,
She'll be in a fine mood!
We'll have fun. We'll have fun.
Tune: "Where is Thumbkin?"
From Songs from A to Z
Phonics Picture Posters and Cards

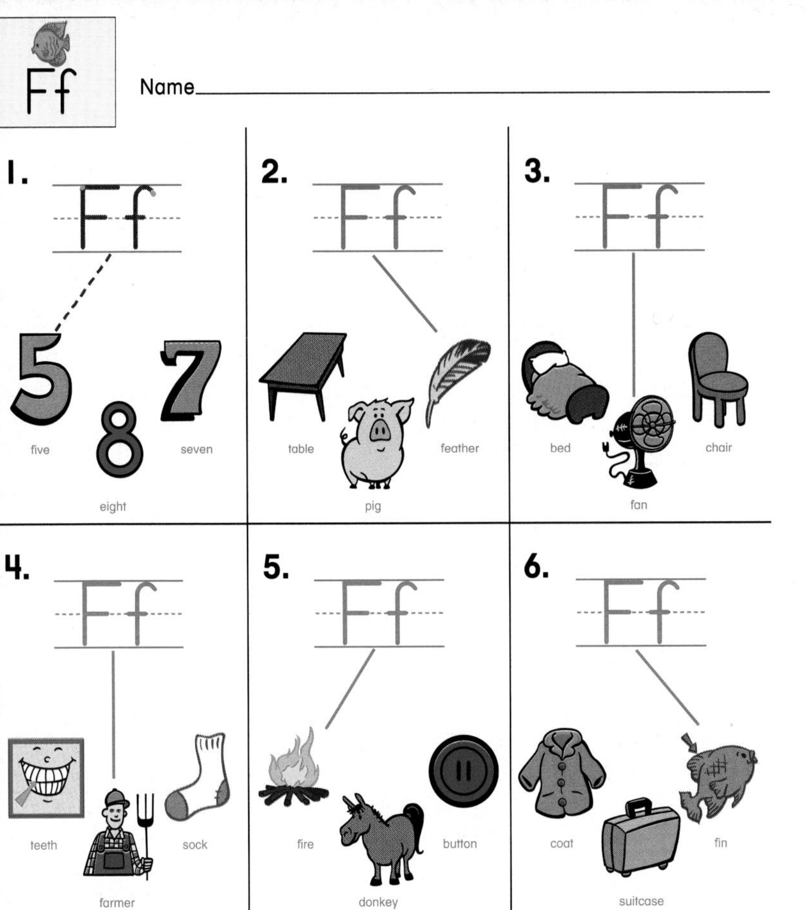
Ff Name________________

1. Ff — five, eight, seven
2. Ff — table, pig, feather
3. Ff — bed, fan, chair
4. Ff — teeth, farmer, sock
5. Ff — fire, donkey, button
6. Ff — coat, suitcase, fin

McGraw-Hill School Division

Write the letters *Ff*. • Say the name of each picture. • Draw a line from *Ff* to the picture whose name has the same beginning sound as *fish*.

52 Review Initial /f/Ff

Review

Initial /f/*Ff*

Children will identify initial /f/*Ff*.

PREPARE

PHONOLOGICAL AWARENESS Review singing the song "Finny the Fish" with children. Then say each sentence slowly. Have children count the number of words in each sentence.

Say the following words and have the children repeat the words that begin with the /f/ sound: *fan, fish, egg, duck, fun, thumb, fence, van, finger. Phonemic Awareness*

TEACH

IDENTIFY INITIAL /f/*Ff* On the chalkboard, write the letters *Ff*. Remind children that the letters *Ff* stand for /f/. Then write *fox* and have a volunteer circle the letters *Ff*. Invite children to write the letters *Ff* on paper and draw a picture of a fox. Then ask them to write *Ff* and draw two other objects beginning with /f/. Call on volunteers to show and tell about their pictures.

PRACTICE

COMPLETE THE PUPIL PAGE Before children begin, read the directions aloud and help children identify the pictures.

ASSESS/CLOSE

IDENTIFY AND USE INITIAL /f/*Ff* Use page 52 to assess children's progress with initial /f/*Ff*. Have children write the letter that stands for the initial sound in *fin*.

ALTERNATE TEACHING STRATEGY

Play "True or False." Explain that you will say something and children have to decide whether it is true or false. Say: *Feet begins with /f/. True or False? Goose begins with /f/. True or False?* Use words that do and do not begin with *f*.

▶ **Linguistic/Auditory**

Review

/o/o, /f/f

Children will identify /o/*o* and /f/*f* in words.

PREPARE

PHONOLOGICAL AWARENESS Say the following word pairs and have children raise a hand if the words rhyme: *fox, box; hat, hot; fan, fin; top, mop; clock, fawn.*

Read the following sentences aloud. Have children listen for the sounds /o/ or /f/ in the initial or medial position. Ask children to nod when they hear a word with that sound.

initial /o/ *An ostrich is a very tall bird.*
medial /o/ *A baby ostrich has spots.*
initial /f/ *Ostrich feathers are beautiful.*

TEACH

REVIEW /o/*o*, /f/*f* Write *o* and *f* on the chalkboard. Draw three blank letter boxes on the chalkboard. Distribute letter cards *o* and *f* from the Word Building Manipulative Cards. Tell children that they will listen for the sound /o/ and the sound /f/ in words. Say *hot.* Invite a volunteer to place the *o* letter card in the correct box to show where he or she hears the sound—at the beginning, in the middle, or at the end of the word. Repeat with the words *dog, fit, fun.*

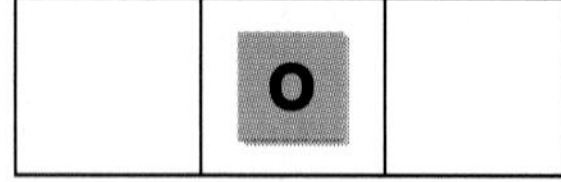

PRACTICE

COMPLETE THE PUPIL PAGE Before children begin, read the directions aloud and help children identify the pictures.

ASSESS/CLOSE

IDENTIFY AND USE /o/*o*, /f/*f* Use page 53 to assess children's progress with /o/o, /f/f.

Name____________________

1. o — ox — | o | | |
2. o — top — | | o | |
3. f — four — | f | | |
4. f — fish — | f | | |

Trace the letter. • Say the picture name. • If you hear the sound the letter stands for at the beginning of the picture name, write the letter in the first box. • If you hear the sound in the middle, write the letter in the middle box. • If you hear the sound at the end, write the letter in the last box.

Name______________________________

1. 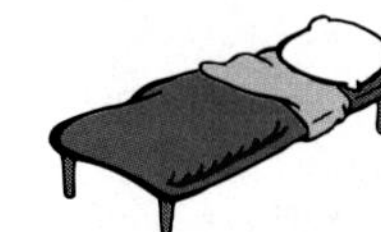

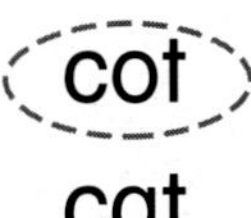

cat

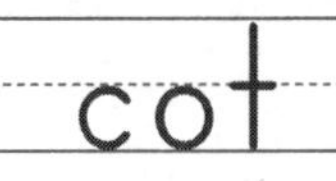

2. 

fan

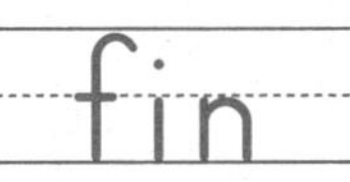

3. 

Sam

Nan

4. 

man

mad

5. 

dad

dot

Read the words. • Circle the word that names the picture. • Then write the word.

ALTERNATE TEACHING STRATEGY

Give each child one of the following words on an index card: *hot, cat, mat, fit, Tom, man, Dan, sit, sat, cot, not, Min, Tim, Nan, dad, nod*. Ask volunteers to hold up their card, then blend and read the word aloud.

▶ **Linguistic/Auditory**

Blending with Short *a, i, o*

TESTED OBJECTIVES

Children will blend and read short *a*, *i*, and *o* CVC words.

PREPARE

Display the *a, c, f, i, m, n, o, t* letter cards from the Word Building Manipulative Cards. Hold up each letter and review its sound. Have children say each sound.

TEACH

MODEL AND GUIDE PRACTICE Place the *o* letter card on the chalkboard ledge and say /o/. Have children repeat /o/.

- Place the *m* letter card next to the *o* letter card.
- Blend the sounds /o/ and /m/ together and have children repeat the sounds after you.
- Place the *T* letter card before the *o* letter card.
- Blend the sounds /t/, /o/, /m/ together to read Tom. Have children repeat the name *Tom* after you.

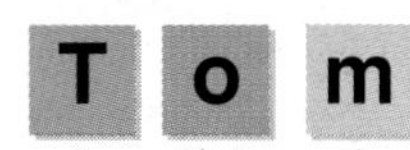

USE THE WORD IN CONTEXT Use *Tom* in a sentence to reinforce its meaning, for example: *My brother's name is Tom.*

REPEAT THE PROCEDURE Continue modeling and guided practice with short *a*, *i*, and *o* and the words: *cat, fan, fit, not*.

PRACTICE

COMPLETE THE PUPIL PAGE Read the directions aloud and then guide children through the steps. Help children name the pictures.

ASSESS/CLOSE

BLEND AND READ WORDS Use page 54 to assess children's skill in blending with short *a*, *i*, and *o*.

Read the Story

OBJECTIVES

Children will use their knowledge of phonics and decoding and high-frequency words to read.

BEFORE READING

Tom

PREVIEW Talk about the cover of the story, *Tom*. Introduce the main character, Tom. Then have children take a **picture walk** through pages 2-5 to preview the story. Ask children to look at the sentences on these pages. Point to and say the following high-frequency words and invite volunteers to point to each word after you: *he*, *see*. Invite children to look through the story to locate these words. (p. 3: he; p. 5: see)

MAKE PREDICTIONS Encourage children to look at the pictures again and predict what the story is about. Record children's predictions on the chalkboard.

DURING READING

READING SUGGESTIONS Encourage children to continue using picture clues. Remind the children that they begin reading on the left and follow the words to the right. On page 2, have the children find the word *Tom*. Remind them that this is where they should begin reading. Encourage children to track print with their finger as they read the story. Review that the name of a story character begins with a capital letter.

Tom is fat.

2

Can he fit?

3

Tom can sit.

4

Tom can see Tam.

5

TEACHING TIP

MANAGEMENT Help children put together their own take-home story. Give the following directions to the children. Demonstrate as needed.

To put book together,
Tear out the story page.
Cut along the dotted line.
Fold each section on the fold line.

Tam is with Mom.

6

Tam can see Tom.

7

Tom can sit on Tam.

8

AFTER READING

RETURN TO PREDICTIONS Read aloud children's predictions from the chalkboard. Discuss whether their predictions matched what happened in the story. Talk about whether or not the story ended as children thought it would end.

RETELL THE STORY Encourage children to retell the story in their own words. Ask the children to tell you what happened first, next and last.

STORY QUESTIONS Ask the following questions about the story.

- *What does Tom do at the beginning of the story?* (Climbs into the windowsill.) ***Literal/Story Details***
- *Why do you think Tom sits in the window?* (Answers will vary, but can include: waiting for Tam, watching things outside.) ***Critical/Make Inferences***
- *What would Tom do if he got to go outside?* (Answers vary.) ***Critical/Make Predictions***

Cross Curricular: Dramatic Arts

ACT LIKE THE CAT Invite the children to imagine that they are cats just waking up from a nap.

- Have children curl up on the floor in the manner of a sleeping cat.
- Then have children make the movements of a cat waking up and stretching its paws and legs while it yawns.
- Then have the children begin meowing like a cat.
- Continue by having children make suggestions for what the cat may do next.

▶ **Kinesthetic**

Introduce

Shapes

OBJECTIVES

Children will identify and describe the shapes *circle* and *square*.

PREPARE

INTRODUCE SHAPES Tell children they will learn about shapes today. Discuss with children what they know about shapes. Tell children they will learn about two kinds of shapes today: *circles* and *squares*.

TEACH

IDENTIFY SHAPES Tell children that you will show them some shapes. Hold up a *circle* cut from construction paper, and say *This is a circle*. Tell children that circles are round and have no sides. Repeat with a construction paper *square*. Tell children that squares have four sides that are all the same length.

Gather together objects that are circular and square in shape. Tell children to raise their hands when they see an object in the shape of a *circle*. Show an object that is a *circle*, such as a plate. Repeat with *square* objects.

PRACTICE

COMPLETE THE PUPIL PAGE Before children begin, read the directions aloud. Then name each shape and color at the top of the pupil page. Explain to children that they should color the shapes in the picture the same color as indicated at the top of the page.

ASSESS/CLOSE

REVIEW THE PAGE Use page 57 to assess children's knowledge of *circle* and *square* shapes. Have children name other objects in the classroom that are the same shape.

Name________________________________

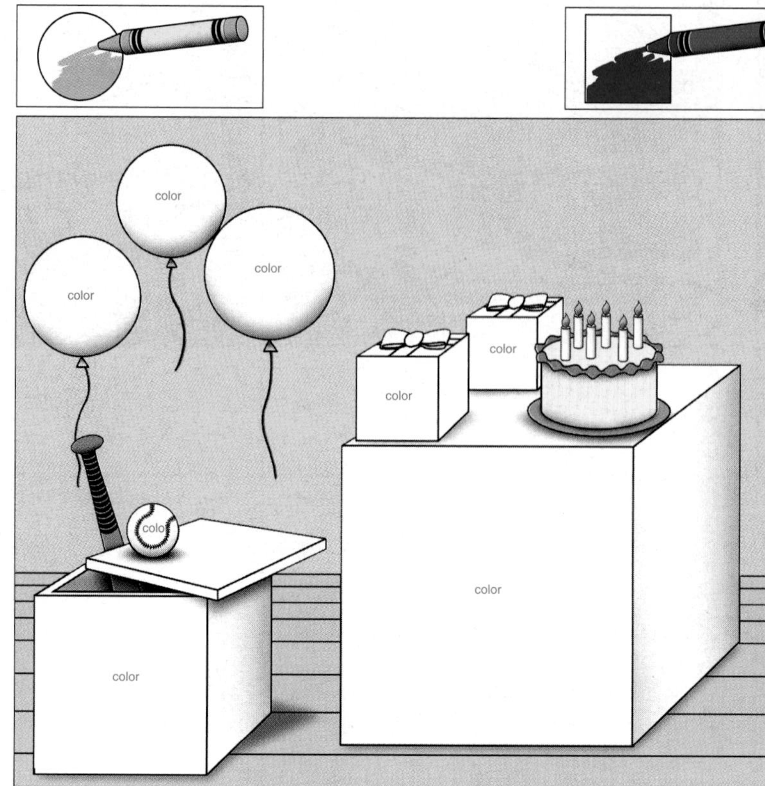

Name each color and shape. • Then find and color the shapes in the picture the same color.

Beginning Reading Concepts: *Shapes* 5

ALTERNATE TEACHING STRATEGY

ESL APPROPRIATE **Have children trace cut-outs of a *circle* on one half of a piece of paper and a *square* on the other half. Hold up a circular or square object. Ask children to hold up their paper to show the side with the matching shape. Repeat with different circular and square objects.**

▶ **Kinesthetic/Spatial**

ame

McGraw-Hill School Division

ame each color and shape. • Then find and color the shapes in the picture the same color.

8 Beginning Reading Concepts: *Shapes*

ALTERNATE TEACHING STRATEGY

ESL APPROPRIATE Have children place paper shapes of *circles, squares, triangles* and *rectangles* on a piece of construction paper to make a picture. Have children glue their shapes to the page and help them label their pictures. Have children describe their picture and name the shapes they used.

▶ **Kinesthetic/Spatial**

Introduce

Shapes

Children will identify and describe the shapes *triangle* and *rectangle*.

PREPARE

INTRODUCE SHAPES Review the shapes *circle* and *square* with children. Have them point to something in the room that is circular or square in shape. Then tell children they will learn about two new shapes: *triangles* and *rectangles*.

TEACH

IDENTIFY SHAPES Draw a *triangle* and a *rectangle* on opposite sides of the board. Describe the number of sides in each shape. Invite children to point to the *triangle* and say its name with you. Repeat with the *rectangle*. Hold up a *triangular* object, such as a triangular block. Tell children to point to the same shape on the board and say the name of the shape. Repeat with other *triangular* and *rectangular* shapes.

PRACTICE

COMPLETE THE PUPIL PAGE Before children begin, read the directions aloud. Then name each shape and color at the top of the pupil page. Tell children to color the objects in the picture the same color as indicated at the top of the page.

ASSESS/CLOSE

REVIEW THE PAGE Use page 58 to assess children's progress with the *triangle* and *rectangle* shapes. Challenge children to name other objects in the classroom that are those shapes.

Review

OBJECTIVES

Children will review /a/a, /i/i, /o/o, /k/c, /d/d, /f/f, /m/m, /n/n, /s/s, /t/t.

PREPARE

PHONOLOGICAL AWARENESS Say the following sentences and have children blend the sounds together to answer your questions:

Listen

/M/ /o/ /m/ raked leaves. Who raked leaves? (Mom)
/S/ /i/ /d/ is late. Who is late? (Sid)
/D/ /o/ /t/ found a feather. Who found a feather? (Dot)
The doll can /n/ /o/ /d/. What can the doll do? (nod)
Coins are in the /k/ /a/ /n/. What are the coins in? (a can)

TEACH

REVIEW SOUND/SYMBOL RELATIONSHIPS Draw three blank letter boxes on the chalkboard. Ask children to listen to the words you say and hold up the letters that stand for the beginning, middle, and ending sounds. Invite volunteers to place letter cards in the correct boxes to show where they hear each sound. Then have them read the word aloud. Distribute letter cards i, o, c, d, m to partners and say: *dim, cod*. Then distribute cards a, f, n, s, t and say: *sat, fat, tan*.

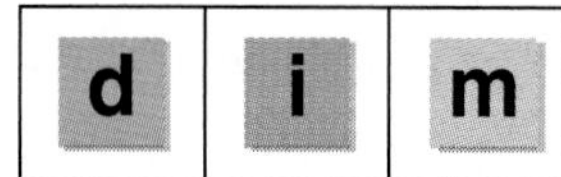

PRACTICE

COMPLETE THE PUPIL PAGE Read the directions aloud and complete the page with children.

ASSESS/CLOSE

IDENTIFY AND USE *a, i, o, c, d, f, m, n, s, t* Use page 59 to assess children's progress.

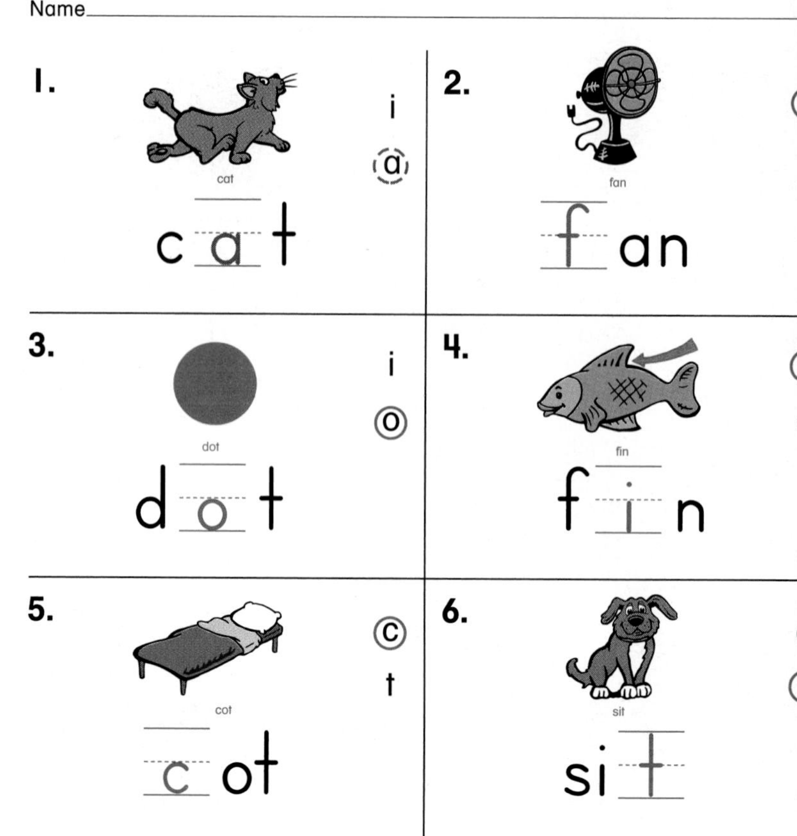

Name________

1. cat — i, (a) — c a t
2. fan — f an
3. dot — i, (o) — d o t
4. fin — f i n
5. cot — (c), t — c ot
6. sit — si t

Say each picture name. • Circle the missing letter. • Then write the letter. • Read the word.

Cumulative Review: Phonics 5

Name

1\. Sam is sad. — is / the

2\. Nan can see the fan. — with / see

3\. Dan has a cat. — has / the

4\. The cat is with Sam. — with / has

5\. Nan sat on the cot. — he / the

Read the sentence. • Then circle the word that completes the sentence. • Write it on the line.

60 Cumulative Review: High-Frequency Words

ALTERNATE TEACHING
STRATEGY

Distribute word cards for *the*, *is*, *with*, *has*, *he*, and *see*, so that each child gets one card. Say a word and ask children who have that word to stand up and show their word. Invite volunteers to use the word in their own sentences. Repeat until all the words have been identified. You may wish to repeat by having children exchange their cards.

▶ **Auditory/Linguistic**

Cumulative Review

Children will review the high-frequency words *the*, *is*, *with*, *has*, *he*, *see*.

PREPARE

LISTEN TO WORDS Tell children you will read some sentences aloud. Ask children to listen for the word you say at the beginning of each sentence. Have them touch their nose when they hear the word.

has *A rabbit has a funny nose.*
is *It is a nose that wiggles.*
with *It is a nose with whiskers.*
the *Most of the time, a rabbit sniffs things.*
see *A rabbit does not see as well as it smells.*

TEACH

IDENTIFY THE WORDS Write *the*, *is*, *with*, *has*, *he*, *see* across the chalkboard, leaving space under the words for word cards. Distribute word cards for these words. Say each word and have volunteers place matching cards under the words on the chalkboard ledge. Then write the sentences from the Prepare section. As you read them aloud, invite children to hold up words that match the ones they hear and see.

PRACTICE

COMPLETE THE PUPIL PAGE Before children begin, read the directions aloud. Complete the page with children.

ASSESS/CLOSE

REVIEW THE PAGE Use page 60 to assess children's progress with the words *the*, *is*, *with*, *has*, *he*, *see*. Invite children to write two of the words and use them in an oral sentence.

Develop

Phonological Awareness

Identify Rhyming Words

Teach Read the poem *"Pets in a Tub"* aloud. Say: *The words* tub *and* rub *rhyme because they have the same ending sound.* Then say the following words and have children say "rub" when they hear a word that rhymes with it: *hub, ran, up, stub, cub, under, ball, flub.*

Practice Say the following groups of three words and have children tell which two words rhyme: *ran/man/moon; top/slip/tip; tack/sack/sock; bed/mad/head; Sam/him/limb.*

Pets in a Tub

Ten peppy kids pile into the tub
With Mom and Dad Goat
They slip and tip and soap-a-rub-rub
They even dip and float!
Then Mack and Ben, the pups, pop in.
Hop in ducks, Nan and Min.
Goats and pups and ducks in a tub –
How can the pets fit in?

Identify Beginning Sounds

Phonemic Awareness

MATERIALS
- Phonics Picture Posters *rabbit, pig*
- Beanbag

Teach Display the Phonics Picture Poster (picture side only) for *rabbit*. Tell children the word *rabbit* begins with the sound /r/. Have children repeat the word and initial /r/. Repeat with words from the poem: *Ron, ran, rim*. Repeat using the Phonics Picture Poster for *pig* and the beginning /p/ sound. Have chidren say the words *paint, penny* and *pin*, while emphasizing the /p/ sound.

Practice Play *"What Do You Hear"?* Begin by saying *"What do you hear at the beginning of* right?" Toss the beanbag to a volunteer who responds with *"I hear /r/."* The child tosses the beanbag back to you. To continue, use these words: *pet, run, pup, rack, rain, poppy, real, peck, pal, riddle.*

Identify Ending Sounds

Phonemic Awareness

MATERIALS

- Word Building Manipulative Cards
  cap

Teach Display the Word Building Manipulative Card (picture side only) for *cap*. Tell children the word *cap* ends with the /p/ sound. Have children repeat the word and ending sound. Have children listen to pairs of words and tell which end with /p/: *cap/cat; mat/map; hop/hot; sip/Sid.*

Practice Play a version of "*I'm Thinking of a Word.*" Say: "*I'm thinking of a word that is something to drink from and ends with /p/.*" Call on a volunteer to answer: *cup*. Continue making up clues for the following words: *hop, up, pup, skip, lip, trip, snap, mop.*

Blend Sounds

Phonemic Awareness

MATERIALS

- Yarn or string with 3 moveable beads

Teach Tell children you will put some sounds together to say a word. Display the string with the beads separated. Stretch out the sounds /r/-/o/-/n/, moving the beads closer, until you blend *Ron*. Have children repeat the sounds and blend them into the word. Tell children you will say the sounds of another name and they should blend the sounds to say the name: /p/-/a/-/m/ as you move the beads together.

Practice Have volunteers push the beads together to blend the sounds of the following names: *Page, Rose, Matt, Sue, Sam, Tom, Paul.* Continue until all children have had a chance.

Introduce

Initial /r/*Rr*

OBJECTIVES

Children will identify initial /r/*Rr* and form the letters *Rr*.

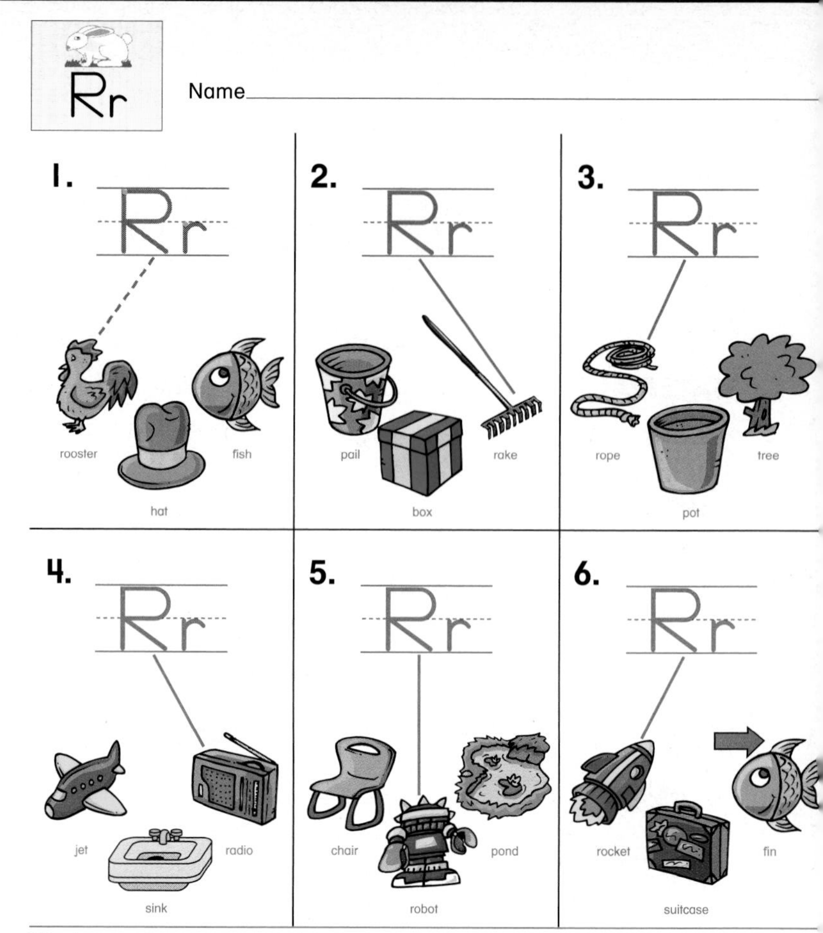

Rr Name______________

1. Rr — rooster, hat, fish
2. Rr — pail, box, rake
3. Rr — rope, pot, tree
4. Rr — jet, sink, radio
5. Rr — chair, robot, pond
6. Rr — rocket, suitcase, fin

Write the letters *Rr*. • Say the name of each picture. • Draw a line from *Rr* to each picture whose name begins like *rabbit*.

Introduce Initial /r/*Rr* 61

PREPARE

PHONOLOGICAL AWARENESS Say the following words: *best*, *rides*, *rest*. Ask the children to name the two words that rhyme.

Listen

While holding up the Phonics Picture Poster for *rabbit*, sing the song, "Ricky the Rabbit." Have the children hop like a rabbit each time they hear the /r/ sound at the beginning of the word. *Phonemic Awareness*

TEACH

IDENTIFY INITIAL /r/*Rr* Write the letters *Rr* on the chalkboard and tell children that the letters *Rr* stand for the sound /r/. Ask children to say the name *Ron*. Write *Ron* and invite volunteers to circle the letter *R* and say /r/. Then write: *He ran up to the rim.* Read the sentence aloud. Invite children to circle *r* and say /r/.

FORM *Rr* Review how to write *R* and *r*. Encourage children to trace the letters on the Handwriting Models in the back of the Pupil's Edition.

PRACTICE

COMPLETE THE PUPIL PAGE Have children identify the key picture *rabbit*, and say its beginning sound, /r/. Read the directions aloud and help children identify the pictures.

ASSESS/CLOSE

IDENTIFY AND USE INITIAL /r/*Rr* Use page 61 to assess children's knowledge of initial /r/*Rr*. Ask children to answer this riddle: *My name begins with the letter* r. *I am an animal with long ears and a fluffy tail. Who am I?* (rabbit)

Listen

Ricky the Rabbit

Ricky the rabbit rides his bike,
Rides his bike, rides his bike.
Ricky the rabbit rides his bike,
Then he stops to rest.

Tune: "The Wheels on the Bus"
From **Songs from A to Z**

Phonics Picture Posters and Cards

Name ____________________

Rr

1. 
rose
Rr

2. 
robot
Rr

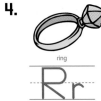

3. 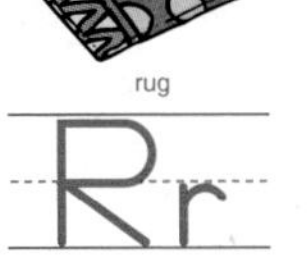
rug
Rr

4. 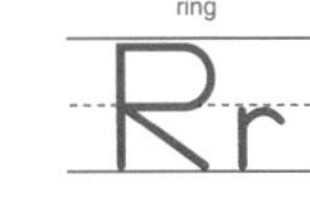
ring
Rr

5.
teeth

6. 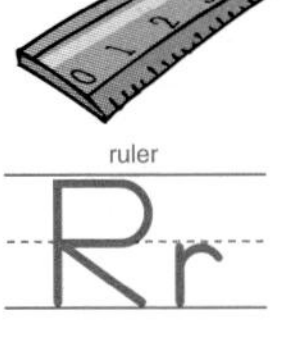
ruler
Rr

7.
rake
Rr

8. 
leaf

Say the name of each picture. • If the name begins with the same sound as *rabbit*, write *Rr* on the line.

62 Review Initial /r/*Rr*

TEACHING TIP

INSTRUCTIONAL Because *r* and *n* have similar shapes, you may want to provide extra handwriting practice for these letters. If children confuse the capital letters *R* and *B* when writing, review their formation, focusing on the differences between the two.

ALTERNATE TEACHING STRATEGY

Make a road using a length of brown wrapping paper and tape it onto the floor. Tell children that they will play a game, "Cross the Road." Explain that they can "cross the road" only if they say a word that begins with /r/. Have children walk, skip, or jump across the road when they respond correctly.

▶ **Linguistic/Kinesthetic**

Review

Initial /r/*Rr*

TESTED OBJECTIVES

Children will identify initial /r/*Rr*.

PREPARE

PHONOLOGICAL AWARENESS Say the sentence:

Ricky the Rabbit rides his bike. Have children clap and count the number of words in the sentence.

While holding up the Phonics Picture Poster for *rabbit*, review the song, "Ricky the Rabbit." Then have children take turns saying a word that begins with the /r/ sound. ***Phonemic Awareness***

TEACH

IDENTIFY INITIAL /r/*Rr* Remind children that the letters *Rr* stand for /r/. On the chalkboard, write *ran* and *rim*. Point to each word and read it aloud with children. Circle the *r* that begins each word and ask children to say the sound it stands for. Then invite volunteers to think of other words that begin with *Rr*. Write their responses on the chalkboard. Point to and read each word, and have children say the beginning sound.

PRACTICE

COMPLETE THE PUPIL PAGE After reading the directions aloud and helping children identify the pictures, complete the first item together. Then have children complete the rest of the page on their own.

ASSESS/CLOSE

IDENTIFY AND USE INITIAL /r/*Rr* Use page 62 to assess children's progress with initial /r/*Rr*. Also have children answer this riddle: *My name begins with the letter* r. *I am a color. What am I?* (red)

Initial /p/*Pp*

OBJECTIVES

Children will identify initial /p/*Pp* and form the letters *Pp*.

PREPARE

PHONOLOGICAL AWARENESS Say the following words, *pets*, *pigs*, *pickles*, and *ponies*. Have children clap out the syllables in each word with you.

While singing the song "Penny the Pig", hold up the Phonics Picture Card of a *pig*. Have the children tap their pencil each time they hear a /p/ sound at the beginning of the word. *Phonemic Awareness*

TEACH

IDENTIFY INITIAL /p/*Pp* Distribute the *Pp* letter card from the Word Building Manipulative Cards. Tell children that the letters *Pp* stand for the sound /p/. Point to objects around the classroom that begin with /p/*Pp*. Have volunteers name the object and place their letter card by it. Objects might include *pen*, *pencil*, *pin*, *paper*, *pail*, *paste*, *peg*, *puzzle*.

FORM *Pp* Review how to write *P* and *p*. Have children write sets of *Pp* on lined paper to practice correct placement of capital and lowercase letters.

PRACTICE

COMPLETE THE PUPIL PAGE Before children begin the page, read the directions aloud and help them identify the pictures. Work through the first item with children, then have them complete the page on their own.

ASSESS/CLOSE

IDENTIFY AND USE INITIAL /p/*Pp* Use page 63 to assess children's knowledge of initial /p/*Pp*. Have children draw a picture of an object that begins with /p/.

Name

Pp

1. parachute Pp
2. paint Pp
3. pin Pp
4. bottle
5. piano Pp
6. pencil Pp
7. carrot
8. pillow Pp

Say the name of each picture. • If the name begins with the same sound as *pig*, write *Pp* on the line.

Introduce Initial /p/*Pp* 63

Listen

Penny the Pig

Penny the Pig likes pickles and peas,
Pickles and peas, pickles and peas.
Penny the Pig likes pickles and peas.
Penny is a pig.

Sung to the tune: "Here We Go 'Round the Mulberry Bush"
From Songs from A to Z

Phonics Picture Posters and Cards

Name ________________

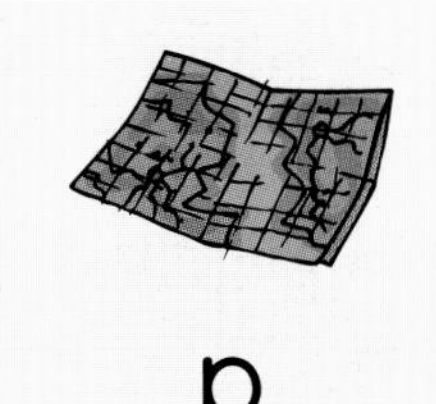

—p

1. 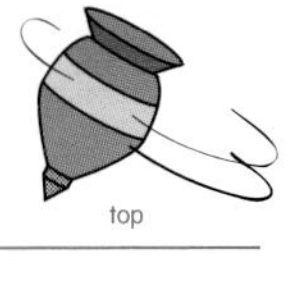

p

2. 

p

3. cloud

4. 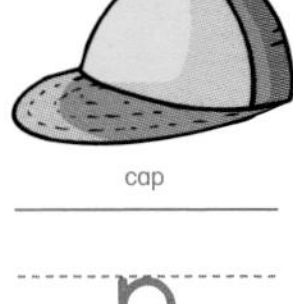

p

5. rake

6. jeep

p

7. 

p

8. mop

p

Say the name of each picture. • Write *p* on the line if the name has the same ending sound as *map*.

Introduce

Final /p/*p*

OBJECTIVES

Children will identify final /p/*p*.

PREPARE

PHONOLOGICAL AWARENESS Say the following sets of words and have children say the two words in each set that rhyme: *tap, cap, car; tin, sip, tip; hop, hand, stop; cup, pup, pen.*

Listen

Then say the following words and have children tap their pencil each time they hear a /p/ sound at the end of the word: *sip, cap, hat, tap, cup, rod, hot, top, top. Phonemic Awareness*

TEACH

IDENTIFY FINAL /p/*p* Say *hop* and invite a volunteer to write the letter for the ending sound on the chalkboard. Review that the letter *p* stands for the sound /p/. Write this sentence on the chalkboard: *Skip had a dip in a pool.* Have volunteers circle each letter *p* at the end of a word and say /p/.

PRACTICE

COMPLETE THE PUPIL PAGE Before children begin, read the directions aloud, help them identify the pictures, and complete the first item together. Have children complete the remaining items on their own.

ASSESS/CLOSE

IDENTIFY AND USE FINAL /p/*p* Use page 64 to assess children's knowledge of final /p/*p*. Ask children to name a word that ends with /p/.

LANGUAGE SUPPORT

Non-English-speaking children may not understand the meanings of the following words in Pets in a Tub: *peppy, kids, pile, soap-a-rub-rub*. Explain how they are used in the rhyme. You may want to have classmates act out the rhyme with puppets or toy animals.

ALTERNATE TEACHING STRATEGY

Have children repeat tongue twisters with words that begin with *p*:

Peter Piper picked a peck of pickled peppers.
If Peter Piper picked a peck of pickled peppers,
How many pickled peppers did Peter Piper pick?

Encourage children to make up their own tongue twisters with words that begin or end with *p*.

▶ **Linguistic/Auditory**

Review

/r/r, /p/p

Children will identify /r/*r* and /p/*p* in words .

PREPARE

PHONOLOGICAL AWARENESS Read the following sentences and have children clap out the syllables in each word.

initial /p/ *I sit on the porch with my friend.*
initial /r/ *We see rabbits on the grass.*
final /p/ *Then they hop away quickly.*

Reread the sentences aloud slowly. Tell children to nod when they hear a word with the sound you say. *Phonemic Awareness*

TEACH

REVIEW /r/*r*, /p/*p* Distribute letter cards *r* and *p* from the Word Building Manipulative Cards. Encourage children to say the sound each letter stands for. Then draw three blank letter boxes on the chalkboard. Say *tip* and have children identify whether they hear /r/ or /p/ by holding up the letter *r* or *p*. Ask a volunteer to place the letter card *p* in the correct box to show where he or she hears the sound—at the beginning, in the middle, or at the end of the word. Repeat with other words, for example: *pet*, *rib*, *run*.

PRACTICE

COMPLETE THE PUPIL PAGE Read the directions aloud and complete the page with children.

ASSESS/CLOSE

IDENTIFY AND USE /r/*r*, /p/*p* Use page 65 to assess children's progress with /r/r, /p/*p*.

Name__________

1. r (rug) r

2. r (rip) r

3. p (pot) p

4. p (cap) p

Trace the letter. • Say the picture name. • If you hear the sound the letter stands for at the beginning of the picture name, write the letter in the first box. • If you hear the sound at the end, write the letter in the last box.

Review /r/r, /p/p 65

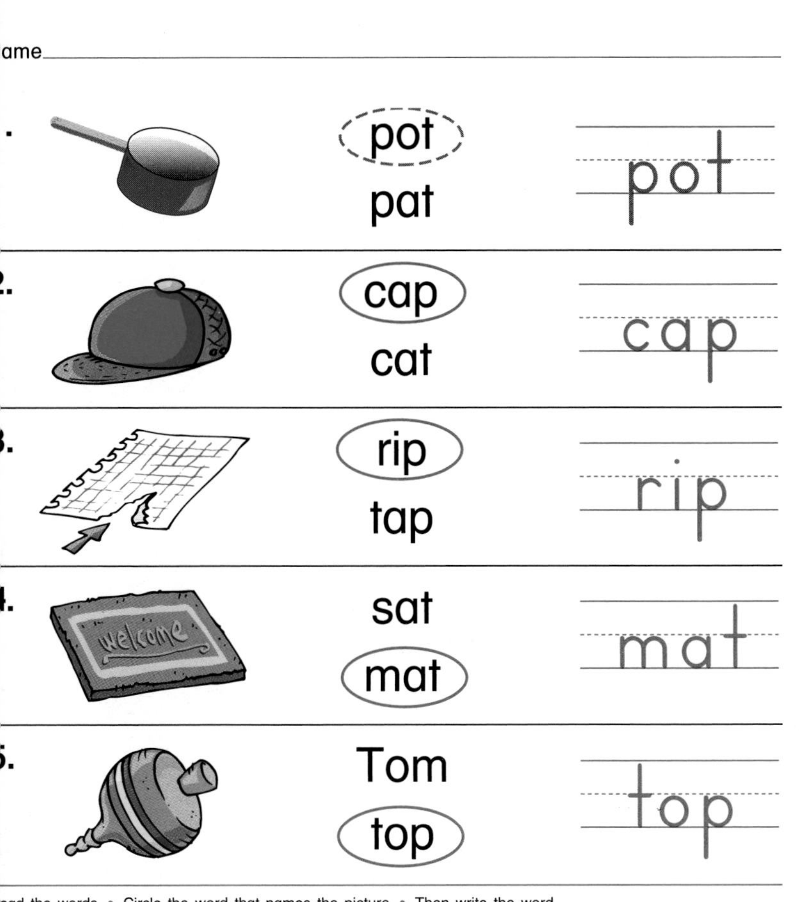
ame____________

1. pot pat — pot
2. cap cat — cap
3. rip tap — rip
4. sat mat — mat
5. Tom top — top

ead the words. • Circle the word that names the picture. • Then write the word.

McGraw-Hill School Division

6 Blending with Short *a*, *i*, and *o*

Blending with
Short *a, i, o*

TESTED OBJECTIVES

Children will blend and read short *a*, *i*, and *o* CVC words.

PREPARE

Display these letter cards from the Word Building Manipulative Cards and briefly review the sounds they stand for: *a*, *c*, *d*, *i*, *m*, *o*, *p*, *r*.

TEACH

MODEL AND GUIDE PRACTICE Place the *o* letter card on the chalkboard ledge and say /o/. Have children repeat /o/.

- Place the *d* letter card next to the *o* letter card.
- Blend the sounds /o/ and /d/ together and have children repeat the sounds after you.
- Place the *p* letter card before the *o* letter card.
- Blend the sounds /p/, /o/, /d/ together to read *pod*. Have children repeat the word *pod* after you.

USE THE WORD IN CONTEXT Use *pod* in a sentence to reinforce its meaning, for example: *Peas grow in a pod.*

REPEAT THE PROCEDURE Use these words to continue modeling and guided practice: *cot*, *map*, *rim*, *rip*.

PRACTICE

COMPLETE THE PUPIL PAGE Read the directions aloud and help children name the pictures. After completing the first item with children, have them finish on their own.

ASSESS/CLOSE

BLEND AND READ WORDS Use page 66 to assess children's skill in blending with short *a*, *i*, and *o*.

ALTERNATE TEACHING STRATEGY

Give each child a word card with a simple action, such as *tap*, *sit*, *pat the cat*. Have children read the word on their card and pantomime the action. Children can exchange cards and play several rounds of the game.

▶ **Linguistic/Kinesthetic**

Introduce

High-Frequency Words: *and, you, a*

Children will identify and read the high-frequency words *and, you,* and *a.*

PREPARE

LISTEN TO WORDS Read the following sentences aloud and ask children to listen for these words: *and, you, a.* Have them clap when they hear the word you name.

you—*Do you like pets?*
a—*I have a goat.*
and—*She is brown and white.*

TEACH

IDENTIFY THE WORDS Distribute the High-Frequency word cards *and, you, a,* from the back of Pupil's Edition. Place one set on the chalkboard ledge. Point to each word, read it aloud, and ask children to repeat each word. Then write the sentences from the Prepare section on the chalkboard and reread them pointing to each word as you read. Invite children to hold up the correct word card when you point to and say the words *and, you,* and *a.*

PRACTICE

COMPLETE THE PUPIL PAGE Read the directions aloud and make sure children understand that they should circle more than one word in each row.

ASSESS/CLOSE

REVIEW THE PAGE Use page 67 to assess children's recognition of the words *and, you,* and *a.* Have children use the word *and* in an oral sentence.

Name____________________

1.	and	(and)	you	a	(and)
2.	you	and	(you)	and	(you)
3.	a	(a)	and	you	(a)
4.	you	(you)	and	a	(you)
5.	and	(and)	you	a	(and)

Read the first word in each row. • Circle the words in that row that are the same.

ame

.	and	a	and
2.	you	the	you
3.	has	and	and
4.	a	has	a
.	you	with	with
6.	the	and	the

sten to the word. • Circle the word you hear. • Then write the word.

ALTERNATE TEACHING STRATEGY

Ask children to copy the words *and*, *you*, *a*, *with*, and *the* onto cards, one word per card. Partners combine their cards, shuffle them, and then deal them out so each player gets five cards. Players take turns drawing a card from their partner's hand and trying to match it with their own. The first player to match all of his or her cards is the winner.

▶ Interpersonal/Kinesthetic

Review

High-Frequency Words

Children will identify and read the high-frequency words *and*, *you*, *a*, *with*, and *the*.

PREPARE

LISTEN TO WORDS Invite children to guess the riddle below. Then assign each child a word (*a*, *with*, *and*, *the*, *you*). As you reread the riddle, have them raise their hands when they hear their word. Reassign the words and repeat. *I am a bug with wings. I fly and light up in the night. Can you guess my name?* (firefly)

TEACH

IDENTIFY THE WORDS Write *and*, *you*, *a*, *with*, *the* in a row on the chalkboard. Place the High-Frequency Word Cards from the back of the Pupil's Edition on the chalkboard ledge under each word in this order: *you*, *and*, *the*, *a*, *with*. As you say each word, invite volunteers to draw a line from the word to the matching word card. Then arrange children in pairs and give partners the five word cards. Write and read aloud the riddle from the Prepare section. Ask partners to point to the words *and*, *you*, *a*, *with*, and *the* when they hear each word.

PRACTICE

COMPLETE THE PUPIL PAGE Read the directions aloud. Tell children to listen to each word you say, circle it, and then write it. Say: (1) *and*; (2) *you*; (3) *and*; (4) *a*; (5) *with*; (6) *the*.

ASSESS/CLOSE

REVIEW THE PAGE Use page 68 to assess children's recognition of the words *and*, *you*, *a*, *with*, and *the*. Have children say and write the word *and*.

Develop

Phonological Awareness

Count Words

MATERIALS
- blocks (five per child)

Teach Read aloud the poem "*A Pup Named Tom*." Tell children they will help you count the number of words in the title. Then call four children to the front and assign one word of the title to each child. Have children say the words "*A Pup Named Tom*" in order. Tell children there are four words in this title.

Practice Distribute 5 blocks to pairs of children. Have the pairs use the blocks to count the number of words in each of the following: *Tom is a good pup. Don is a hog. Don and Tom have fun. They are friends.*

A Pup Named Tom

A pup named Tom rolls in the mud,
While a hog named Don sits on a log.
When Tom is done, he gets right up
To run and sniff a buttercup.
Then Don says, "What a lot of fun!"
And runs to join Tom in the sun.

Identify Beginning Sounds

Phonemic Awareness

MATERIALS
- Phonics Picture Posters
  lion, umbrella

Teach Display the Phonics Picture Poster (picture side only) for *lion*. Tell children the word lion begins with the sound /l/. Have children repeat the word and the sound with you. Repeat using the Phonics Picture Poster for *umbrella*, focussing on the beginning /u/ sound.

Practice Display both posters and have children point to the picture that has the same beginning sound as they following words: *lap, uncle, under, laugh, lily, up, light, until, log, upside-down, look, lamp.*

Identify Middle Sounds

Phonemic Awareness

MATERIALS

- **Phonics Picture Poster**
  sun
- **Beanbag**

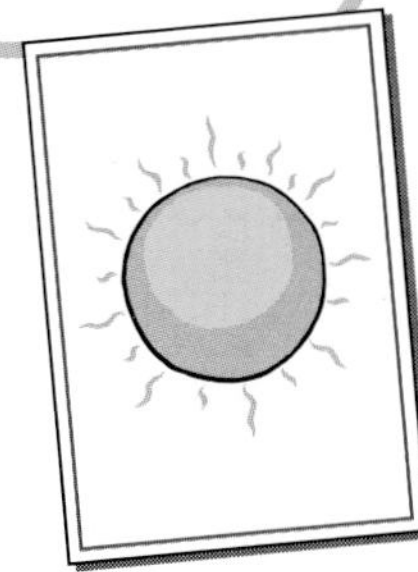

Teach Display the Phonics Picture Poster (picture side only) for *sun*. Tell children to listen to the middle sound in the word. Tell children the middle sound in the word sun is /u/. Have children repeat the sound with you.

Practice Say pairs of words and toss the beanbag to a child. Have the child identify which word has the middle /u/ sound. Use these words: *fun/fan; not/nut; sum/sam; big/bug; bun/bat; run/ram; sip/sun; tug/top; hot/hut; rug/rag.*

Blend Sounds

Phonemic Awareness

Teach Model asking the children a riddle. Tell children you are thinking of something people use to write with. Say the sounds /p/-/e/-/n/. Then tell children if you put the sounds together, they make the word *pen*. Continue by saying the sounds of other classroom objects, such as *book*, *pad*, *desk*, *chair*, *light* and so on.

Practice Tell children you are going to play a name game called "*I'm Going to Grandma's House*." Start by saying "*I'm going to grandma's house and I'm taking* /p/-/a/-/m/." The class blends the name or word. Repeat with other simple names such as *Paul*, *Rob*, *Tom*, *Tam*, *Sam*, *Kim*, *Tory*, *Dave* and so on.

Introduce

Initial /l/*Ll*

OBJECTIVES

Children will identify initial /l/*Ll* and form the letters *Ll*.

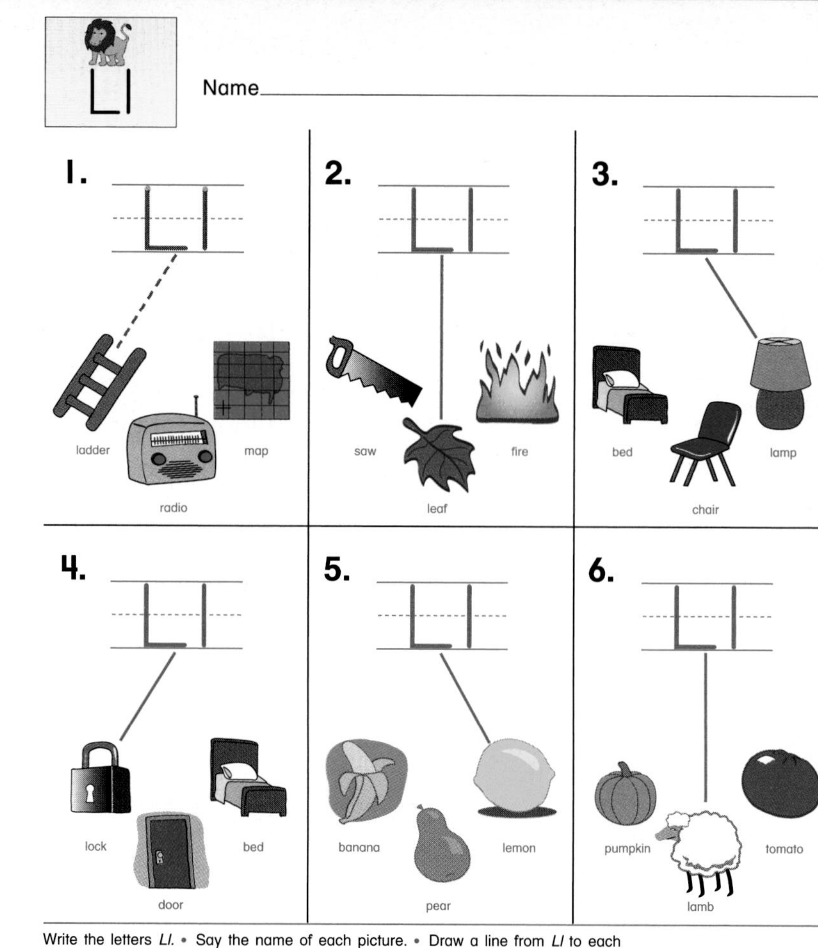
Ll Name

1\. ladder radio map

2\. saw leaf fire

3\. bed chair lamp

4\. lock door bed

5\. banana pear lemon

6\. pumpkin lamb tomato

Write the letters *Ll*. • Say the name of each picture. • Draw a line from *Ll* to each picture whose name begins like *lion*.

Introduce Initial /l/*Ll* 69

PREPARE

PHONOLOGICAL AWARENESS Say the following words, *laugh*, *lion*, *likes* and *loudly*. Have children clap the syllables in each word with you.

Listen

While singing the song "Lucy Lion," hold up the Phonics Picture Poster for *lion*. Have the children raise their left hand every time they hear a /l/ sound at the beginning of a word. Point out to children that *left* begins with /l/. ***Phonemic Awareness***

Lucy Lion

Lucy Lion likes to laugh,
Likes to laugh, likes to laugh.
Lucy Lion likes to laugh,
She laughs loudly!

Sung to the tune: "London Bridge"
From Songs from A to Z

TEACH

IDENTIFY INITIAL /l/*Ll* Write *Ll* on the chalkboard and review that the letters *Ll* stand for the sound /l/. Then write: *Leo met a little leopard.* Ask volunteers to circle the letters *Ll* and say /l/.

FORM *Ll* Some children may need to review how to write *L* and *l*. Invite children to draw a picture of a little *lion* and to write *L* and *l* around the lion. Have them use the letter cards from the Word Building Manipulative Cards as reference.

PRACTICE

COMPLETE THE PUPIL PAGE Read the directions aloud and help children identify the pictures. Work through the first item together and let children do the other items independently.

ASSESS/CLOSE

IDENTIFY AND USE INITIAL /l/*Ll* Use page 69 to assess children's knowledge of initial /l/*Ll*. Have children say a word and a name that begin with /l/.

Phonics Picture Posters and Cards

Name________________________________

Ll

1. 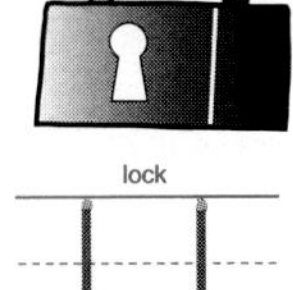
lock
Ll

2. 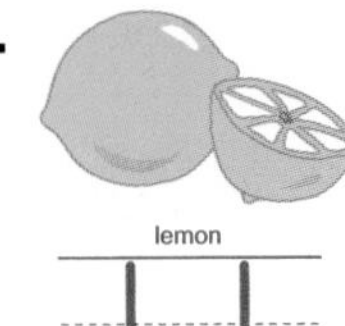
lemon
Ll

3. 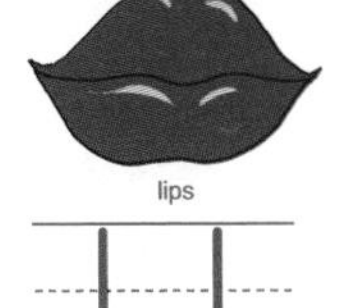
lips
Ll

4. 
rabbit

5. 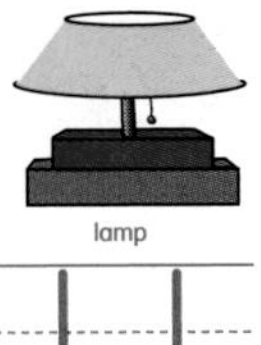
lamp
Ll

6. 
letter
Ll

7. 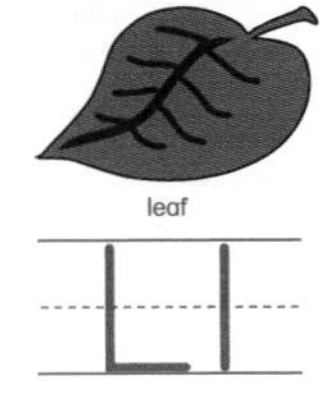
leaf
Ll

8. 
nurse

Say the name of each picture. • If the name begins with the same sound as *lion*, write *Ll* on the line.

TEACHING TIP

INSTRUCTIONAL You may wish to provide sandpaper letters for children to practice tracing before they write the letters *Ll*.

ALTERNATE TEACHING STRATEGY

Draw a ladder on the chalkboard or chart paper. On each rung, write a decodable word that begins with *l*, such as *lip*, *lot*, *lap*, *lid*, *lit*, *Lin*, *lad*. Call on volunteers to blend sounds to read words as they "climb the ladder."

▶ **Visual/Linguistic**

Review

Initial /l/*Ll*

TESTED OBJECTIVES

Children will identify initial /l/*Ll*.

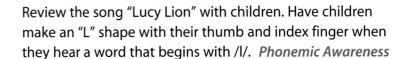

PREPARE

PHONOLOGICAL AWARENESS Say the following sounds and have children blend them to say the words: /l/-/ot/; /l/-/ip/; /l/-/ad/; /l/-/it/.

Listen

Review the song "Lucy Lion" with children. Have children make an "L" shape with their thumb and index finger when they hear a word that begins with /l/. *Phonemic Awareness*

TEACH

IDENTIFY INITIAL /l/*Ll* Provide small groups of children with a large sheet of drawing paper, scissors, paste, and magazines. Write *Ll* on the chalkboard and remind children that the letters *Ll* stand for /l/. Have children write *Ll* on their papers, cut out pictures beginning with /l/, and paste them on the paper. Call on groups to show and tell about their pictures.

PRACTICE

COMPLETE THE PUPIL PAGE Read the directions aloud, identify the pictures, and complete the first item together with children. Then have children finish the page independently.

ASSESS/CLOSE

IDENTIFY AND USE INITIAL /l/*Ll* Use page 70 to assess children's progress with initial /l/*Ll*. Have children draw a picture of an object that begins with /l/ and write *Ll* under it.

Introduce

Initial /u/*Uu*

OBJECTIVES

Children will identify initial /u/*Uu* and form the letters *Uu*.

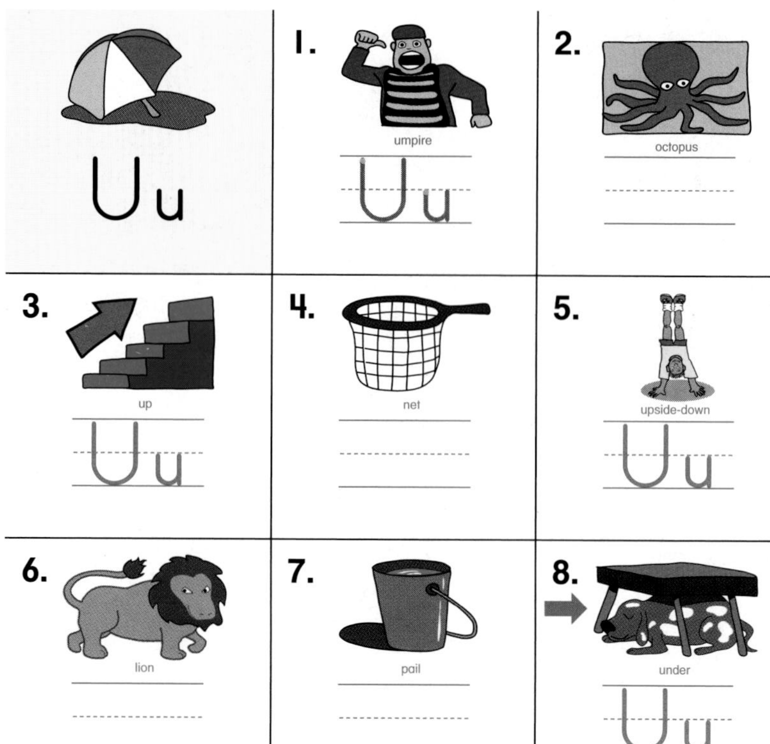

Name

Uu

1. umpire Uu

2. octopus

3. up Uu

4. net

5. upside-down Uu

6. lion

7. pail

8. under Uu

Say the name of each picture. • If the name begins with the same sound as *umbrella*, write *Uu* on the line.

Introduce Initial /u/*Uu* 71

PREPARE

PHONOLOGICAL AWARENESS Sing the song "Uncle Joe's Umbrella." Sing the first line again changing the word *climb* to *walk*. Ask children to say the word that was changed.

As you sing the song "Uncle Joe's Umbrella," hold up the Phonics Picture Poster for *umbrella*. Have the children point their thumb up each time they hear a /u/ sound at the beginning of the word. *Phonemic Awareness*

TEACH

IDENTIFY INITIAL /u/*Uu* Draw an umbrella on the chalkboard and write *Uu* on it. Explain that the letters *Uu* stand for the sound /u/. Have children say /u/ as you point to each letter. Write *umbrella* above the picture. Then under the umbrella, write *under, up, us*. Invite volunteers to circle each initial letter *u* while the class says /u/.

FORM *Uu* Some children may need to review how to write *U* and *u*. Have children trace the letter cards *Uu* from the Word Building Manipulative Cards.

PRACTICE

COMPLETE THE PUPIL PAGE Read the directions aloud. Help children identify the pictures and complete the first item. Have them finish the other items on their own.

ASSESS/CLOSE

IDENTIFY AND USE INITIAL /u/*Uu* Use page 71 to assess children's recognition of initial /u/*Uu*.

Phonics Song

Listen

Uncle Joe's Umbrella

Climb up the hill with Uncle Joe,
Uncle Joe, Uncle Joe,
Up the hill in the rain we go,
Under his umbrella!

Sung to the tune: "Here We Go 'Round the Mulberry Bush"
From **Songs from A to Z**

Phonics Picture Posters and Cards

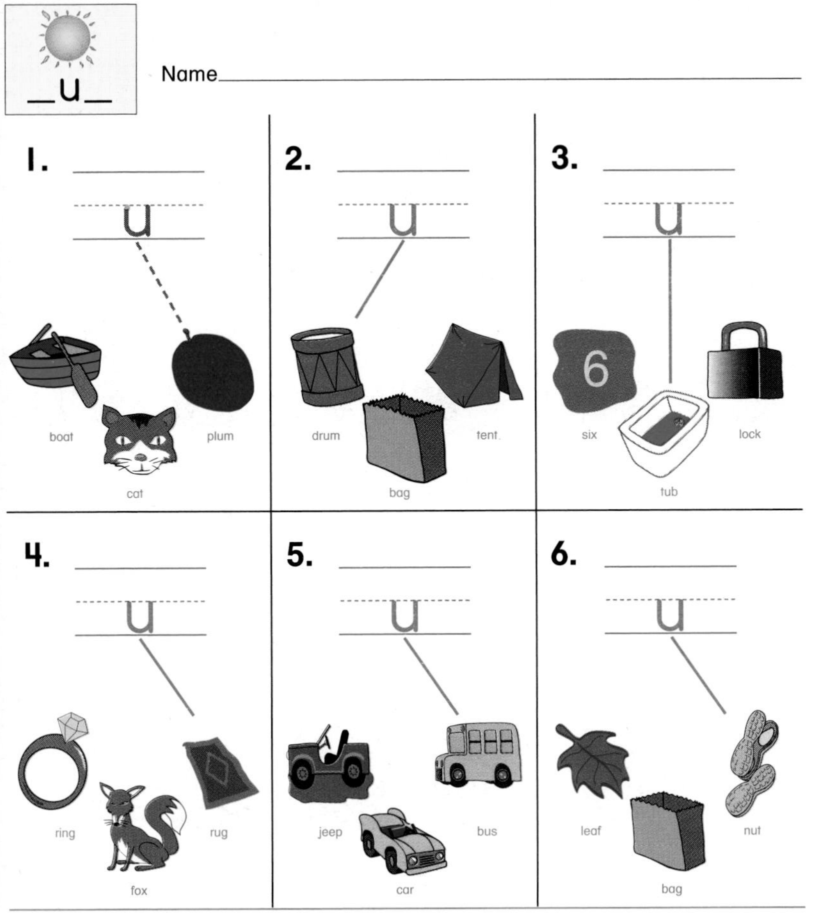
_u_ Name________________

1. ______ u
boat plum cat

2. ______ u
drum tent bag

3. ______ u
six lock tub

4. ______ u
ring rug fox

5. ______ u
jeep bus car

6. ______ u
leaf nut bag

McGraw-Hill School Division

Write the letter *u.* • Say the name of each picture. • Draw a line from the *u* to each picture whose name has the same middle sound as *sun.*

72 Introduce Medial /u/*u*

Introduce

Medial /u/*u*

Children will identify medial /u/*u*.

PREPARE

PHONOLOGICAL AWARENESS Tell children the words *run* and *sun* rhyme because they have the same ending sound. Have children think of other words that rhyme with *run*.

Listen

Say the following words and have children say /u/ each time they hear that sound in the middle of a word: *cup*, *hut*, *rat*, *pen*, *bun*, *pup*, *tap*, *sit*, *sun*. ***Phonemic Awareness***

TEACH

IDENTIFY MEDIAL /u/*u* Write *u* on the chalkboard and remind children that the letter *u* stands for the sound /u/. Display an assortment of pictures on the chalkboard ledge, most of which have medial /u/*u*, such as *pup*, *sun*, *bug*, *cup*, *bus*. Invite volunteers to point to a picture with medial /u/, name it, and write the letter *u* above it.

PRACTICE

COMPLETE THE PUPIL PAGE Before children complete the page on their own, read the directions aloud and help them identify the pictures. Encourage children to say *sun* after they name each picture and compare middle sounds.

ASSESS/CLOSE

IDENTIFY AND USE MEDIAL /u/*u* Use page 72 to assess children's progress with medial /u/*u*. Say *fun* and ask children to tell you in which position they hear /u/.

LANGUAGE SUPPORT

ESL In Spanish and in many other languages, the sound for the vowel *u* is /ü/ as in the word *moon*. You may want to provide extra practice for non-English-speaking children who have difficulty with the short *u* sound.

ALTERNATE TEACHING STRATEGY

Have children use clay to make a lowercase *u* and then use their finger to trace it. Ask children the sound that their clay letters stand for.

▶ **Kinesthetic**

Review

/l/*l*, /u/*u*

Children will identify /l/*l* and /u/*u* in words .

PREPARE

PHONOLOGICAL AWARENESS Say: *The lions and hippos are playing ball.* Have children clap out the syllables.

Then read aloud the following sentences. Have children raise their left thumb when they hear a word with the sound you say. *Phonemic Awareness*

initial /l/ *Leo the Lion hits the ball with his bat.*
middle /u/ *He runs to first base.*
initial /u/ *The umpire yells "safe."*

TEACH

REVIEW /l/*l*, /u/*u* Write the letters *l* and *u* on the chalkboard and distribute these letter cards from the Word Building Manipulative Cards. Say the word *tub* and ask children which sound they hear in the word, /l/ or /u/. Then ask children to hold up the letter that stands for /u/. Draw three blank letter boxes on the chalkboard. Invite a volunteer to place the letter card *u* in the correct box to show where he or she hears the sound—at the beginning, in the middle, or at the end of the word. Repeat with other words such as *lid, sun, let.*

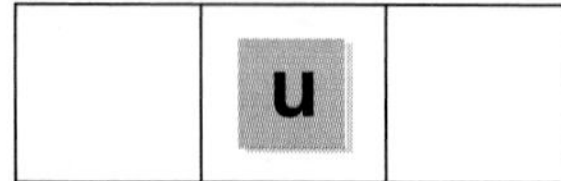

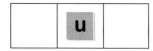

PRACTICE

COMPLETE THE PUPIL PAGE Read the directions aloud, help identify pictures, and complete the first item together.

ASSESS/CLOSE

IDENTIFY AND USE /l/*l*, /u/*u* Use page 73 to assess children's progress with /l/l, /u/u.

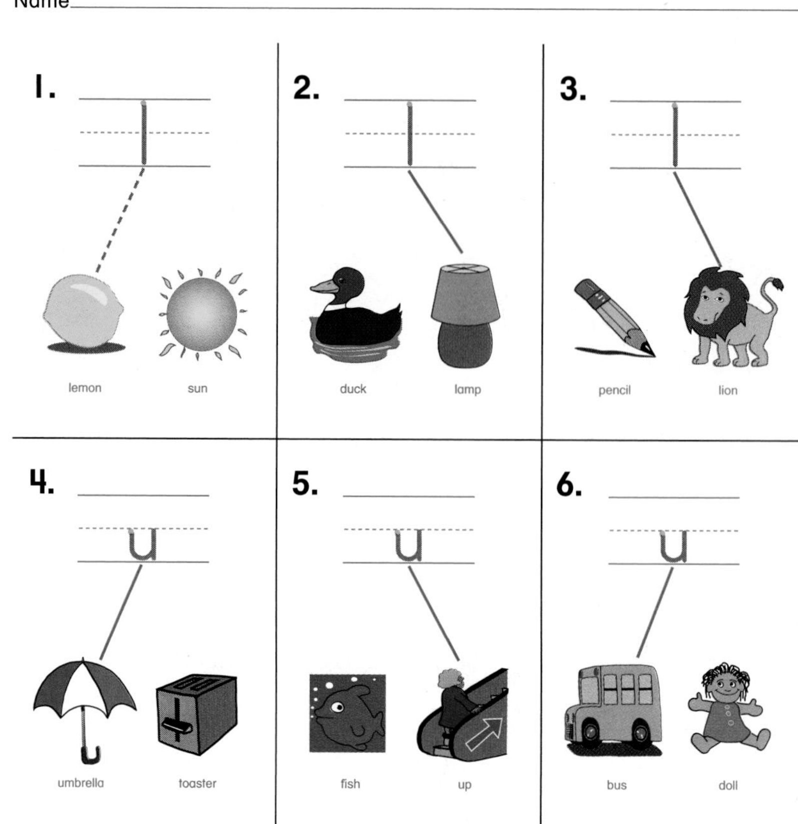

Trace the letter. • Say the sound it stands for. • Say the names of the pictures. • Draw a line from the letter to the picture whose name has the same sound as the letter.

Review /l/, /u/u 73

Name

1. nut (u, a)

2. fan (c, f)

3. mud (p, d)

4. sun (n, m)

5. pot (i, o)

6. lip (l, f)

McGraw-Hill School Division

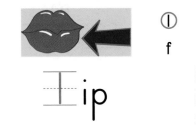

Say each picture name. • Circle the missing letter. • Then write the letter. • Read the word.

ALTERNATE TEACHING STRATEGY

Prepare word cards with short *a*, *i*, *o* and *u* words such as: *pup*, *pet*, *top*, *sat*, *kit*, *not*, *mud*. Display them on the chalkboard ledge. Point to each word and read it aloud. Then call out a word and have a volunteer find it, hold it up, and read it aloud.

▶ Linguistic/Auditory

Blending with Short *a, i, o, u*

OBJECTIVES

Children will blend and read short *a*, *i*, *o* and *u* CVC words.

PREPARE

Display the *a*, *f*, *i*, *n*, *o*, *p*, *t*, *u* letter cards from the Word Building Manipulative Cards. Point to each letter and review the sound for each letter.

TEACH

MODEL AND GUIDE PRACTICE Place the *u* letter card on the chalkboard ledge and say /u/. Have children repeat /u/.

- Place the *n* letter card next to the *u* letter card.
- Blend the sounds /u/ and /n/ together and have children repeat the sounds after you.
- Place the *f* letter card before the *u* letter card.
- Blend the sounds /f/, /u/, /n/ together to read *fun*. Have children repeat the word *fun* after you.

USE THE WORD IN CONTEXT Use *fun* in a sentence to reinforce its meaning, for example: *Riding a bike is fun.*

REPEAT THE PROCEDURE Use the following words to continue modeling and guided practice with short *a*, *i*, *o*, and *u*: *pin*, *tan*, *not*, *pat*.

PRACTICE

COMPLETE THE PUPIL PAGE Read the directions aloud and complete the page with children.

ASSESS/CLOSE

BLEND AND READ WORDS Use page 74 to assess children's skill in blending with short *a*, *i*, *o*, and *u*.

Introduce

High-Frequency Words: *that, for, go*

Children will identify and read the high-frequency words *that, for,* and *go.*

PREPARE

LISTEN TO WORDS Have children stand as you read aloud the sentences below. Have them listen for the key word in each sentence and jump when they hear the word.

that—*Look at that rabbit.*
go—*She can go fast.*
for—*I have a carrot for her.*

TEACH

IDENTIFY THE WORDS Hold up and read the word cards *that, go, for* from the High-Frequency Word Cards in the back of the Pupil's Edition. Write each sentence from the Prepare section on the chalkboard. Read each sentence aloud and have volunteers draw a line under the high-frequency words. Say those words aloud. Then distribute word cards and erase *that, go,* and *for*. Reread the sentences, pointing to each word, and have children hold up the card for the missing word.

PRACTICE

COMPLETE THE PUPIL PAGE Read the directions aloud and work through the first item with children. Remind them to circle more than one word in each row.

ASSESS/CLOSE

REVIEW THE PAGE Use page 75 to assess children's recognition of the words *that, for,* and *go*. Have children use these words in a sentence and hold up word cards as they say each word.

Name____________________

1.	that	for	that	go	that
2.	for	that	for	for	go
3.	go	for	go	that	go
4.	for	for	go	that	for
5.	that	that	go	that	for

Read the first word in each row. • Circle the words in that row that are the same.

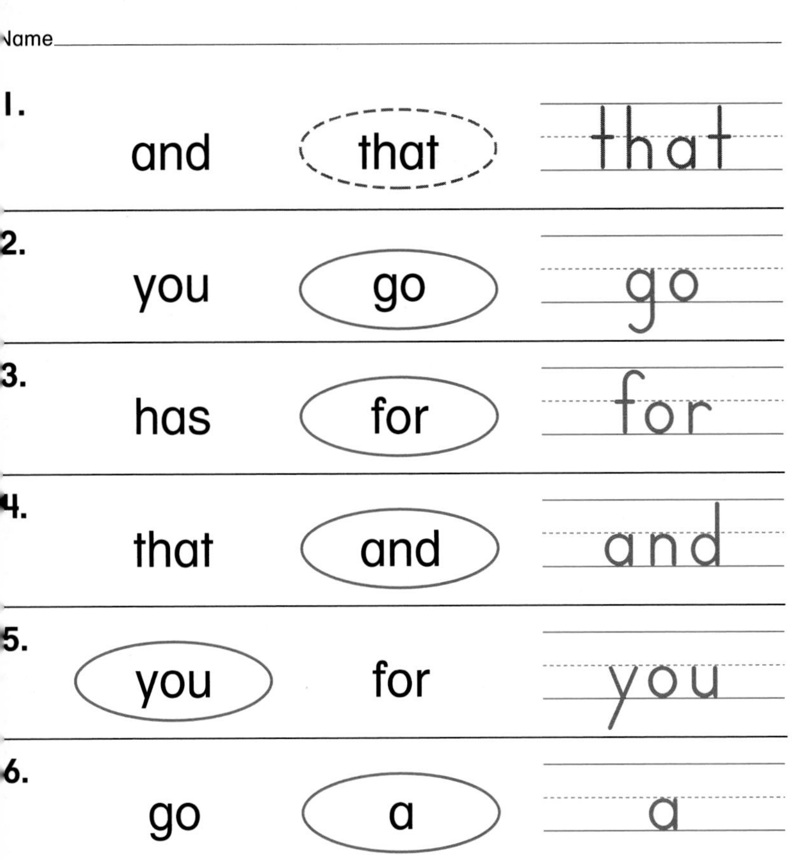

Name

1.	and	that	that
2.	you	go	go
3.	has	for	for
4.	that	and	and
5.	you	for	you
6.	go	a	a

Listen to the word. • Circle the word you hear. • Then write the word.

76 Review High-Frequency Words

Review

High-Frequency Words

TESTED OBJECTIVES

Children will identify and read the high-frequency words *that, for, go, and, you,* and *a*.

PREPARE

LISTEN TO WORDS Assign each child a word to listen for as you slowly read the following sentences aloud: *go, for, a, and, you, that*. Have them stand up when they hear their word. Reassign the words and repeat the sentences.

I will go for a walk.
You and your friend can come.
Wait for me by that door.

TEACH

IDENTIFY THE WORDS Have children work in small groups. Write *that, for, go, and, you,* and *a* on the chalkboard and read each word aloud. Distribute these word cards from the back of the Pupil's Edition to each group. Point to and say a word and invite each group to use the word in a spoken sentence.

PRACTICE

COMPLETE THE PUPIL PAGE Read the directions aloud. Tell children to listen to each word you say, circle it, and write it. Say: (1) *that*; (2) *go*; (3) *for*; (4) *and*; (5) *you*; (6) *a*.

ASSESS/CLOSE

REVIEW THE PAGE Use page 76 to assess children's recognition of the words *that, for, go, and, you,* and *a*. Have children say and write the word *that*.

ALTERNATE TEACHING STRATEGY

Give pairs of children a high-frequency word card. Have children search for their word in books or magazines. Help children read aloud the sentence in which their word appears.

▶ **Linguistic/Visual**

Develop

Phonological Awareness

Blend Syllables

Teach Read aloud the poem *"Sun Up."* Tell children that the name Rex in this poem has one word part. Say the two word parts of *bet-ty* and blend them to say the name. Have children repeat the word parts and then blend them to say the word.

Practice Children sit in a circle and take turns saying the word parts of words that fit a category. For example, start with foods, such as *crack-er*. A volunteer blends the syllables and takes the next turn. When no one can think of any other foods, start a new category such as colors, animals, or furniture.

Sun Up

Tick tock. Sun up.
Rex sips from the cup.
Hot buns. Red jam.
And a bit of ham.
Back pack. Red cap.
Dad gets Rex a map.
Tick tock. Run. Run.
It is time for fun.

Identify Beginning Sounds

Phonemic Awareness

MATERIALS

- **Phonics Picture Posters**
  kite, dog, sock, bear, hen, rope

Teach Display the Phonics Picture Poster (picture side only) for *kite*. Tell children the word kite begins with the sound /k/. Say pairs of words and have children repeat the word that begins with /k/: *key/tea; mitten/kitten; wing/king.*

Practice Play *"I'm thinking of a word that begins with the sound _"* Display the Phonics Picture Posters (picture side only) for *kite, dog, sock, bear, hen* and *rope*. Begin by giving the clues to the class. As children become more comfortable identifying beginning sounds, add more Phonics Picture Posters and allow children to give the clues.

Identify Ending Sounds

Phonemic Awareness

MATERIALS
- Word Building Manipulative Cards
  clock
- Puppet

Teach Display the Word Building Manipulative Card for *clock* (picture side only). Tell children the word *clock* has the ending sound /k/. Have children say the word and sound with you. Have children identify which of a pair of words ends with the /k/ sound: *pack/pat; sad/sack; dug/duck; den/deck.*

Practice Have children sit in a circle. Tell children that the puppet only knows how to say words that end with the /k/ sound. Have the puppet say the word *sock*. Then pass the puppet to the child next to you, who will make the puppet say another word that ends with the /k/ sound.

Blend Sounds

Phonemic Awareness

MATERIALS
- blocks or cubes (three per child)

Teach Display three blocks and point to each as you say the individual sounds in a three-sound word such as *sick*: /s/-/i/-/k/. Stretch out the sounds and move the blocks together until you blend the word. Have children take turns coming up and moving a block for each sound as you say and then blend other words such as: *map*, *sack*, *lock*, *fit*, *sun*, *dig*, *name*, *nick*, *tack*.

Practice Distribute three blocks to each pair of children. Give the individual sounds in three-sound words for the pairs to blend. Call on volunteers to say the blended words. Use such words as: *sick*, *dip*, *fat*, *bun*, *lack*, *net*, *knock*, *rock*, *men*.

Introduce

Initial /k/*Kk*

Children will identify initial /k/*Kk* and form the letters *Kk*.

PREPARE

PHONOLOGICAL AWARENESS Listen Say the following words and have children repeat after you and clap the syllables: *kite*, *kangaroo*, *kitten*, and *key*.

While singing the song "Kenny's Kite," hold up the Phonics Picture Poster of *kite*. Have the children say /k/ each time they hear a /k/ sound at the beginning of a word. *Phonemic Awareness*

TEACH

IDENTIFY INITIAL /k/*Kk* Tell children that the sound /k/ can be spelled with the letters *Kk*. Write *Kk* on the chalkboard and have children say /k/ and point to the letter. Then write this sentence: *Karen had a little kitty*. Invite volunteers to draw a line from *Kk* to the words beginning with *Kk*.

FORM *Kk* Review how to write *K* and *k*. Have children practice writing the letters on lined paper, using letter cards from the Word Building Manipulative Cards as a reference.

PRACTICE

COMPLETE THE PUPIL PAGE Read the directions aloud and have children name the key picture *kite*. Help them identify the pictures and complete the first item.

ASSESS/CLOSE

IDENTIFY AND USE INITIAL /k/*Kk* Use page 77 to assess children's knowledge of initial /k/*Kk*. Have children draw a picture of something that begins with /k/.

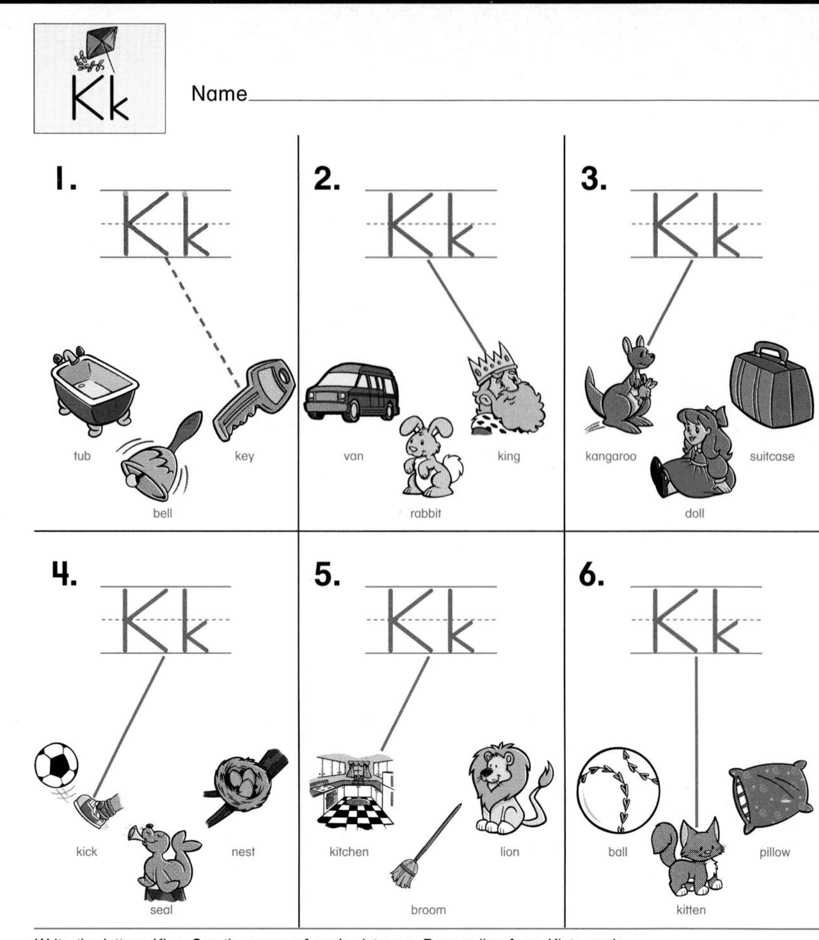

Kk Name

1. Kk — tub, bell, key
2. Kk — van, rabbit, king
3. Kk — kangaroo, doll, suitcase
4. Kk — kick, seal, nest
5. Kk — kitchen, broom, lion
6. Kk — ball, kitten, pillow

Write the letters *Kk*. • Say the name of each picture. • Draw a line from *Kk* to each picture whose name begins like *kite*.

Introduce Initial /k/*Kk* 77

Kenny's Kite

Kenny Kangaroo likes flying kites,
Flying kites, flying kites,
Kenny Kangaroo likes flying kites,
Flying kites is fun!

Sung to the tune:
"The Wheels on the Bus"
From **Songs from A to Z**

Phonics Picture Posters and Cards

Name_______________

Kk

1. 

king

Kk

2. wig

3. 

kitchen

Kk

4. 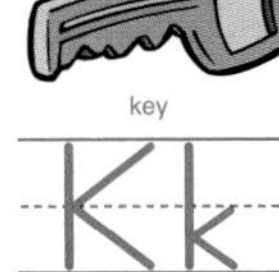

key

Kk

5. 

pots

6. 

kitten

Kk

7. 

kick

Kk

8. 

kangaroo

Kk

Say the name of each picture. • If the name begins with the same sound as *kite*, write *Kk* on the line.

Review

Initial /k/*Kk*

Children will identify initial /k/*Kk*.

PREPARE

PHONOLOGICAL AWARENESS Invite children to play a game in which they listen to things you name that a kangaroo might keep in its pouch. Explain the kangaroo only collects things beginning with /k/. Say, for example, *Will I find a kite in the pouch? Kitten? Apple? Key? Ball? King? Queen?* *Phonemic Awareness*

TEACH

IDENTIFY INITIAL /k/*Kk* Write *Kk* on the chalkboard in a circle and remind children that the letters *Kk* stand for /k/. Then write the following words around the circle: *kite*, *key*, *bat*, *king*, *kick*, *man*, *kitty*. Read aloud each word and invite volunteers to repeat the word after you and draw a line from the word to the circle if it begins with /k/*Kk*. If it does not begin with /k/*Kk*, have children cross out the word.

PRACTICE

COMPLETE THE PUPIL PAGE Before children begin, read the directions aloud and help children identify the pictures. After working on the first item together, encourage children to finish the other items on their own.

ASSESS/CLOSE

IDENTIFY AND USE INITIAL /k/*Kk* Use page 78 to assess children's progress with initial /k/*Kk*. Say the following words and have children clap when they hear a word that begins with /k/: *kind*, *sun*, *keep*, *kitten*, *ball*. Then have them write the letter that stands for the sound /k/ as in *kitten*.

TEACHING TIP

INSTRUCTIONAL Explain to children that the sound /k/ can be spelled with the letter *c* or with the letter *k*. Provide cards with initial /k/*c* words and initial /k/*k* words. Help children say the words and sort them into "c" and "k" groups.

ALTERNATE TEACHING STRATEGY

Draw a large kite on chart paper and print *k* all around the edge of the outline. Have children find and cut out pictures that begin with *k* and paste them in the middle of the kite. Draw a kite string and have volunteers write the letter *k* along the string.

▶ Spatial/Visual

Introduce

Final /k/ck

OBJECTIVES

Children will identify final /k/*ck* and form the letters *ck*.

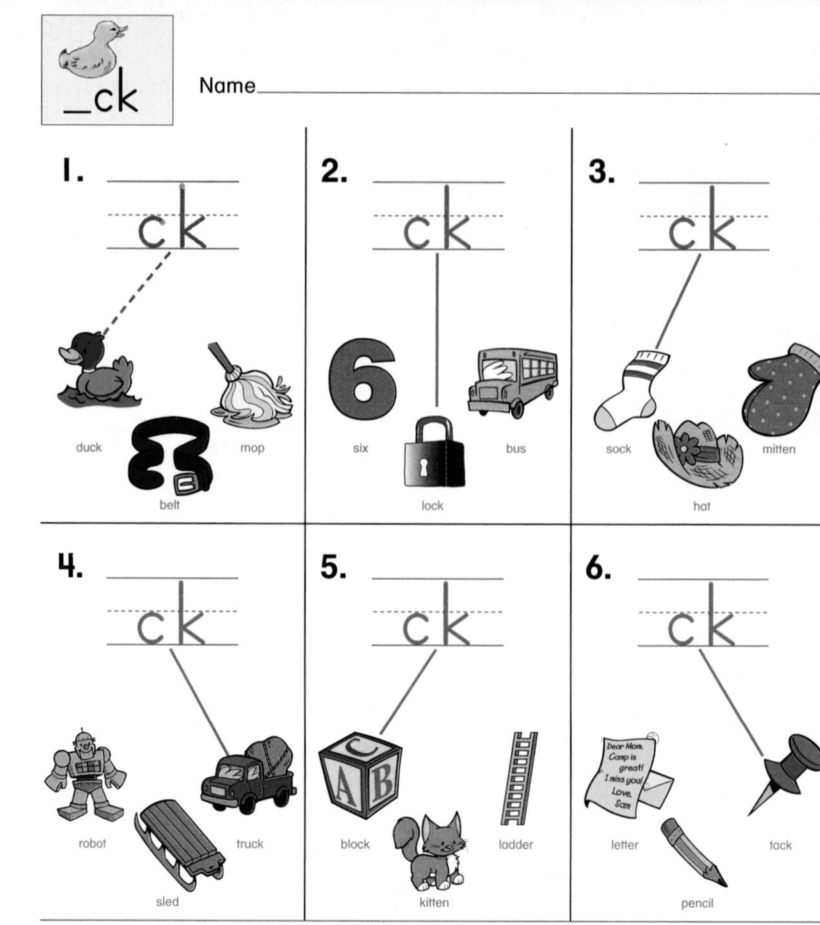

_ck Name________

1. ck — duck, mop, belt
2. ck — six, bus, lock
3. ck — sock, mitten, hat
4. ck — robot, truck, sled
5. ck — block, ladder, kitten
6. ck — letter, tack, pencil

Write the letters *ck*. • Say the name of each picture. • Draw a line from *ck* to each picture whose name has the same ending sound as *duck*.

Introduce Final /k/*ck* 79

PREPARE

PHONOLOGICAL AWARENESS Say the following sets of words and have children identify the two words that rhyme: *duck, big, luck; rock, ten, sock; rabbit, sick, lick; neck, nine, peck.*

Then hold up the Phonics Picture Poster for *duck*. Tell children the word duck ends with the /k/ sound. Say the following words and ask children to identify the ending sound of each word: *duck, sock, pick, sip, neck, ten, luck.* ***Phonemic Awareness***

TEACH

IDENTIFY FINAL /k/*ck* Write *clock, sock, block* on the chalkboard. Underline the letters *ck* and tell children that the letters *ck* can stand for the ending sound /k/. Have children say the words after you.

FORM *ck* Review how to write the letters *ck*. Encourage children to trace *ck* on the letter cards from the Word Building Manipulative Cards. Then have children write the letters on a piece of paper and draw a picture of a *duck*.

Phonics Picture Posters and Cards

PRACTICE

COMPLETE THE PUPIL PAGE Read the directions aloud and identify the key picture *duck*. Help children identify the pictures before they work on their own.

ASSESS/CLOSE

IDENTIFY AND USE FINAL /k/*ck* Use page 79 to assess children's recognition of final /k/*ck*. Have children write *ck* and say two words that end with /k/*ck*.

ame______________________________

___ck

1. 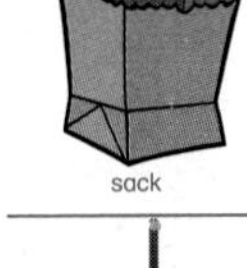

sack

ck

2. 

truck

ck

3. 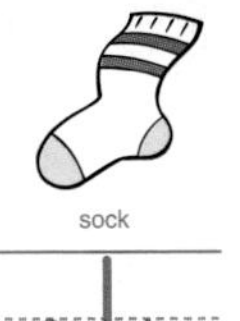

sock

ck

4. 

duck

ck

5. 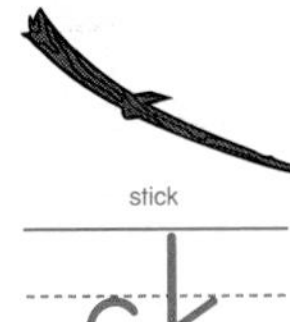

stick

ck

6. 

neck

ck

7. 

five

8. 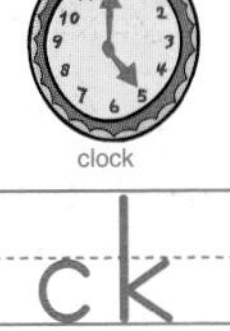

clock

ck

McGraw-Hill School Division

ay the name of each picture. • If the name ends with the same sound as *lock*, rite *ck* on the line.

0 Review Final /k/ck

ALTERNATE TEACHING STRATEGY

Explain that *unlock* ends with /k/. Have children pretend to use a key to unlock a lock. Then have children pretend to unlock a lock when they hear a word that ends like *lock*. Say these words: *pick, map, sock, luck, pack, table, kitten, stack*.

▶ **Auditory/Kinesthetic**

Review

Final /k/ck

Children will identify final /k/*ck*.

PREPARE

PHONOLOGICAL AWARENESS Say the words *quack* and *tack*. Tell children that these words rhyme because they have the same ending sounds. Say the following words and have children say "quack" if the word rhymes with *quack*: *rack, tan, pack, dog, bear, stack, lack, pun*.

Say *truck* and have children identify the ending sound. Invite children to play a game in which they pretend to load things into a truck. Explain that the objects must end with the /k/ sound. Ask: *Can we take a duck? A clock? A cat? A hen?* *Phonemic Awareness*

TEACH

IDENTIFY FINAL /k/*ck* Remind children that the letters *ck* can stand for the sound /k/ at the end of a word. Write this sentence on the chalkboard: *I put the black rock in my sack.* Read the sentence aloud and have volunteers circle final *ck* and say /k/.

PRACTICE

COMPLETE THE PUPIL PAGE Before inviting children to complete the page on their own, read the directions aloud and help them identify the pictures. Do the first item together.

ASSESS/CLOSE

IDENTIFY AND USE FINAL /k/*ck* Use page 80 to assess children's progress with final /k/*ck*. You may wish to have children draw a picture of an object that ends with *ck* and write *ck* under it.

Review

/k/*k*, *ck*

OBJECTIVES

Children will identify /k/*k*, *ck* in words .

PREPARE

PHONOLOGICAL AWARENESS Have children think of words that rhyme with *sock* and say them aloud.

Read this sentence and tell children to listen for a word with /k/ at the beginning: *My aunt is a kind person.* Tell them to listen for a word with /k/ at the end in this sentence: *She cares for people who are sick.* *Phonemic Awareness*

TEACH

REVIEW /k/*k*, *ck* Write the letters *k* and *ck* on the chalkboard. Remind children that the letter *k* stands for /k/ at the beginning of a word and the letters *ck* stand for /k/ at the end of a word. Draw three blank letter boxes. Say the word *kit* and ask children where they hear the sound /k/. Have a volunteer write *k* or *ck* to show where he or she hears the sound—at the beginning or at the end of the word. Repeat with other words such as *kid, pick, back.*

PRACTICE

COMPLETE THE PUPIL PAGE Read the directions aloud, help children name the pictures, and do the first item together. Then encourage children to finish the page on their own.

ASSESS/CLOSE

IDENTIFY AND USE /k/*k*, *ck* Use page 81 to assess children's progress with /k/*k*, *ck*. Say *Ken* and ask children to tell you in which position they hear /k/. Repeat with the word *lock.*

Name____________________

1. k — ladder, kite	2. k — kangaroo, rose	3. k — kitchen, telephone
4. ck — duck, ant	5. ck — bread, truck	6. ck — baby, lock

Trace the letter or letters. • Say the sound they stand for. • Say the names of the pictures. • Draw a line from the letter or letters to the picture whose name has the same sound.

Review /k/*k*, *ck* 81

Name

1\. cup (u / i) — c u p

2\. duck (ck / t) — du ck

3\. kick (o / i) — k i ck

4\. mop (m / r) — m op

5\. fan (s / n) — fa n

6\. rod (r / t) — r od

McGraw-Hill School Division

Say each picture name. • Circle the missing letter or letters. • Then write the letter or letters. • Read the word.

82 Blending with Short *a, i, o,* and *u*

ALTERNATE TEACHING STRATEGY

Create word cards for the following words: *pack, pick, tick, tock, tuck, sick, sock, sack, dock,* and *duck.* Show each word card and have children repeat each word as you read it aloud. Clarify word meanings. Then ask children to sort the word cards for beginning sounds and then for middle sounds.

▶ **Linguistic/Logical**

Blending with
Short *a, i, o, u*

TESTED OBJECTIVES

Children will blend and read short *a, i, o,* and *u* CVC words.

PREPARE

Display the *a, d, i, l, o, r, u,* and *ck* letter cards from the Word Building Manipulative Cards. As you say the sound for each letter, have a volunteer remove the appropriate card.

TEACH

MODEL AND GUIDE PRACTICE Place letter card *i* on the chalkboard ledge and say /i/. Have children say the sound /i/.

- Place the *ck* letter card next to the *i* letter card.
- Blend the sounds /i/ and /k/ together and have children repeat the sounds after you.
- Place the *R* letter card before the *i* letter card.
- Blend the sounds /r/, /i/, /k/ together to read *Rick.* Have children repeat the name *Rick* after you.

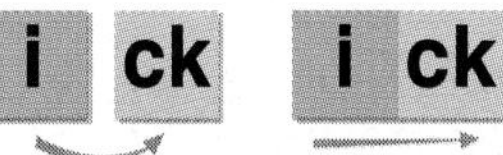

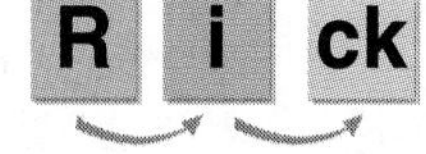

USE THE WORD IN CONTEXT Use *Rick* in a sentence to reinforce its meaning, for example: *I know a boy named Rick.*

REPEAT THE PROCEDURE Use the following words to continue modeling and guided practice: *luck, dock, rid, lad.*

PRACTICE

COMPLETE THE PUPIL PAGE Read the directions aloud and complete the first item with children.

ASSESS/CLOSE

BLEND AND READ WORDS Use page 82 to assess children's skill in blending with short *a, i, o, u.* Have children use the letter cards to build and read a CVC word.

Read the Story

OBJECTIVES

Children will use their knowledge of phonics and decoding and high-frequency words to read.

Kit can run a lot.

2

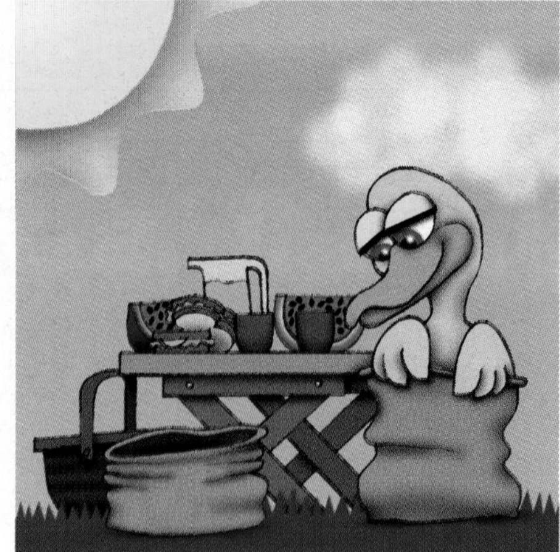

Duck has a sack.

3

BEFORE READING

PREVIEW After reading the story title, *Kit and Duck*, talk about the picture on the cover. Invite the children to discuss what the story is about by looking at the picture on the cover. Invite volunteers to name the sound at the beginning of *Kit*. (/k/) Write the following high-frequency words on the chalkboard: *and, you, a, that, for, go*. Read each of these words aloud to the children as you point to them. Have children look through the story to find these words.

Kit and Duck

MAKE PREDICTIONS Invite children to take a **picture walk** through pages 2, 3, and 4. Have children use the pictures to make predictions about the story. Ask: *What is the story about? How do children think the story will end?* List children's ideas on the chalkboard.

"Can you fit?"

4

Kit can fit.

5

DURING READING

READING SUGGESTIONS Tell children to look at the pictures as they read to help them better understand the story. Have children track the print with their finger. Remind them to pay attention to the marks at the ends of sentences, such as the question mark on page 4 and the exclamation point on page 6.

TEACHING TIP

MANAGEMENT Help children put together their own take-home story. Give the following directions to the children. Demonstrate as needed.

To put book together,
Tear out the story page.
Cut along the dotted line.
Fold each section on the fold line.

Duck can go for that cup!

6

Duck can pack the cup.

7

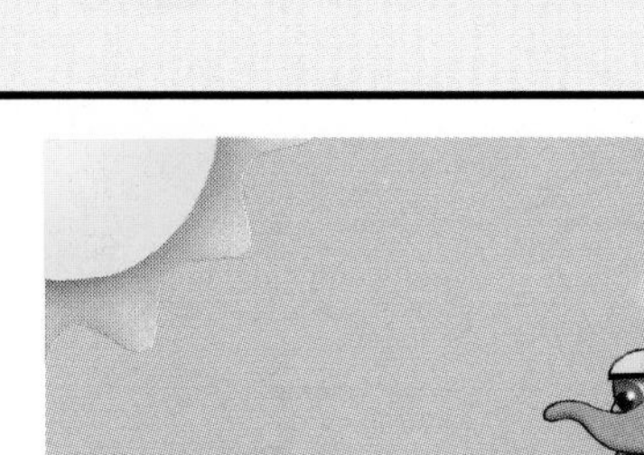

Kit can pack the cup!

8

Read the Story

AFTER READING

RETURN TO PREDICTIONS Read aloud children's predictions from the chalkboard. Discuss whether their predictions matched what happened in the story. Talk about whether or not the story ended as children thought it would end.

RETELL THE STORY Invite volunteers to retell the story in their own words. Use sentence starters to help them tell the story in sequence. For example, say, "In the beginning of the story..." and have a volunteer finish the sentence. Continue with sentence starters for the middle and end of the story.

STORY QUESTIONS Ask the following questions about the story.

- *Who ran to the top of the hill first?* (Kit the cat.) ***Literal/Story Details***
- *Why do Duck and Kit want to hop around in burlap sacks?* (Because it is fun.) ***Inferential/Story Details***
- *What could Kit do if he does not fit in his sack?* (Answers will vary, find another game, get a bigger sack) ***Critical/Make Predictions***

CENTER Activity

Cross Curricular: Music

CREATE A SONG Help children create a song about the story *Kit and Duck* to the tune of "Old MacDonald." Here is a possible sample verse: *Old MacDonald had a picnic. E-I-E-I-O. And at this picnic there was some food. E-I-E-I-O. With a munch munch here, and a munch, munch there, here a munch, there a munch, everywhere a munch, munch. Old MacDonald had a picnic. E-I-E-I-O.* Brainstorm other lines for the song such as ants marching, animals running, and so on.

▶ **Auditory/Musical**

Introduce

Positional Terms

Children will identify left-to-right directionality.

PREPARE

INTRODUCE LEFT TO RIGHT Draw a picture of a dog on the left side of the chalkboard. Then draw a bone to the right of the dog. Stand with your back to the class and tell children the dog is on the left side. Have children hold up their left hand. Then point to the bone and tell children the bone is on your right side. Have children hold up their right hands.

TEACH

IDENTIFY LEFT-TO-RIGHT Then tell children that if the dog wants to get the bone, he must move from left to right. Draw a straight line from the dog to the bone. Then write the following sentence under the pictures: *"The dog ran to the bone."* Explain that when we read we move from left to right. Reread the sentence while tracking print.

PRACTICE

COMPLETE THE PUPIL PAGE Before children begin, read the directions aloud. Identify the pictures with children. Tell children to draw a line to connect each animal on the left with the food it likes to eat on the right.

ASSESS/CLOSE

REVIEW THE PAGE Use page 85 to assess children's knowledge of left-to-right directionality. Have children say aloud an animal on the left and the food it likes to eat on the right.

Name______________________________

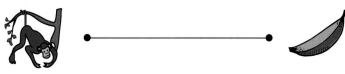

Draw a line from left to right to connect each animal with the food it likes to eat.

Beginning Reading Concepts: *Positional Terms* 85

ALTERNATE TEACHING STRATEGY

ESL APPROPRIATE Place word cards for the following sentence in a pocket chart: *My pup Sam is fun*. Explain to children that when we read, we move from left to right. Read the sentence aloud, tracking print as you read each word. Have volunteers read the sentence while tracking print. Repeat with other sentences.

▶ Spatial/Visual

ame

McGraw-Hill School Division

raw a line from top to bottom to connect each kite with a person.

6 Beginning Reading Concepts: *Positional Terms*

TEACHING TIP

TOP-TO-BOTTOM Invite children to play a game of "Simon Says." Instruct them to touch their head, shoulders, tummy, knees, and toes. Repeat to reinforce that they are going from the top to the bottom of their bodies.

Introduce

Positional Terms

Children will demonstrate knowledge of top-to-bottom movement.

PREPARE

INTRODUCE TOP AND BOTTOM Use different colored linking cubes to build a tower. Show children which cube is at the top of the tower and which cube is at the bottom of the tower. Repeat with a different combination of colored cubes.

TEACH

IDENTIFY TOP-TO-BOTTOM Use a marker to draw a sun at the top of a piece of chart paper. Say: *The sun is at the top*. Use a marker to draw grass at the bottom of the paper. Say: *This grass is at the bottom*. Tell children that we read from left-to-right and top-to-bottom. Demonstrate by tracking print in a classroom big book.

PRACTICE

COMPLETE THE PUPIL PAGE Before children begin, read the directions aloud. Tell children to draw a line from each kite at the top to a person at the bottom of the page.

ASSESS/CLOSE

REVIEW THE PAGE Use page 86 to assess children's skill in demonstrating top-to-bottom movement. Ask children to use a finger to trace a line from a kite to the person below.

Develop

Phonological Awareness

Blend Onsets and Rimes

Teach Read aloud *"Meg and Her Duck."* Tell children you will say some words from the poem by saying their beginning sound separately from the rest of the word. Demonstrate by saying: /m/-/eg/. Then blend the sounds to say the word: *Meg*.

Practice Have children blend the following sounds to say other words from the poem: /b/-/ig/: *big*; /d/-/uk/: *duck*; /w/-/et/: *wet*.

Meg and Her Duck

A girl named Meg got a duck.
The duck was big and yellow.
Meg named the duck Luck.
He was a good, happy fellow.
Meg gave Luck a hug each day.
Then they'd play tag in the sun.
Meg and Luck would go get wet.
They had so much fun!

Identify Beginning and Ending Sounds

Phonemic Awareness

MATERIALS

- Phonics Picture Posters

  goat, egg

Teach **FOCUS ON BEGINNING SOUNDS**

Display the Phonics Picture Poster for *goat*. Say the word and then the sound /g/. Have children repeat the word and sound after you. Reread the poem and have children raise a hand when they hear a word beginning with /g/: *girl, good, go*. Repeat with the beginning /e/ sound and the Phonics Picture Poster for *egg*.

Practice Play *"Go!"* Say a word beginning with /g/ and then say *"Go* (name a child)*!"* to someone in the class. That child says a word with initial /g/ and says *"Go* (names another child)*!"* Continue the game with the beginning /e/ sound, as in *egg*.

FOCUS ON ENDING SOUNDS

Repeat the activity with the ending sound /g/. Point to a child and say "Egg!". Have each child say a word that ends with the final /g/ sound.

Identify Middle Sounds

Phonemic Awareness

MATERIALS

- **Phonics Picture from Word Building Cards**
  web

Teach Tell children the word *Meg* has the middle sound /e/. Then display the Phonics Picture of a *web* from the Word Building Manipulative Cards. Tell children the words Meg and web have the middle /e/ sound. Have children repeat after you: web: /e/. Have children tell which of pairs has middle /e/: *met/mat; sill/sell; peg/pig*.

Practice Have children stand in a circle and pretend they are a web. Have children take turns stepping into the middle of the web and giving the middle sound of the following words: *men, Zeb, cap, sock, led, head, tub, pen, win*.

Segment Sounds

Phonemic Awareness

MATERIALS

- **Three pieces of paper**

Teach Tell children they will count the number of sounds in words. Tape three pieces of paper next to each other on the wall. Say the word *pen*. Tell children to listen for three sounds; then point to each paper as you say the sounds /p/-/e/-/n/. Demonstrate and lead children to do the same with other two- and three-sound words, such as: *get, by, men, egg, set, ran, at, peg*.

Practice Put children in groups of three. Tell each group a word and have the group separate the word into individual sounds. Then groups share their words, tell how many sounds, and identify the individual sounds. Use these words: *bet, well, men, hen, wet, leg, pen, ten*.

Introduce

Initial /g/*Gg*

Children will identify initial /g/*Gg* and form the letters *Gg*.

PREPARE

PHONOLOGICAL AWARENESS Say the following words and have children tell you which words rhyme: *goat, gate, late*. Repeat with the words *hog, sock, log*.

While singing the song "My Goat Gary" hold up the Phonics Picture Poster of a *goat*. Afterwards, say the words of the song slowly and have children say /g/ each time they hear a /g/ sound at the beginning of the word. *Phonemic Awareness*

TEACH

IDENTIFY INITIAL /g/*Gg* Distribute the *Gg* letter card from the Word Building Manipulative Cards. Tell children that the letters *Gg* can stand for the sound /g/. Ask children to say /g/ and point to their letter cards. Draw a grid with 9 boxes on chart paper and write a word in each box: *go, say, get, girl, to, give, goat, pet, got*. Have volunteers put letter cards on words with initial /g/*g*.

FORM *Gg* Review how to write *G* and *g*. Encourage children to write the letters on paper folded into fourths, using their letter cards as reference.

PRACTICE

COMPLETE THE PUPIL PAGE Read the directions aloud and help children identify the key picture *goat* and the other pictures.

ASSESS/CLOSE

IDENTIFY AND USE INITIAL /g/*Gg* Use page 87 to assess children's recognition of initial /g/*Gg*. Ask: *My name begins with /g/. I am a place to keep a car. What am I?* (garage)

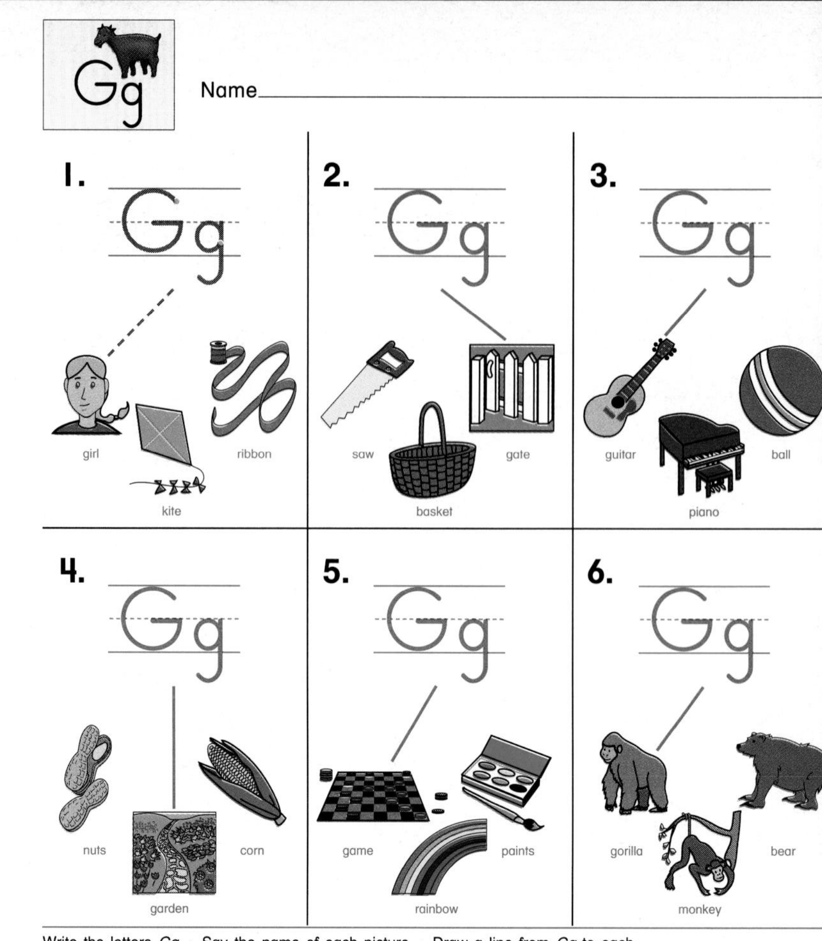

Gg Name________

1. Gg — girl, ribbon, kite
2. Gg — saw, gate, basket
3. Gg — guitar, ball, piano
4. Gg — nuts, corn, garden
5. Gg — game, paints, rainbow
6. Gg — gorilla, bear, monkey

Write the letters *Gg*. • Say the name of each picture. • Draw a line from *Gg* to each picture whose name begins like *goat*.

Introduce Initial /g/*Gg* 87

Phonics Song

My Goat Gary

My goat Gary plays guitar,
I think he will be a star!
Gary plays by the garden gate.
All the geese think he's just great.
My goat Gary plays guitar.
I think he will be a star!

Tune: "Twinkle, Twinkle Little Star"
From **Songs from A to Z**

Phonics Picture Posters and Cards

Name

–g

1. 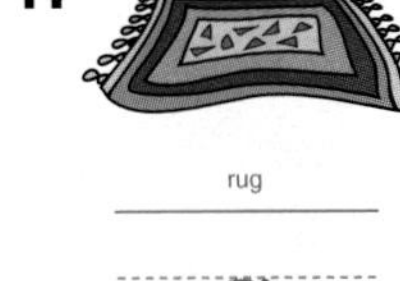

rug

g

2. 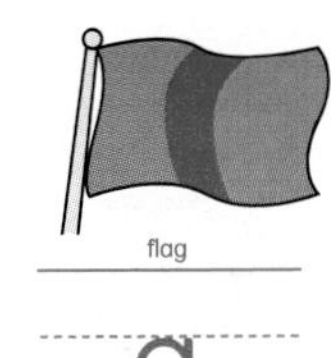

flag

g

3. 

truck

4. 

boat

5. 

pig

g

6. 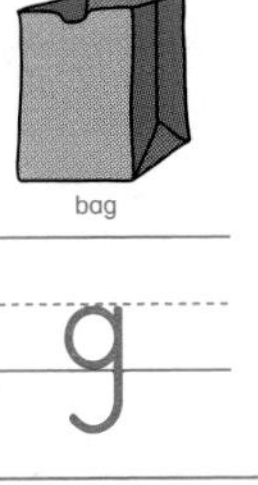

bag

g

7. 

mug

g

8. 

dog

g

Say the name of each picture. • If the name ends with the same sound as *frog*, write *g* on the line.

TEACHING TIP

MANAGEMENT When you teach initial /g/*g*, you may want to have children work in groups. If so, prepare a list of children for each group ahead of time.

ALTERNATE TEACHING STRATEGY

Demonstrate how to gallop like a horse. Then have children listen as you say some words. If they begin with *g*, have children gallop. If they end with *g*, children should stand still. Use words such as these: *girl, jug, gate, gallon, mug, get, go, gone, lag, pig.*

▶ **Auditory/Kinesthetic**

Introduce

Final /g/g

Children will identify final /g/*g*.

PREPARE

PHONOLOGICAL AWARENESS Have children clap out the syllables for the following pairs of words: *big/yellow; luck/fellow; happy/good.* Ask children which word in each pair is longer.

Listen

Display and name pictures of these animals: *pig, frog, dog, bug.* Have children identify the ending sound in each animal name. *Phonemic Awareness*

TEACH

IDENTIFY FINAL ***/g/g*** Say *pig* and have a volunteer write on the chalkboard the letter that stands for the final sound. Remind children that *g* can stand for /g/. Then write this tongue twister and invite children to circle final *g* and say /g/: *I saw a big pig in a wig eat a fig.*

PRACTICE

COMPLETE THE PUPIL PAGE Read the directions aloud, identify each picture, and work through the first item with children. Then have them complete the page independently.

ASSESS/CLOSE

IDENTIFY AND USE FINAL ***/g/g*** Use page 88 to assess children's knowledge of final /g/*g*. Ask children to name an animal whose name ends with /g/*g*.

Introduce

Initial /e/Ee

Children will identify initial /e/*Ee* and form the letters *Ee*.

PREPARE

PHONOLOGICAL AWARENESS Say the words *end* and *lend*. Have children think of other words that rhyme with them.

Listen

As you sing the song "Ed's Eggs," hold up the Phonics Picture Poster for *egg*. Have the children touch their elbow each time they hear the /e/ sound at the beginning of a word. *Phonemic Awareness*

TEACH

IDENTIFY INITIAL /e/*Ee* Write each word on a large envelope: *egg, ever, Emma*. Hold up the *Ee* letter card from the Word Building Manipulative Cards and tell children that the letters *Ee* stand for /e/, the beginning sound of *envelope*. Read the words on the envelopes aloud. Have volunteers say /e/, and put the matching letter card in the envelope.

FORM *Ee* Some children may need to review how to write *E* and *e*. Have children write capital *E* and lowercase *e* on a partner's back while the partner guesses which letter it is.

PRACTICE

COMPLETE THE PUPIL PAGE Read the directions aloud and help children identify the pictures. Have children finish the page on their own.

ASSESS/CLOSE

IDENTIFY AND USE INITIAL /e/*Ee* Use page 89 to assess children's knowledge of initial /e/*Ee*. Have them name initial /e/ words in this sentence and write *Ee*: *Every egg is blue.*

Name______________________________

Ee	1. elevator Ee	2. apple
3. elephant Ee	4. envelope Ee	5. gorilla
6. escalator Ee	7. elbow Ee	8. pail

Say the name of each picture. • If the name begins with the same sound as *egg*, write *Ee* on the line.

Introduce Initial /e/*Ee* 89

Listen

Phonics Song

Ed's Eggs

My friend Ed likes hard boiled eggs,
Hard boiled eggs, hard boiled eggs.
My friend Ed likes hard boiled eggs,
Morning, noon, and night.

Sung to the tune:
"The Wheels on the Bus"
From **Songs from A to Z**

Phonics Picture Posters and Cards

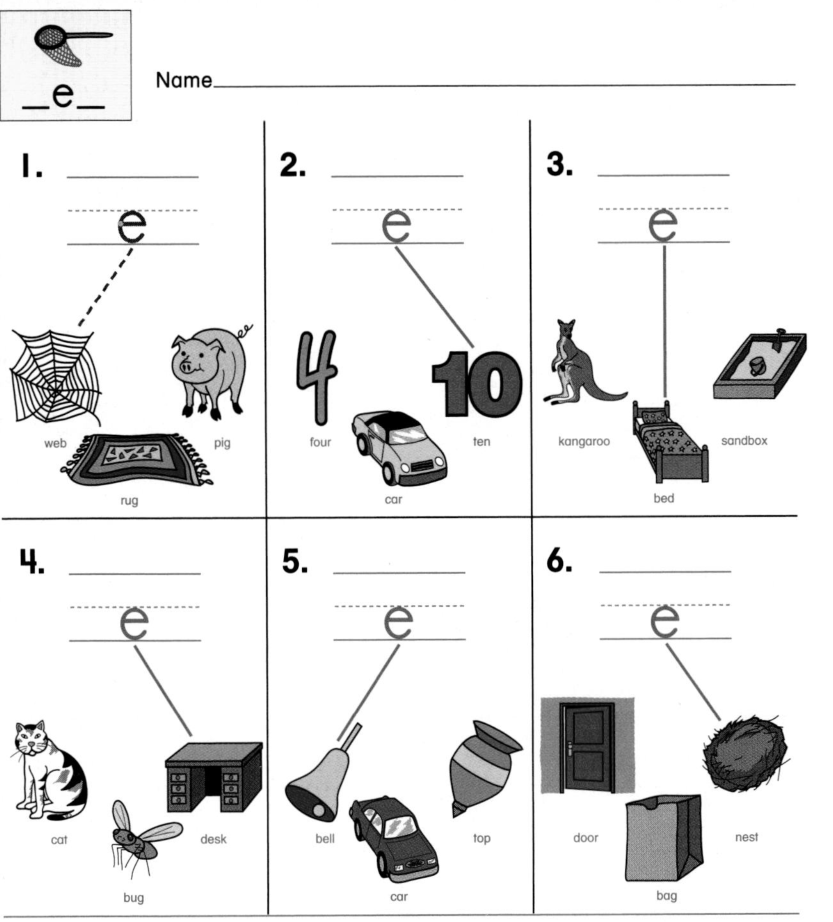

Introduce

Medial /e/e

Children will identify medial /e/e.

PREPARE

PHONOLOGICAL AWARENESS Say the following words and have children clap the syllables in each word with you: *Ed, eggs, morning, friend, elephant.*

Listen

Say the following words and have the children tap their legs each time they hear the /e/ sound in the middle of the word: *web, peg, ball, out, ten, pet, run, men.* *Phonemic Awareness*

TEACH

IDENTIFY MEDIAL /e/e Draw a web on the chalkboard with the letter *e* in the center. Remind children that the letter *e* stands for the sound /e/ as in *web.* Have children say /e/ as you point to each letter. Then say these words and write them in the web: *red, tell, best, Ken.* Invite volunteers to circle each medial letter *e* and say /e/.

PRACTICE

COMPLETE THE PUPIL PAGE After reading the directions aloud, help children identify the key picture, and the other pictures. Complete the first item with children and then encourage them to work independently.

ASSESS/CLOSE

IDENTIFY AND USE MEDIAL /e/e Use page 90 to assess children's progress with medial /e/e. Have children complete this oral sentence with a word with medial *e*: *I would like a red* ____.

ALTERNATE TEACHING STRATEGY

Create simple crossword puzzles that have intersecting boxes—three going down and three going across. In the puzzles, write words with the short *e* sound, such as *net/pet, beg/leg, pet/set, fed/led, men/pen*. Have children blend the sounds to read words and then use the words in their own silly sentence.

▶ **Visual/Linguistic**

Review

/g/g, /e/e

Children will identify /g/*g*, and /e/*e* in words .

PREPARE

PHONOLOGICAL AWARENESS Read the following sentences aloud, having children count the number of words in each sentence.

initial /g/ *The girl has a pet.*
final /g/ *Her pet is a dog.*
initial /e/ *The dog's name is Emma.*
medial /e/ *Emma is red.*

Slowly reread the sentences aloud. Tell children to listen for /g/ or /e/ in the initial, medial, or final position. Have them tap a finger on their desk when they hear a word with the indicated sound. *Phonemic Awareness*

TEACH

REVIEW /g/*g*, /e/*e* Distribute the *G, g, E, e* letter cards from the Word Building Manipulative Cards. Say *Emma* and ask children whether they hear /g/ or /e/ in this word. Have children hold up the letter card that stands for the sound /e/. Draw three letter boxes on the chalkboard. Invite a volunteer to place the letter card *E* in a box to show where he or she hears the sound in the word *Emma*. Repeat with *Gus, rag, fed.*

PRACTICE

COMPLETE THE PUPIL PAGE Read the directions aloud and help identify the pictures.

ASSESS/CLOSE

IDENTIFY AND USE /g/*g*, /e/*e* Use page 91 to assess children's progress with /g/*g*, /e/*e*.

Name______________________________

1. g — gas — | g | | |

2. g — pig — | | | g |

3. e — eggs — | e | | |

4. e — web — | | e | |

Trace the letter. • Say the picture name. • If you hear the sound the letter stands for at the beginning of the picture name, write the letter in the first box. • If you hear the sound in the middle, write the letter in the middle box. • If you hear the sound at the end, write the letter in the last box.

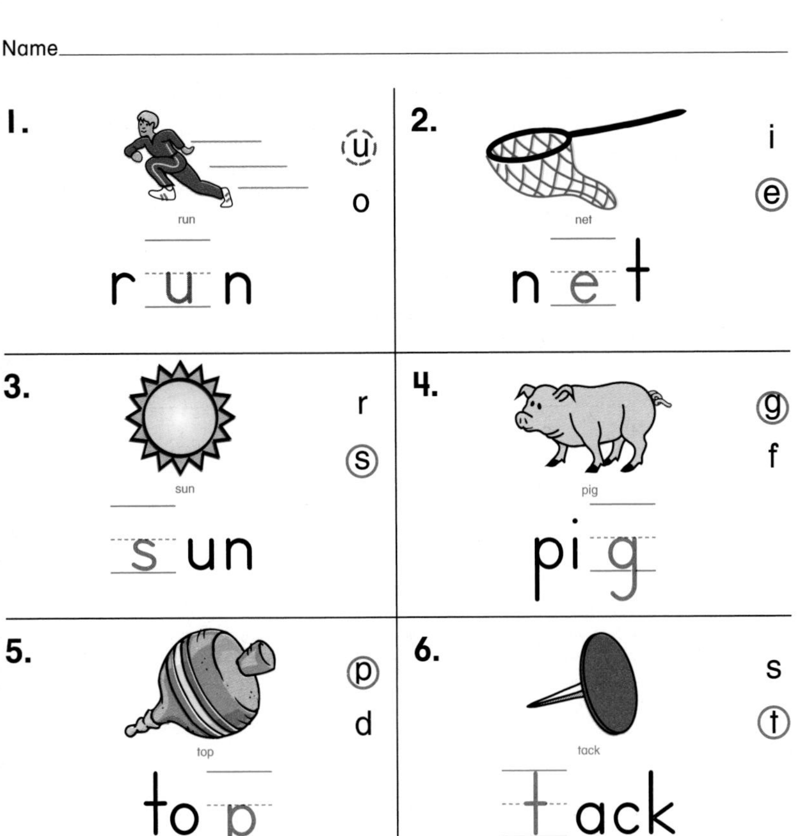

Name____

1. run — u / o — r u n

2. net — i / e — n e t

3. sun — r / s — s un

4. pig — g / f — pi g

5. top — p / d — to p

6. tack — s / t — t ack

Say each picture name. • Circle the missing letter. • Then write the letter. • Read the word.

ALTERNATE TEACHING STRATEGY

Have children repeat each short *a, e, i, o, u* word you write on the chalkboard, blending the sounds of the letters together to read the word aloud: *fan, bat, pet, dip, rip, mop, lock, hug, cup*. Show gestures to pantomime the words and ask children to act them out as they read the words.

▶ Auditory/Kinesthetic

Blending with

Short *a, i, o, u, e*

TESTED OBJECTIVES

Children will blend and read short *a, i, o, u* and *e* CVC words.

PREPARE

Display the *a, e, g, i, o, p, t, u* letter cards from the Word Building Manipulative Cards. As you say a sound for one of the letters, have volunteers remove the appropriate card.

TEACH

MODEL AND GUIDE PRACTICE Place the *e* letter card on the chalkboard ledge and say /e/. Have children repeat /e/.

- Place the *t* letter card next to the *e* letter card.
- Blend the sounds /e/ and /t/ together and have children repeat the sounds after you.
- Place the *g* letter card before the *e* letter card.
- Blend the sounds /g/, /e/, /t/ together to read *get*. Have children repeat the word *get* after you.

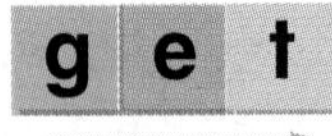

USE THE WORD IN CONTEXT Use *get* in a sentence to reinforce its meaning, for example: *What did you get at the store?*

REPEAT THE PROCEDURE Use the following to continue modeling and guided practice: *tip, pug, got, tag*.

PRACTICE

COMPLETE THE PUPIL PAGE Read the directions aloud and complete the first item with children.

ASSESS/CLOSE

BLEND AND READ WORDS Use page 92 to assess children's skill in blending with short *a, i, o, u,* and *e*. Have children use the letter cards to build and read a CVC word.

Introduce

High-Frequency Words: *to, are, do*

BJECTIVES

Children will identify and read the high-frequency words *to*, *are*, and *do*.

PREPARE

LISTEN TO WORDS Have children walk in a circle and listen for the words *are*, *to*, and *do* as you read aloud the following sentences. Ask them to stop when they hear the words.

are—*Here are some books.*
to—*Please give them to Sam.*
do—*Will you do this for me?*

TEACH

IDENTIFY THE WORDS Distribute High-Frequency Word Cards *to*, *are*, *do* from the back of the Pupil's Edition. Hold up and say each word and have children hold up the same word card. Write the sentences from the Prepare section on the chalkboard, omitting the high-frequency words. Read the sentences and have volunteers fill in the blanks orally. Write the missing words and have children hold up the matching word cards.

PRACTICE

COMPLETE THE PUPIL PAGE Read the directions aloud and remind children that they should circle more than one word in each row.

ASSESS/CLOSE

REVIEW THE PAGE Use page 93 to assess children's recognition of the words *to*, *are*, and *do*. Ask children to write the word *do* and use it in a sentence.

Name____________________

1.	to	do	to	are	to
2.	are	to	do	are	are
3.	do	do	are	to	do
4.	are	are	to	are	to
5.	to	do	are	to	to

Read the first word in each row. • Circle the words in that row that are the same.

Name______________________________

1.	and	(are)	are
2.	(to)	go	to
3.	(do)	for	do
4.	are	(and)	and
5.	do	(for)	for
6.	to	(you)	you

Listen to the word. • Circle the word you hear. • Then write the word.

McGraw-Hill School Division

94 Review High-Frequency Words

Review
High-Frequency Words

Children will identify and read the high-frequency words *for*, *go*, *and*, *you*, *to*, *are*, and *do*.

PREPARE

LISTEN TO WORDS Slowly read aloud the following sentences and ask children to listen for the words you name. Invite children to raise a hand when they hear the words.

are, to—*We are going to the park.*
do, you—*Do you want to come?*
go—*We will go soon.*
for, and—*We will wait for you and Kim.*

TEACH

IDENTIFY THE WORDS Display High-Frequency Word Cards *for*, *go*, *and*, *you*, *to*, *are*, *do*, from the back of the Pupil's Edition, on the chalkboard ledge. Arrange children in small groups and distribute these seven word cards to each group. Point to and say each word and ask children to find and hold up the matching card. Then write the sentences from the Prepare section on the chalkboard. Read the sentences aloud, pause after each high-frequency word, and ask children to hold up the matching card.

PRACTICE

COMPLETE THE PUPIL PAGE Read the directions aloud. Then read aloud these words for children to circle and write: (1) *are*; (2) *to*; (3) *do*; (4) *and*; (5) *for*; (6) *you*.

ASSESS/CLOSE

REVIEW THE PAGE Use page 94 to assess children's recognition of the words *for*, *go*, *and*, *you*, *to*, *are*, and *do*.

ALTERNATE TEACHING STRATEGY

Write the high-frequency words, omitting a letter from each word: *y_u*, *f_r*, *g_*, *_nd*, *t_*, *_re*, *_o*. Point to each word and ask a question, for example: *What letter can I add to make this word* for? After each correct response, complete the word and have children read it aloud with you. Repeat the activity, omitting different letters from the words.

▶ **Visual/Logical**

Develop

Phonological Awareness

Blend Onsets and Rimes

Teach Read aloud the poem *"Rob the Hog."* Ask children to tell what word you are saying: /r/-/ob/. Then say the onset and rime for the word *ten*: /t/-/en/. Lead children to blend the sounds to say the words.

Practice Begin a circle game by holding a beenbag in your hand and saying: "/b/ and /at/ make *bat*." Then pass the beenbag to the child next to you. Say the sounds: /m/-/at/ and have the child say: "/m/ and /at/ make *mat*." Then the child passes the beenbag to the next child. Continue with words from the same word family: *cat*, *sat*, *rat*, and *fat*.

Rob the Hog

Ten little kittens can fit in a bed
With Cat and Duck and Frog.
But one big pet could not fit in –
Great big Rob, the hog.
So Rob gave his pals a goodnight hug
And went to sleep on a soft, red rug.

Identify Beginning Sounds

MATERIALS
- Phonics Picture Posters
  bear, hen
- Ball

Teach Display the Phonics Picture Poster for *bear*. Tell children the word *bear* begins with the sound /b/. Have children repeat these words and tell which begin with /b/: *pack, back, met, bet, jig, bat, big, ten, bell*. Repeat the activities for initial /h/ using the Phonics Picture Poster for *hen* and words such as: *happy, mat, hope, hog, let, high, hat, wet, hungry*.

Practice Begin a bouncing game with a word that begins with /b/. Say: *I bounce the ball on bat*. As you say the word *bat*, bounce the ball once in front of you. Then pass the ball to a child to bounce the ball on another word beginning with /b/. Repeat the game using the /h/ sound and the sentence *"I hand the ball on hat."*

Identify Ending Sounds

Phonemic Awareness

MATERIALS

- Ball of yarn

Teach Say the word *Rob* and tell children the word *Rob* ends with the /b/ sound. Have children repeat after you: *rob*: /b/. Then have children tell the ending sound in these words: *cab, cap, tub, put, web, tab,* and *rub.*

Practice Play *"Come Into My Web."* Have children sit in a circle. Tell children that you are the spider. Ask them to listen closely as you name someone to come into your web in the middle of the circle. For example, say: *Cameron, come into my web.* If the child can name the sound at the end of their name, that person can get out of the web. Repeat by calling other children into your web.

Segment Sounds

Phonemic Awareness

MATERIALS

- Cards or blocks numbered 1, 2, and 3

Teach Say: *I hear three sounds in this word:* hog. *The sounds are:* /h/-/o/-/g/. Ask how many sounds children hear in the word *wet.* (3) Show the numbered cards or blocks. Identify which sound is first (/w/), which is second (/e/), and which is third (/t/). Then point to the second block and ask, *Which sound is in the middle?* (/e/) Ask where the /t/ is in the word *wet* (the third sound).

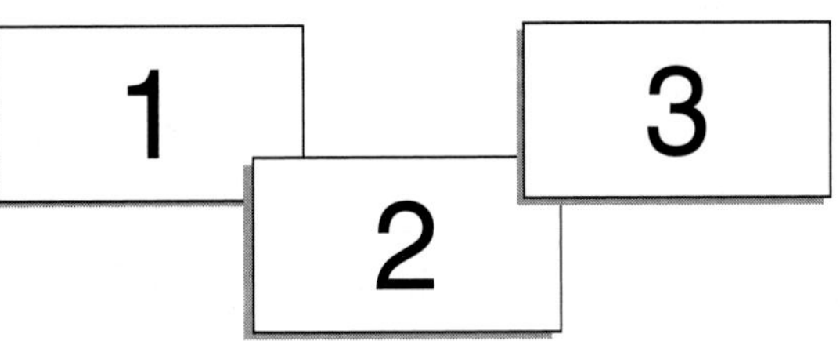

Practice Distribute numbered cards or blocks to three children at the front of the room. Say a word with three sounds such as *cat.* Then give directions for volunteers to follow such as: *What is the middle sound?* (/a/); *What is the last sound?* (/t/); *What do you hear first?* (/k/). Then have a different group of three come up and repeat the activity with a different word.

Introduce

Initial /b/*Bb*

OBJECTIVES

Children will identify initial /b/*Bb* and form the letters *Bb*.

PREPARE

PHONOLOGICAL AWARENESS Say the following words and have children repeat after you and clap the syllables: *bear*, *balloon*, *big*, and *bottle*.

Listen

While singing the song "Bobby the Bear," hold up the Phonics Picture Poster for *bear*. Ask the children to bounce in their seats when they hear the /b/ sound at the beginning of a word. *Phonemic Awareness*

TEACH

IDENTIFY INITIAL /b/*Bb* Draw a large bus on the chalkboard. Write *Bb* on the bus and tell children that the letters *Bb* stand for the sound /b/. Write *ball* on the bus and encourage children to suggest other words that begin with /b/*Bb*, for example: *book*, *bear*, *bell*, *Bob*, *bird*. Write the words on the bus and have volunteers circle the letters *Bb* and say /b/.

FORM *Bb* Some children may need to review how to write *B* and *b*. Have children fold a sheet of paper into four boxes and write *Bb* in each box, using the Handwriting Models from the back of the Pupil's Edition.

PRACTICE

COMPLETE THE PUPIL PAGE Read the directions aloud and help children identify the pictures.

ASSESS/CLOSE

IDENTIFY AND USE INITIAL /b/*Bb* Use page 95 to assess children's knowledge of initial /b/*Bb*. Ask children to answer this riddle: *I am a word that begins with the letters Bb. I am something you bounce. What am I?* (ball)

Name____________________

Bb	1. banana Bb	2. fox
3. book Bb	4. desk	5. bell Bb
6. bus Bb	7. bird Bb	8. belt Bb

Say the name of each picture. • If the name begins with the same sound as *bear*, write *Bb* on the line.

Introduce Initial /b/*Bb* 95

Listen

Bobby the Bear

Bobby the bear likes big balloons,
Big balloons, big balloons.
Bobby the bear likes big balloons,
Bobby is a bear!

Sung to the tune: "Here We Go 'Round the Mulberry Bush"
From **Songs from A to Z**

Phonics Picture Posters and Cards

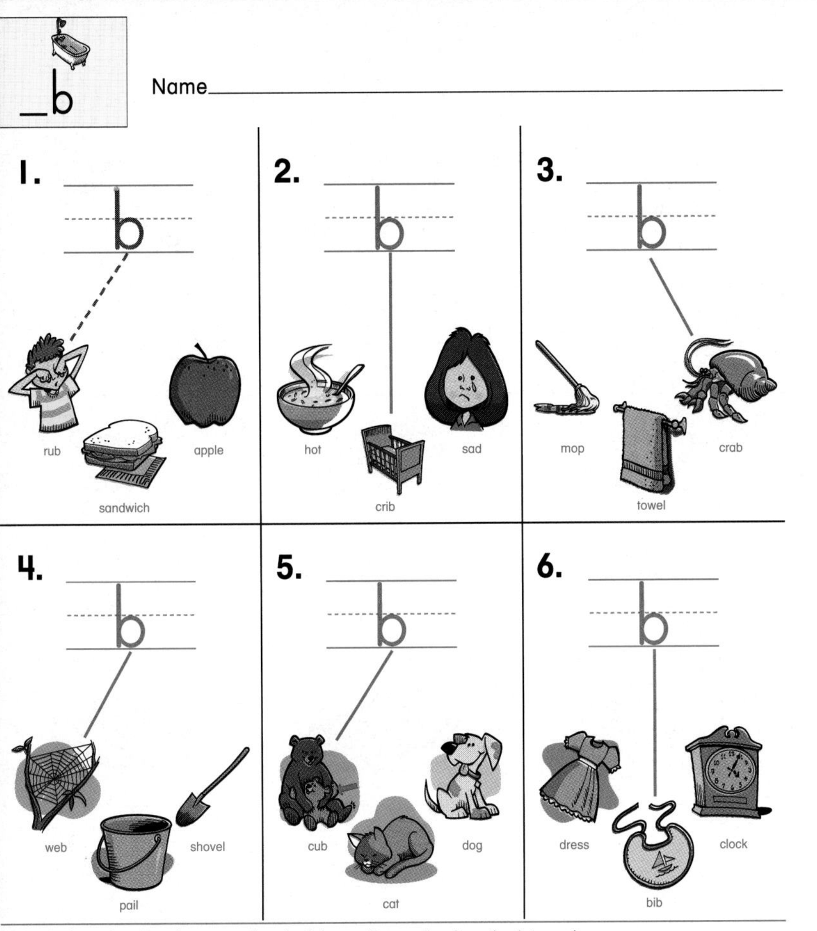

Write the letter *b*. • Say the name of each picture. • Draw a line from the *b* to each picture whose name has the same ending sound as *tub*.

96 Introduce Final /b/*b*

Introduce

Final /b/*b*

Children will identify final /b/*b*.

PREPARE

PHONOLOGICAL AWARENESS Say the following sets of words and have children repeat the two words that rhyme: *tub, sock, rub; ball, sob, rob.*

Say the following words and have children say the word *tub* when they hear the /b/ sound at the end of a word: *can, rock, web, cub, pail, cap, rub, sob.* *Phonemic Awareness*

TEACH

IDENTIFY FINAL /b/*b* Write *b* at the top of a sheet of chart paper and review that the letter *b* stands for /b/. Then write the following grid of words and have volunteers say /b/ and circle each word that ends with *b*:

Bob	not	tub	Meg
had	Rob	web	Ned
cab	man	put	cub

PRACTICE

COMPLETE THE PUPIL PAGE Identify the key picture for children. Then read the directions aloud and identify the pictures. Complete the first item together, then encourage children to complete the page independently.

ASSESS/CLOSE

IDENTIFY AND USE FINAL /b/*b* Use page 96 to assess children's knowledge of final /b/*b*. Have children draw a picture of an object that ends with /b/ and write *b* under it.

TEACHING TIP

MANAGEMENT Prepare the grid of words ahead of time, leaving enough space around each word so children can easily circle words. Provide a marking pen for children to use.

ALTERNATE TEACHING STRATEGY

Lead children in singing "The Bear Went Over the Mountain." Point out that *bear* begins with *b*. Help children brainstorm additional words that begin or end with *b* to replace *bear*, such as *bug, baboon, bat,* or *cab*. Guide children as they sing the new verses.

▶ Auditory/Musical

Introduce

Initial /h/*Hh*

Children will identify initial /h/*Hh* and form the letters *Hh*.

PREPARE

PHONOLOGICAL AWARENESS Have children say the two rhyming words in each set of words: *hen, hot, pen; hail, pail, hunt; cot, cob, hot.*

Listen

While singing the song "Hungry Helen Hen," hold up the Phonics Picture Poster for *hen*. Have the children put their hand on their head each time they hear the /h/ sound at the beginning of a word. *Phonemic Awareness*

TEACH

IDENTIFY INITIAL /h/*Hh* Hold up letter card *Hh* from the Word Building Manipulative Cards. Explain that the letters *Hh* stand for the sound /h/. Then give clues to words with initial /h/*Hh* and invite children to guess the words. Write the words on the chalkboard and have volunteers circle the letters *Hh* and say /h/. Clues might include: *something you wear on your head* (hat), *what you do with a bat* (hit), *not low* (high), *not cold* (hot).

FORM *Hh* Some children may need to review how to write *H* and *h*. Ask children to use the Handwriting Models at the back of the Pupil's Edition to trace the letters.

PRACTICE

COMPLETE THE PUPIL PAGE Before children complete the page independently, read the directions aloud and help children identify the pictures. Do the first item together.

ASSESS/CLOSE

IDENTIFY AND USE INITIAL /h/*Hh* Use page 97 to assess children's recognition of initial /h/*Hh*. Have children say a word beginning with /h/.

Name__________

Hh	1. horse Hh	2. hammer Hh
3. nails	4. hose Hh	5. hand Hh
6. duck	7. hippopotamus Hh	8. house Hh

Say the name of each picture. • If the name begins with the same sound as *hen*, write *Hh* on the line.

Listen

Hungry Helen Hen

Hungry Helen Hen,
Hungry Helen Hen,
Helen had a hearty lunch,
But hopes to eat again.

Sung to the tune:
"The Farmer in the Dell"
From **Songs from A to Z**

Phonics Picture Posters and Cards

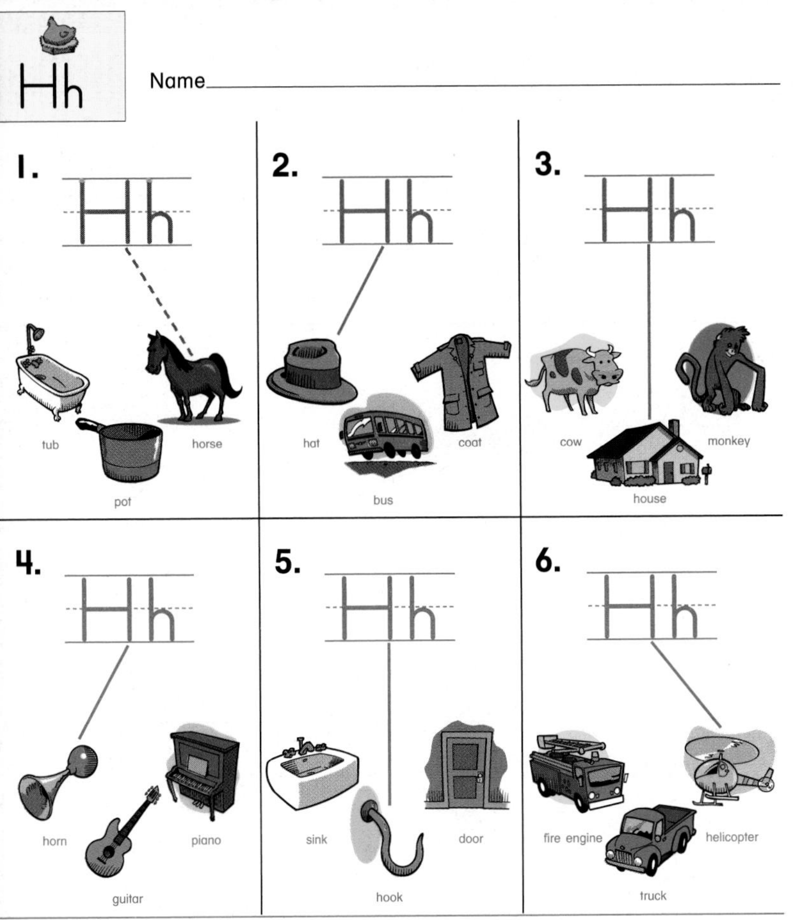

Write the letters *Hh*. • Say the name of each picture. • Draw a line from *Hh* to each picture whose name has the same beginning sound as *hen*.

98 Review Initial /h/*Hh*

Review

Initial /h/*Hh*

Children will identify initial /h/*Hh*.

PREPARE

PHONOLOGICAL AWARENESS Have children think of as many words as they can that rhyme with *hen* such as *men, when, pen, ten, Ben, den* and so on.

Listen

Review singing the song "Hungry Helen Hen" while holding up the Phonics Picture Poster for *hen*. Then have each child take a turn saying a word that begins with the /h/ sound. *Phonemic Awareness*

TEACH

IDENTIFY INITIAL /h/*Hh* Invite a volunteer to name the letters that stand for the sound /h/. Write *Hh* on the chalkboard. Distribute letter card *Hh* from the Word Building Manipulative Cards. Then write this sentence: *They hum and hop all day.* Read it aloud and ask volunteers to match *h* to words beginning with /h/. Reread the sentence and invite all children to hold up *h* to match the words.

PRACTICE

COMPLETE THE PUPIL PAGE Read the directions aloud and work through the first item with children. Help them identify each picture before they complete the page independently.

ASSESS/CLOSE

IDENTIFY AND USE INITIAL /h/*Hh* Use page 98 to assess children's progress with initial /h/*Hh*. Ask children to draw a picture of something that begins with /h/ and write *Hh* under it.

TEACHING TIP

INSTRUCTIONAL In some languages, the initial *h* is silent. Provide practice in pronouncing the initial /h/ by using words with *h* in simple commands such as: *Hold his hand. Hop here. Hold your head.* Pair a non-English-speaking child with an English-speaking child and have them take turns giving and following commands.

ALTERNATE TEACHING STRATEGY

Show children how to make paper plate hats. Have them decorate their hats with words that begin with *h*. Assist children in punching holes and putting strings on hats. Invite children to show and discuss their hats.

▶ **Linguistic/Interpersonal**

Review

/b/*b*, /h/*h*

Children will identify /b/*b* and /h/*h* in words.

PREPARE

PHONOLOGICAL AWARENESS Have children say a word that rhymes with *rub*.

Read the following sentences aloud and ask children to tap a finger on their desk when they hear a word with each sound. *Phonemic Awareness*

Initial /h/ *It is a hot day.*
Initial /b/ *A boy decides to go swimming.*
Final /b/ *The boy's name is Jeb.*

TEACH

REVIEW /b/*b*, /h/*h* Write the letters *b* and *h* on the chalkboard. Draw three letter boxes on the chalkboard and distribute letter cards *B*, *b*, *H*, *h* from the Word Building Manipulative Cards. Say the name *Hal* and ask children whether they hear /b/ or /h/ in this word. Ask them to hold up the letter that stands for the sound /h/. Have a volunteer place the letter card *H* in a box to show where they hear the sound—at the beginning, in the middle, or at the end of the word. Repeat with *rib, had, Ben*.

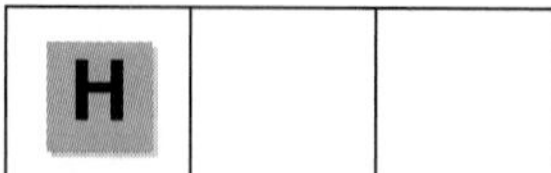

PRACTICE

COMPLETE THE PUPIL PAGE Read the directions aloud and identify pictures with children. Do the first item together.

ASSESS/CLOSE

IDENTIFY AND USE /b/*b*, /h/*h* Use page 99 to assess children's progress with /b/*b*, /h/*h*.

Name________________________

1. h — hat — h
2. b — cub — b
3. h — hen — h
4. b — bat — b

Trace the letter. • Say the picture name. • If you hear the sound the letter stands for at the beginning of the picture name, write the letter in the first box. • If you hear the sound at the end, write the letter in the last box.

Review /b/b, /h/h 99

Name___________________________

1. b h — b at

2. u i — l i ck

3. s r — r ug

4. f g — le g

5. e o — p e n

6. m t — do t

McGraw-Hill School Division

Say the picture name. • Circle the missing letter. • Then write the letter. • Read the word.

100 Blending with Short *a*, *i*, *o*, *u*, and *e*

Blending with

Short *a, i, o, u, e*

Children will blend and read short *a*, *i*, *o*, *u* and *e* CVC words.

PREPARE

Display the *a*, *b*, *e*, *h*, *i*, *m*, *o*, *u* letter cards from the Word Building Manipulative Cards. Point to each letter and have children say the sound for that letter.

TEACH

MODEL AND GUIDE PRACTICE Place the *e* letter card on the chalkboard ledge and say /e/. Have children repeat /e/.

- Place the *m* letter card next to the *e* letter card.
- Blend the sounds /e/ and /m/ together and have children repeat the sounds after you.
- Place the *h* letter card before the *e* letter card.
- Blend the sounds /h/, /e/, /m/ together to read the word *hem*. Have children repeat the word *hem* after you.

USE THE WORD IN CONTEXT Use *hem* in a sentence to reinforce its meaning: *The tailor sewed a hem in the skirt.*

REPEAT THE PROCEDURE Use these words to continue modeling and guided practice: *ham*, *hum*, *mob*, *bib*, *red*.

PRACTICE

COMPLETE THE PUPIL PAGE After reading the directions aloud, help children name the pictures. Using the first item, guide children through each step.

ASSESS/CLOSE

BLEND AND READ WORDS Use page 100 to assess children's skill in blending with short a, i, o, u, and e.

ALTERNATE TEACHING STRATEGY

Ask children to chant the initial *h* short vowel sounds *ha-*, *he-*, *hi-*, *ho-*, *hu-* several times each as you point to them on the chalkboard. Then have them chant these words: *hat*, *hen*, *him*, *hot*, *hum*.

▶ **Auditory/Linguistic**

Read the Story

OBJECTIVES

Children will use their knowledge of phonics and decoding and high-frequency words to read.

Ed got a pup.

2

The pup is Bob.

3

BEFORE READING

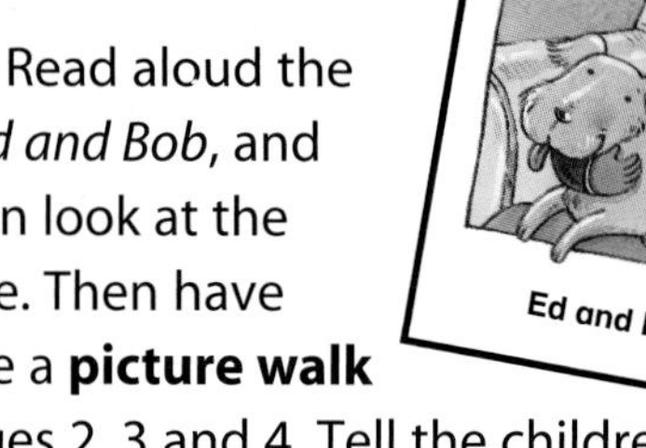

PREVIEW Read aloud the story title, *Ed and Bob*, and have children look at the cover picture. Then have children take a **picture walk** through pages 2, 3 and 4. Tell the children that this story is about a boy and his dog. Encourage children to tell what the boy and his dog are doing in the pictures. Read aloud the sentences from these pages. Ask children to look at the sentences and point to these high-frequency words as you say them aloud: *a, is, do.*

MAKE PREDICTIONS Invite children to think about the pictures and predict what will happen in the story. Ask: *Why is Ed begging at the table?* List children's ideas on the chalkboard.

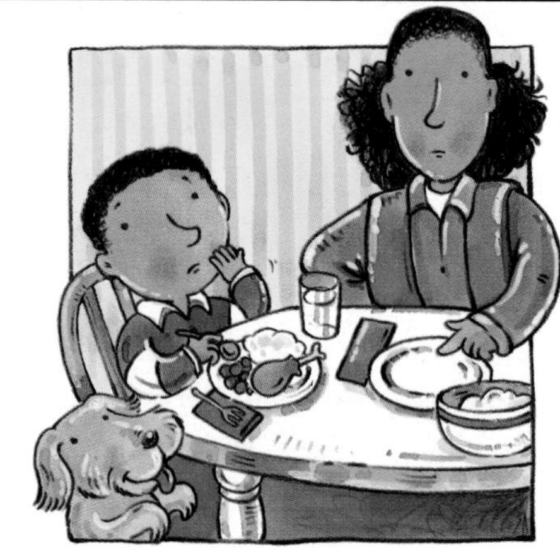

Do not beg, Bob!

4

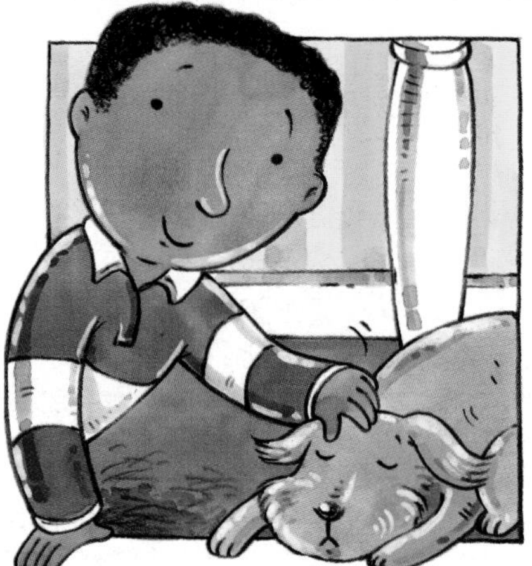

Ed and Bob are sad.

5

DURING READING

READING SUGGESTIONS Encourage children to track the print with their finger as they read. Point to the period on page 3. Explain that a period tells us where the sentence ends. Point to the exclamation points on this page and on page 8. Ask *What do exclamation points tell us?* (That the speaker is excited and speaking loudly.)

TEACHING TIP

MANAGEMENT Help children put together their own take-home story. Give the following directions to the children. Demonstrate as needed.

To put book together,
Tear out the story page.
Cut along the dotted line.
Fold each section on the fold line.

Bob has to sit.

6

Ed can pet Bob.

7

Bob is not sad!

8

Read the Story

AFTER READING

RETURN TO PREDICTIONS Discuss what children predicted would happen and what actually happened in the story. Discuss with the children why Bob is not sad at the end of the story.

RETELL THE STORY Invite the children to retell the story in their own words. Encourage the children to use the pictures to help them recall the story events.

STORY QUESTIONS Ask the following questions about the story.

- *Who is Bob?* (Ed's puppy.) ***Literal/Story Details***
- *On page 5, why are Ed and Bob sad?* (Because they want to be able to feed Bob from the table.) ***Inferential/Use Illustrations***
- *Why is Bob happy at the end of the story?* (Because Ed fed him.) ***Inferential/Use Illustrations***

Cross Curricular: Art

MAKE MOBILES MAKE A MASK Provide paper bags and different colored construction paper for the children to make dog masks. Beforehand you may wish to discuss the different kinds of dogs with children or display pictures of different breeds. Children can use markers or crayons to color the eyes and whiskers. They can cut out the ears, nose and mouth from the construction paper. Display dog masks in center so that children may choose their favorites.

▶ **Visual**

Introduce

Categories

Children will identify categories.

PREPARE

INTRODUCE CATEGORIES Hold up a crayon, marker, and tape. Say: *Which two things belong together?* Tell children the crayon and the marker belong together because they are both used for drawing.

TEACH

IDENTIFY CATEGORIES Place the Phonics Picture Cards of the *dog*, *seal*, and *apple* in the pocket chart. Explain that since the *dog* and the *seal* are both animals, they belong in the same group. Explain that the apple does not belong with the other pictures because it is a food. Repeat with three different cards, two of which have something in common such as the *egg*, *apple*, and *nest*. (The *egg* and *apple* are foods.)

PRACTICE

COMPLETE THE PUPIL PAGE Before children begin, read the directions aloud. Remind children that they should circle the two objects in each row that have something in common. Have children complete the remaining items on their own, identifying the pictures for them as they work.

ASSESS/CLOSE

REVIEW THE PAGE Use page 103 to assess children's recognition of objects that belong in the same category. Invite children to explain what two of the objects in each row have in common.

Name________

1\.

2\.

3\.

4\.

5\.

Say the picture names in each row. • Draw a circle around the two pictures in each row that belong in the same group.

Beginning Reading Concepts: *Categories* 103

ALTERNATE TEACHING STRATEGY

ESL APPROPRIATE Give small groups of children manipulatives, such as attribute blocks, to sort into categories. Begin by having children sort the objects by color. Then have them sort the objects by shape. Encourage children to describe other ways of sorting objects. (by size, texture and so on.)

▶ **Interpersonal/Kinesthetic**

Review

Categories

TESTED OBJECTIVES

Children will identify categories.

PREPARE

INTRODUCE CATEGORIES Invite five volunteers to stand before the class. Invite children to think of ways to put the volunteers into groups. For example, they could put the boys in one group and the girls in another group.

TEACH

IDENTIFY CATEGORIES Place the following picture cards from the Word Building Manipulative Cards in the pocket chart: *elephant*, *mouse*, *pig*, *lamp*, *turtle*, *net*, *game*. Tell children these cards can be sorted into two categories: *animals* and *objects*. Have children help you separate the cards into an *animal* group and an *objects* group.

PRACTICE

COMPLETE THE PUPIL PAGE Before children begin, read the directions aloud. Remind children that they should circle the two objects in each row that belong in the same category. Name the remaining pictures, having children complete the items on their own.

ASSESS/CLOSE

REVIEW THE PAGE Use page 104 to assess children's recognition of objects that belong in the same category. Challenge children to identify the category to which two of the objects in each row belong.

Name________________________________

1.   

2.  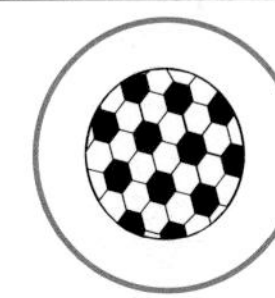 

3. 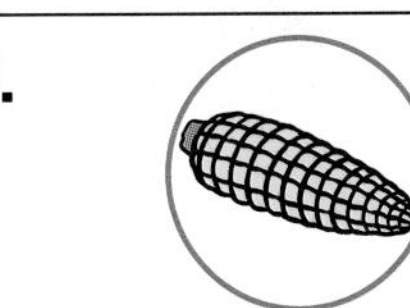  

4.

5.

Say the picture names in each row. • Draw a circle around the two pictures in each row that belong in the same group.

104 Beginning Reading Concepts: *Categories*

TEACHING TIP

CATEGORIES Have children practice the skill of categorizing using your classroom library books. Display three baskets labeled *Animals*, *ABC Books* and *Fairy Tales*. Provide a stack of books, which can be categorized into one of the three baskets. Have children help you categorize the books. Explain that some books may fit into more than one category.

Cumulative Review

Children will review /e/*e*, /u/*u*, /b/*b*, /k/*c*, /g/*g*, /h/*h*, /k/*k*, /l/*l*, /p/*p*, /r/*r*.

PREPARE

PHONOLOGICAL AWARENESS Read the first sentence below. Have children clap out the syllables and identify the longest word.

/b/, /g/ *Have you ever heard a boy giggle?*
/k/, /h/ *When would a king hiccup?*
/b/, /p/ *Have you heard a balloon pop?*
/e/, /r/ *Can an elephant roar?*

Say the first sound shown at the beginning of each question. Read the questions aloud and have children touch an ear when they hear the sound. Repeat, using the second sound. *Phonemic Awareness*

TEACH

REVIEW SOUND/SYMBOL RELATIONSHIPS Draw three blank letter boxes on the chalkboard. Distribute letter cards *e*, *b*, *r* from the Word Building Manipulative Cards to pairs of children. Then say *ran* and have children identify whether they hear /e/, /b/, or /r/ by holding up the correct letter card. Invite a volunteer to place a letter card in the correct box to show in which part of the word the sound is heard. Repeat with /u/*u*, /g/*g*, /l/*l* and *pup*; /h/*h*, /p/*p*, /k/*k* and *pot*.

PRACTICE

COMPLETE THE PUPIL PAGE Before children begin, read the directions aloud and help them identify the pictures.

ASSESS/CLOSE

IDENTIFY AND USE *e, u, b, c, g, h, k, l, p, r* Use page 105 to assess children's progress.

Name________________

1. gate	2. key	3. lamp
(g) f	t (k)	d (l)
4. basket	**5. house**	**6. cat**
p (b)	(h) s	n (c)
7. elephant	**8. apple**	**9. turtle**
(e) i	(a) u	(t) r

Say each picture name. • Circle the letter that stands for the beginning sound.

Name

1. Did Dan go to bed? (go) are

2. The bag is for you. that (for)

3. The dog and cat run. (and) to

4. Kit can do it! you (do)

5. Dad has a map. to (a)

McGraw-Hill School Division

Read the sentence. • Then circle the word that completes the sentence. • Write the word on the line.

106 Cumulative Review: High-Frequency Words

ALTERNATE TEACHING STRATEGY

Write these words on the chalkboard or chart paper: *and*, *you*, *a*, *that*, *for*, *go*, *to*, *are*, and *do*. Assign a word to each child. Then have children look for their word on classroom signs, charts, labels. Call on children, in turn, to point to and read their assigned word in the classroom. Then invite volunteers to use the word in their own sentences.

▶ **Visual/Linguistic**

Cumulative Review

TESTED OBJECTIVES

Children will identify and read the high-frequency words *and*, *you*, *a*, *that*, *for*, *go*, *to*, *are*, *do*.

PREPARE

LISTEN TO WORDS Have children listen to the following sentences and pat their head when they hear the word(s) you name.

you, that *Did you see that squirrel?*
a, and *It found a nut and ran off.*
go *Where did the squirrel go?*
do *What will it do with the nut?*
to *I think it's going to hide the nut.*
for *I think it's saving the nut for winter.*
are *Nuts are hard to find during winter.*

TEACH

IDENTIFY THE WORDS Distribute High-Frequency Word Cards *and*, *you*, *a*, *that*, *for*, *go*, *to*, *are*, and *do* from the back of the Pupil's Edition to pairs of children. Display a set on the chalkboard ledge. Hold up each card, read it aloud, and invite volunteers to hold up the same word. Then write the sentences from the Prepare section on the chalkboard and read them aloud. Ask children to hold up the correct word card when they hear that word in the sentence.

PRACTICE

COMPLETE THE PUPIL PAGE Read the directions aloud and complete the first item with children. Guide children as needed through the remaining items.

ASSESS/CLOSE

REVIEW THE PAGE Use page 106 to assess children's progress with the words *and*, *you*, *a*, *that*, *for*, *go*, *to*, *are*, *do*.

Develop

Phonological Awareness

Recognize Rhyming Words

Teach After reading the poem, repeat the word *wish* and say the rhyming words: *fish, dish*. Tell children the words rhyme because they have the same ending sounds. Model other rhyming words such as *spring/bring/cling/king*.

Practice Say the following sets of words and have children repeat the two words in each set that rhyme: *wet, pen, set; web, wing, spring; wall, door, fall; wait, bait, ball; thin, hat, win.*

We Wish You

We wish you a wonderful winter.
We wish you a wonderful spring.
We wish you a wonderful
summer and fall.
We wish you a wonderful everything.

Identify Beginning Sounds

Phonemic Awareness

MATERIALS

- Phonics Picture Posters
  wagon, van

Teach Display the Phonics Picture Poster for *wagon*. Say the word and the beginning sound /w/. Say the words from the poem: *wish, winter, wonderful*. Each time, have children repeat the word and sound /w/. Then display the Phonics Picture Poster for *van*. Have children say the /v/ sound when they hear you say a word that begins with /v/. Say these words: *van, cat, vet, Vin, will, vine, very*.

Practice Play *"Wiggle."* Children stand in small circles. Say words, some of which begin with /w/. Children hold hands and wiggle when they hear a word beginning with /w/. Use the following words: *wave, can, William, man, warm, water, net, wet, web, willow*.
Repeat the activities with initial /v/ having children say "vroom" when they hear you say a word that begins with the /v/ sound. Say words such as: *vacation, very, ball, vet, Valentine, wet, vest, ten, violin*.

Blend Sounds

Phonemic Awareness

Teach Say a word by segmenting the sounds such as /v/-/e/-/t/. Have children listen as you blend the sounds to say the word *vet*. Then say /w/-/e/-/t/ and lead children to blend the word *wet*.

Practice Tell children you will say a sentence with a mystery word. Tell children after you say the sentence, they are to blend the sounds of the mystery word. Say the following sentence: *Jan and her pup went to the* /v/-/e/-/t/. Have children blend the word *vet*. Repeat with these sentences: *The vet said the pup was very* /s/-/i/-/k/. *Jan and the pup went home in their* /v/-/a/-/n/. Continue with other sentences and sounds.

Segment Sounds

Phonemic Awareness

MATERIALS

- **Word Building Manipulative Cards:** *van, game, jam, key, net, pig, fox, cat*

Teach Display the Word Building Manipulative Card for *van* (picture side only). Say the word *van*. Have children listen to the individual sounds and tell how many. (3). Have children repeat each sound: /v/-/a/-/n/. Repeat with other words such as: *van, wet, wit, wag*.

Practice Play *"How many sounds?"* Begin by holding up the Word Building Manipulative Card for *game* (picture side only). Say: *"How many sounds does the word game have?"* (3: /g/-/ā/-/m/) Encourage children to say the sounds to themselves as they count them. Repeat with the Word Building Manipulative Cards for *jam, key, net, pig, fox, cat*.

/v/-/a/-/n/

Introduce

Initial /w/Ww

Children will identify initial /w/*Ww* and form the letters *Ww*.

PREPARE

PHONOLOGICAL AWARENESS Read the words to the song "Wendy's Wagon" below aloud. Have children clap out the syllables.

Listen

While singing the song "Wendy's Wagon," hold up the Phonics Picture Poster for *wagon*. Have the children wave each time they hear the /w/ sound at the beginning of a word. *Phonemic Awareness*

TEACH

IDENTIFY INITIAL /w/*Ww* Write the letters *Ww* on the chalkboard and tell children that the letters *Ww* stand for the sound /w/. Then create and display cards with these words: *web, was, watched*. Have children say /w/ as you say and point to each word. Write and read aloud these sentences. Invite children to use the cards to fill in the blanks: *I___ a spider.* (watched) *It___ brown.* (was) *It made a___.* (web)

FORM *Ww* Some children may need to review how to write *W* and *w*. Have children draw a window and write *Ww* in each window frame. Children may use the Handwriting Models in the back of the Pupil's Edition for reference.

PRACTICE

COMPLETE THE PUPIL PAGE Read the directions aloud and help identify the pictures.

ASSESS/CLOSE

IDENTIFY AND USE INITIAL /w/*Ww* Use page 107 to assess children's knowledge of initial /w/*Ww*. Have them say the missing word that begins with /w/: *I drank___.* (water)

Name__________

Ww

1. web — Ww
2. nest
3. watermelon — Ww
4. watch — Ww
5. sock
6. worm — Ww
7. waterfall — Ww
8. window — Ww

Say the name of each picture. • If the name begins with the same sound as *wagon*, write *Ww* on the line.

Introduce Initial /w/Ww 107

Listen

Wendy's Wagon

Wendy pulls a wagon made of wood,
Made of wood, made of wood,
I'd want to pull it if I could,
All over town!

Sung to the tune:
"The Wheels on the Bus"
From **Songs from A to Z**

Phonics Picture Posters and Cards

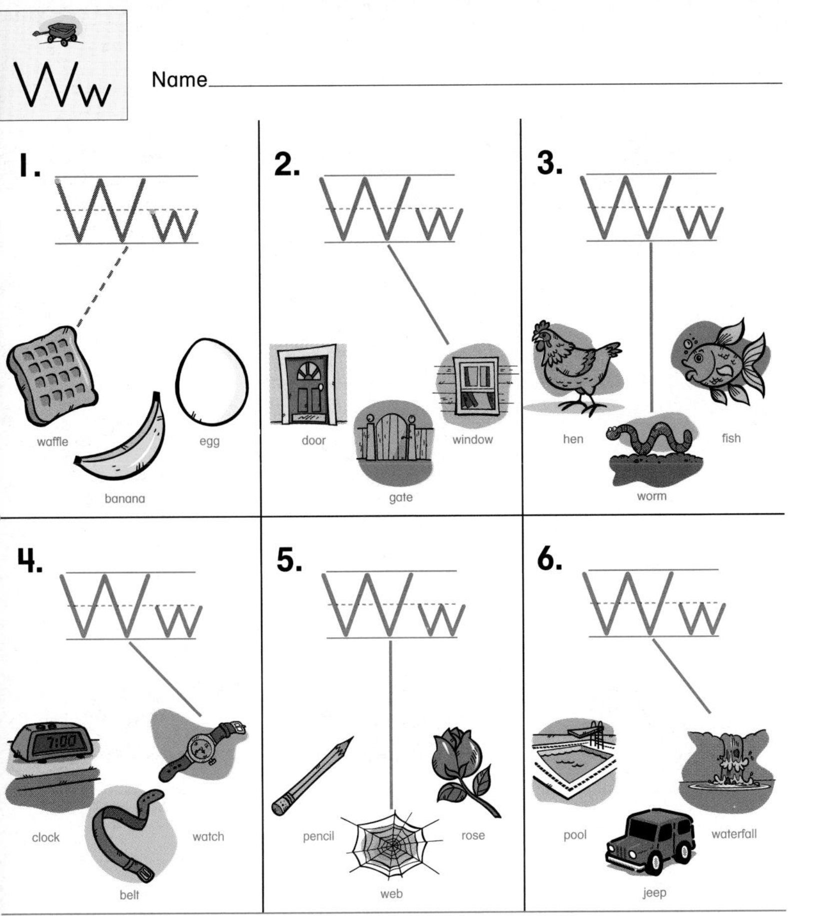

Write the letters *Ww.* • Say the name of each picture. • Draw a line from *Ww* to each picture whose name has the same beginning sound as *wagon.*

108 Review Initial /w/*Ww*

Review

Initial /w/*Ww*

Children will identify initial /w/*Ww*.

PREPARE

PHONOLOGICAL AWARENESS Tell children the words *wood* and *good* rhyme because they have the same ending sounds. Have children clap when they hear you say other words that rhyme with *wood*: *hood, for, dog, should, could, took.*

Review singing the song "Wendy's Wagon" while holding up the Phonics Picture Poster for *wagon*. Afterwards have children think of words that begin with the /w/ sound. *Phonemic Awareness*

TEACH

IDENTIFY INITIAL /w/*Ww* Distribute the letter card *Ww* from the Word Building Manipulative Cards and remind children that the letters *Ww* stand for /w/. Then point to things in the classroom that begin with /w/*Ww* such as *window, wastebasket, watch, wall.* Have volunteers name each thing and place their letter card by it while the class says /w/.

PRACTICE

COMPLETE THE PUPIL PAGE Before children begin, read the directions aloud and help them identify the pictures. Work the first item together. Encourage children to do the rest independently.

ASSESS/CLOSE

IDENTIFY AND USE INITIAL /w/*Ww* Use page 108 to assess children's progress with initial /w/*Ww*. You may wish to have children draw a picture of something that begins with /w/ and write *Ww* under it.

TEACHING TIP

MANAGEMENT You may want to write the letter *w* on self-sticking notes and have children use them instead of letter cards to label classroom things. They might work better, for example, on "wall" and "window."

ALTERNATE TEACHING STRATEGY

Share the following rhyme with children: *The letter* w *begins many words. It begins* word*, in fact, perhaps you heard. What other words begin that way? Well, I wonder what we'll say!* Repeat each line. Have children listen for words that begin like *word* and then answer the question posed in the rhyme.

▶ **Linguistic/Auditory**

Introduce

Initial /v/*Vv*

OBJECTIVES

Children will identify initial /v/*Vv* and form the letters *Vv*.

PREPARE

PHONOLOGICAL AWARENESS Read the words to

Listen

the song "Viv's Van" aloud and have children listen for the words *van* and *vegetable*. Then have children clap and compare the number of syllables in these words.

As you sing the song "Viv's Van," hold up the Phonics Picture Poster for *van*. Have the children clap each time they hear a word that begins with /v/. *Phonemic Awareness*

TEACH

IDENTIFY INITIAL /v/*Vv* Draw a valentine on the chalkboard and write *Vv* in the center. Tell children that the letters *Vv* stand for the sound /v/ they hear in *valentine*. Then write these words around the valentine: *van*, *vet*, *was*, *not*, *Val*. Say each word and invite volunteers to draw a line from those that begin with *Vv* to the center of the valentine as they say /v/.

FORM *Vv* Some children may need to review how to write *V* and *v*. Have children draw a large valentine and write *Vv* around it several times, using the Handwriting Models in the back of the Pupil's Edition for reference.

PRACTICE

COMPLETE THE PUPIL PAGE Read the directions aloud. Identify the key picture of the *van* and the other pictures on the page.

ASSESS/CLOSE

IDENTIFY AND USE INITIAL /v/*Vv* Use page 109 to assess children's knowledge of initial /v/*Vv*. Ask children to say a word that begins with /v/ and write *Vv*.

Name____________________

Vv	1. violin Vv	2. cat
3. valentine Vv	4. vegetables Vv	5. truck
6. lettuce	7. vase Vv	8. vest Vv

Say the name of each picture. • If the name begins with the same sound as *van*, write *Vv* on the line.

Listen

Viv's Van

Viv takes her van today,
To visit her friend Jay.
Viv packs some vegetables
To eat along the way!

Sung to the tune:
"The Farmer in the Dell"
From **Songs from A to Z**

Phonics Picture Posters and Cards

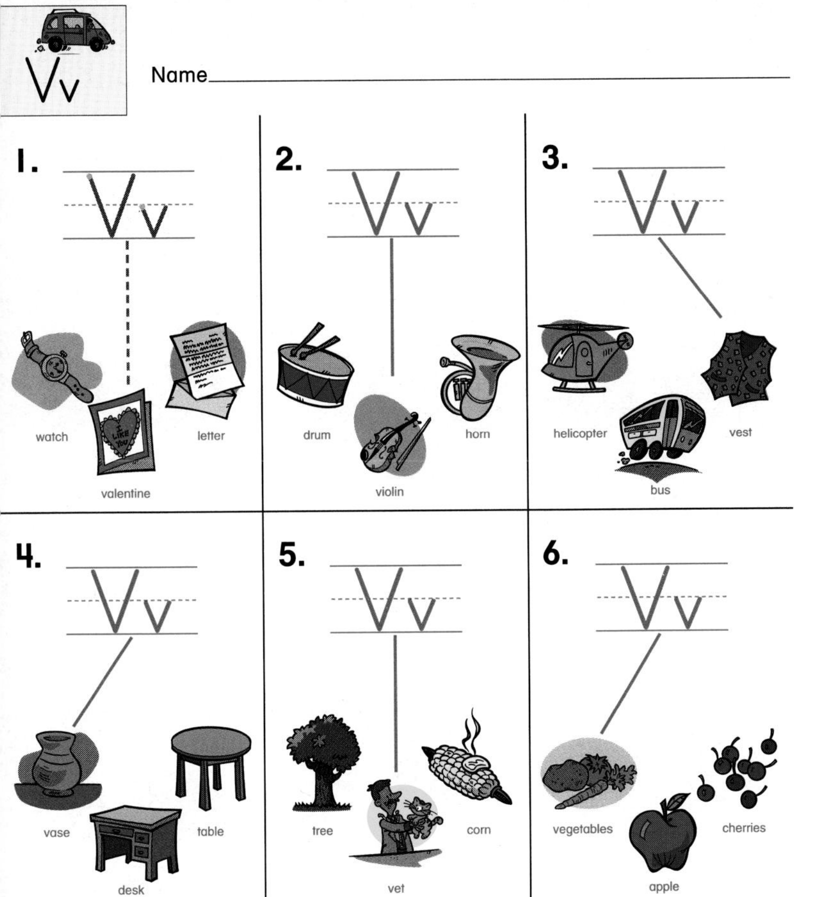

Vv Name______________________________

1. Vv — watch, valentine, letter

2. Vv — drum, violin, horn

3. Vv — helicopter, bus, vest

4. Vv — vase, desk, table

5. Vv — tree, vet, corn

6. Vv — vegetables, apple, cherries

Write the letters *Vv.* • Say the name of each picture. • Draw a line from *Vv* to each picture whose name begins like *van.*

Review

Initial /v/*Vv*

OBJECTIVES

Children will identify initial /v/*Vv*.

PREPARE

PHONOLOGICAL AWARENESS Have children think of as many words as they can that rhyme with *van* such as *man, can, Dan, fan, pan, tan, ran* and so on.

Listen

Review singing the song "Viv's Van," while holding up the Phonics Picture Poster for *van*. Then have the children say vroom each time they hear a word that begins with /v/ as you say the words to the song. *Phonemic Awareness*

TEACH

IDENTIFY INITIAL /v/*Vv* Say *vacation* and invite a volunteer to write the beginning letter of this word on the chalkboard. Remind children that the letters *Vv* stand for /v/. Then write the words *valentine, violin, vegetable,* and *vase* on chart paper and read them aloud. Have children circle each *Vv* and say /v/.

PRACTICE

COMPLETE THE PUPIL PAGE Help children with directions, names of pictures, and the first item. Encourage children to complete the page independently, then review answers.

ASSESS/CLOSE

IDENTIFY AND USE INITIAL /v/*Vv* Use page 110 to assess children's progress with initial /v/*Vv*. Ask children to name two words that begin with initial /v/*Vv*.

ALTERNATE TEACHING STRATEGY

Have each child make a vest by cutting a slit down the front of a large paper bag and then cutting out armholes. Children can decorate their vests with the letter *v* and pictures of objects that begin with /v/*v*. Have children share the vests with classmates.

▶ **Interpersonal/Kinesthetic**

Review

/w/w, /v/v

OBJECTIVES

Children will identify /w/*w* and /v/*v* in words .

PREPARE

PHONOLOGICAL AWARENESS Have children name words that rhyme with *wag*. Then repeat with the word *vet*.

Say the following sentences and encourage children to blend the sounds together to answer your questions: *A spider spun a /w/ /e/ /b/. What did the spider spin?* (a web) *The children rode in a /v/ /a/ /n/. What did the children ride in?* (a van)

TEACH

REVIEW /w/*w*, /v/*v* Write *w* and *v* on the chalkboard. Say *wig* and have children identify whether they hear /w/ or /v/ in this word. Have a volunteer circle the letter that stands for the sound /w/. Then draw three letter boxes and invite a volunteer to write the letter *w* in a box to show where he or she hears the sound—at the beginning, in the middle, or at the end of the word. Repeat with other words such as *wag, vet, Val*.

PRACTICE

COMPLETE THE PUPIL PAGE Before children begin, read the directions aloud. Help them identify the pictures and complete the first item. Invite children to finish the page on their own.

ASSESS/CLOSE

IDENTIFY AND USE /w/*w*, /v/*v* Use page 111 to assess children's progress with /w/*w*, /v/*v*. Ask children to say the sound that each letter stands for: *w, v*.

Name________________

1. w — waterfall, hat
2. v — vase, basket
3. w — mitten, wagon
4. v — valentine, stamp
5. w — watch, fork
6. v — radio, violin

Trace the letter. • Say the sound it stands for. • Say the names of the pictures. • Draw a line from the letter to the picture whose name begins with the sound the letter stands for.

Name

1.   b t

we b

2.   u e

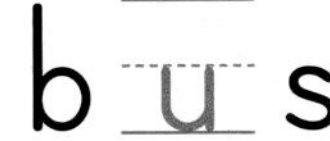
b u s

3.  c d

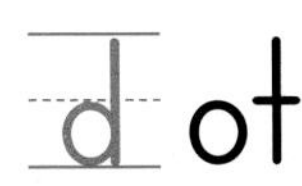
d ot

4.   v p

v an

5.  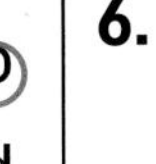 p d

mo p

6.   o a

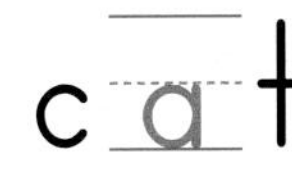
c a t

Say the picture name. • Circle the missing letter. • Then write the letter. • Read the word.

Blending with Short *a, i, o, u, e*

OBJECTIVES

Children will blend and read short *a, i, o, u* and *e* CVC words.

PREPARE

Display and hold up the following letter cards from the Word Building Manipulative Cards: *a, e, i, n, o, t, u, w p, h, v*. Invite children to say the sound each letter stands for.

TEACH

MODEL AND GUIDE PRACTICE Place the *a* letter card on the chalkboard ledge and say /a/. Have children repeat /a/.

- Place the *n* letter card next to the *a* letter card.
- Blend the sounds /a/ and /n/ together and have children repeat the word after you.
- Place the *v* letter card before the *a* letter card.
- Blend the sounds /v/, /a/, /n/ together to read *van*. Have children repeat the word *van* after you.

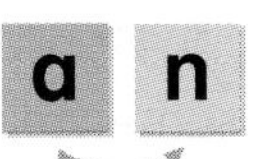 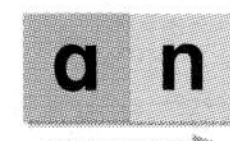 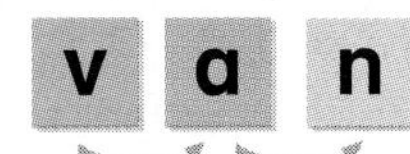 

USE THE WORD IN CONTEXT Use *van* in a sentence to reinforce its meaning, for example: *We drove the van to the park.*

REPEAT THE PROCEDURE Use the following to continue modeling and guided practice: *win, wet, vet, nut, hop.*

PRACTICE

COMPLETE THE PUPIL PAGE Read the directions with children and identify the pictures together.

ASSESS/CLOSE

BLEND AND READ WORDS Use page 112 to assess children's skill in blending with short *a, i, o, u,* and *e*. Have children use the letter cards to build and read a CVC word.

ALTERNATE TEACHING STRATEGY

Give children opportunities to blend and read words by labeling classroom objects, such as: *hat, cap, bag, sack, rock, kit, cup, mug, pin, pen, map*. Talk about how sometimes different words are used for the same or similar objects.

▶ Linguistic/Visual

Introduce

High-Frequency Words: *of, I, was*

Children will identify and read the high-frequency words *of, I,* and *was*.

PREPARE

LISTEN TO WORDS Read aloud the following sentences slowly and have children listen for the words *I, was,* and *of.* Ask children to smile when they hear the high-frequency words: *I went to the zoo. It was a lot of fun.*

TEACH

IDENTIFY THE WORDS Write the sentences from the Prepare section on the chalkboard. Then write the words *of, I,* and *was* under them. Read each word aloud. Encourage children to read the sentences aloud with you as you point to each word in the sentence. Have volunteers draw lines to match the three words to where they appear in the sentences.

PRACTICE

COMPLETE THE PUPIL PAGE Before children begin, read the directions aloud. Emphasize that children are to circle more than one word in each row.

ASSESS/CLOSE

REVIEW THE PAGE Use page 113 to assess children's recognition of the words *of, I,* and *was*. You may wish to have children place the High-Frequency Word Cards from the back of the Pupil's Edition in front of them. Then have children point to the word after you say it aloud.

Name________________

1.	of	was	I	(of)	(of)
2.	I	(I)	was	(I)	of
3.	was	I	(was)	I	(was)
4.	of	was	I	(of)	(of)
5.	was	(was)	of	(was)	of

Read the first word in each row. • Circle the words in the row that are the same.

Introduce High-Frequency Words: *of, I, was* 113

Name

1.	a	(I)	I
2.	has	(was)	was
3.	(of)	for	of
4.	(that)	was	that
5.	I	(for)	for
6.	(go)	of	go

Listen to the word. • Circle the word you hear. • Then write the word.

114 Review High-Frequency Words

ALTERNATE TEACHING STRATEGY

Have children write a story using the high-frequency words *I*, *was*, *of*, *that*, *for*, and *go*. Begin the story for children. Record their story on chart paper. Read the completed story with children. Invite volunteers to look for the word *I* in the story and circle it using a red crayon. Continue with each high-frequency word using a different color crayon.

▶ **Linguistic/Visual**

Review

High-Frequency Words

OBJECTIVES

Children will identify and read the high-frequency words *of*, *I*, *was*, *for*, *that*, and *go*.

PREPARE

LISTEN TO WORDS Tell children to listen for the high-frequency word or words you name as you read each sentence aloud. Have them raise their hand when they hear each word.

of—*The zoo has a room full of birds.*
was, for—*There was a pool for seals.*
I, go, that—*I hope I can go to that zoo again.*

TEACH

IDENTIFY THE WORDS Distribute the High-Frequency Word Cards for the words *of*, *was*, *for*, *I*, *go*, and *that* from the back of the Pupil's Edition. Write the sentences from the Prepare section on the chalkboard and read them aloud. Then ask volunteers to underline each high-frequency word as you name it. Reread the sentences and have children hold up the appropriate word card for each underlined word.

PRACTICE

COMPLETE THE PUPIL PAGE Read the directions aloud. Have children listen to, circle, and write the words you say: (1) *I*; (2) *was*; (3) *of*; (4) *that*; (5) *for*; (6) *go*.

ASSESS/CLOSE

REVIEW THE PAGE Use page 114 to assess children's recognition of the words *of*, *I*, *was*, *for*, *that*, and *go*. You may wish to say each word aloud and have children hold up and read the corresponding word card.

Develop

Phonological Awareness

Count Words

Teach Read the poem aloud. Then say the sentence, *"Come, little fox, let's bake a pie."* Call seven children to the front of the class and assign one word to each child. Have the children say their words in order. Then count the children and explain that this sentence has seven words.

Practice Ask a volunteer to make up a sentence telling something else Little Fox can make: for example, *"Let's bake a meat loaf."* Then count the words and have individuals come up and say the sentence word by word.

Little Fox's Pie

Come, little fox,
Let's bake a pie.
Mix this, mix that!
Pop it in the oven,
Then take it out.
Let it cool awhile,
Place it in a box.
At six o'clock tonight,
Share it with Ox.

Identify Beginning Sounds

Phonemic Awareness

MATERIALS
- Phonics Picture Poster *queen*
- Paper crown

Teach Display the Phonics Picture Poster for *queen*. Tell children the word *queen* begins with the /kw/ sound. Have children say the word and the /kw/ sound with you. Then have children tell which word in each pair begins with /kw/: *quite/kite; sack/quack; kick/quick; guilt/quilt*.

Practice Put the paper crown on a child. Explain that he or she will be called the "King for Now" or the "Queen for Now." The queen chooses a volunteer. If the volunteer can give a word beginning with /kw/, that child can take the crown and become the King or Queen for Now. Continue until children can no longer think of /kw/ words. Then assign a new beginning sound and continue.

Identify Ending Sounds

Phonemic Awareness

MATERIALS

- **Phonics Picture Poster**
  fox

Teach Display the Phonics Picture Poster for *fox*. Tell children the word *fox* ends with the /ks/ sound. Point out that the final sound of the word *fox* is two sounds together /k/ and /s/, /ks/. Give other words and have children repeat the word and final /ks/: *mix, fox, tax.*

Practice Play *"Fox in the Box."* Tell children that only words ending with /ks/ can go in the box. Go around the group asking questions such as: *"Can fox go in the box?"* Children respond *"Yes, fox ends in* /ks/." Use these words: *mix, hog, sick, wax, fix, kit, six, fax, block, tax.*

Blend Sounds

Phonemic Awareness

Teach Say the individual sounds /s/-/i/-/ks/ and then blend the sounds to say the word *six*. Have children repeat the sounds after you and then blend the word: /s/-/i/-/ks/: *six*. Tell children to listen to these sounds and how you blend them: /w/-/i/-/n/: *win*.

Practice Have three children stand slightly apart from each other. Give each a beginning, middle, or ending sound. Children repeat their sounds in order, moving closer and closer together until they join hands and blend the word. Repeat with words such as: *van, fox, mix, quip, quit, quack, hub, hug.*

Introduce

Final /ks/x

OBJECTIVES

Children will identify final /ks/*x* and form the letter *x*.

PREPARE

PHONOLOGICAL AWARENESS Write a large numeral *six* on the chalkboard and ask children to say the name of this number. Then have them name words that rhyme with *six*.

As you sing the song "Felix Fox," hold up the Phonics Picture Poster for *fox*. As you sing the song, emphasize the final /ks/. Have the children raise their hand when they hear final /ks/.
Phonemic Awareness

TEACH

IDENTIFY FINAL /ks/*x* Hold up the *x* letter card from the Word Building Manipulative Cards and explain that the letter *x* stands for the sound /ks/. Distribute *x* letter cards and write this sentence on the chalkboard: *A toy ox and fox were in the box.* Invite children to hold up their letter card when you say and point to a word ending with /ks/*x*. Have children say the word and listen to /ks/.

FORM *x* Review how to write the letter *x*. Invite children to write *x* on index cards, using the Handwriting Models from the back of the Pupil's Edition as a reference.

PRACTICE

COMPLETE THE PUPIL PAGE After reading the directions aloud, work through the first item together.

ASSESS/CLOSE

IDENTIFY AND USE FINAL /ks/*x* Use page 115 to assess children's recognition of final /ks/*x*. Ask children to name a word that ends with the letter *x*.

Name

_x

1. mix x
2. map
3. ox x
4. ax x
5. wagon
6. 6 six x
7. igloo
8. box x

Say the name of each picture. • If the name ends with the same sound as *fox*, write *x* on the line.

Introduce Final /ks/x 11

Phonics Song

Felix Fox

Felix fox likes his own name,
Both of these words end the same,
Xx ends words like six and fox,
Xx ends words like wax and box,
Felix Fox likes his own name,
Both of these words end the same.

Sung to the tune:
"Twinkle, Twinkle, Little Star"
From **Songs from A to Z**

Phonics Picture Posters and Cards

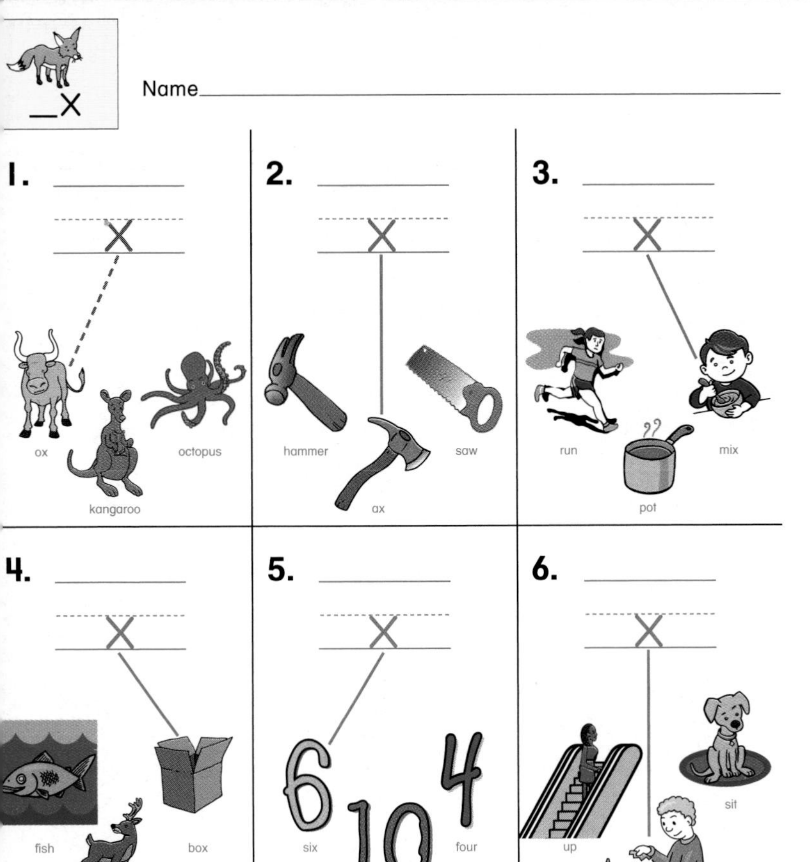

Write the letter *x*. • Say the name of each picture. Draw a line from the *x* to each picture whose name has the same ending sound as *fox*.

16 Review Final /ks/*x*

Review

Final /ks/x

OBJECTIVES

Children will identify final /ks/*x*.

PREPARE

PHONOLOGICAL AWARENESS Have children name words that rhyme with *fix*.

Listen

Say this tongue twister and have children listen for words that end with /ks/: *Mr. Hix will mix and fix dinner for six.* Tell children to raise a hand when they hear words with the ending sound /ks/. *Phonemic Awareness*

TEACH

IDENTIFY FINAL /ks/x Display the letter card *x* from the Word Building Manipulative Cards. Review that the letter *x* stands for the ending sound /ks/. Draw a nine-box grid on the chalkboard and write a word in each space: *ox*, *mix*, *him*, *box*, *cat*, *Max*, *did*, *fox*, *six*. Have children write *x* on words that have final /ks/*x*.

PRACTICE

COMPLETE THE PUPIL PAGE After reading the directions aloud, identify each picture for children. Complete the first item together and then have children work independently.

ASSESS/CLOSE

IDENTIFY AND USE FINAL /ks/x Use page 116 to assess children's progress with final /ks/*x*. You may wish to have children hold up their *x* letter cards when you say a word that ends with *x*. Read aloud the following words: *mat*, *fix*, *clock*, *ox*, *Rex*, *can*.

LANGUAGE SUPPORT

ESL **INSTRUCTIONAL** Some languages do not use the consonant *x*. The equivalent letters are *ks*. You may wish to provide extra writing practice for non-English-speaking children whose native language does not use *x*. Provide labeled final-x pictures and have children copy the words and draw their own pictures.

ALTERNATE TEACHING STRATEGY

Whisper a word that ends with /ks/*x* to a volunteer, such as *mix*, *fix*, *six*, *fox*, *box*. Have the child pantomime the word while the class guesses. As each word is correctly guessed, write it on the chalkboard.

▶ **Kinesthetic/Auditory**

Introduce

Initial /kw/*Qu, qu*

OBJECTIVES

Children will identify initial /kw/*Qu, qu* and form the letters *Qu, qu*.

PREPARE

PHONOLOGICAL AWARENESS Say the following words and have the children clap the syllables in each word: *queen, quiet,* and *question.*

As you sing the song " The Quiet Queen," hold up the Phonics Picture Poster for *queen*. Have the children say the /kw/ quietly when they hear a word beginning with /kw/. *Phonemic Awareness*

TEACH

IDENTIFY INITIAL /kw/*Qu, qu* Write the letters *Qu* and *qu* on the chalkboard and tell children that the letters *q* and *u* together stand for the sound /kw/. Have children point to the letters and say /kw/. Then write these words: *quilt, quarter, web, quart, van, quail*. Play "What Can We Take to the Queen?" Explain to children that they can only take things that begin with /kw/. Invite volunteers to underline the items they can take and circle initial *qu* while the class says /kw/.

FORM *Qu, qu* As a review, have children practice writing *Qu* and *qu* on paper folded into fourths. Children can use the Handwriting Models in the back of the Pupil's Edition.

PRACTICE

COMPLETE THE PUPIL PAGE Read the directions aloud, identify the pictures, and complete the first item together.

ASSESS/CLOSE

IDENTIFY AND USE INITIAL /kw/*Qu, qu* Use page 117 to assess children's knowledge of initial /kw/*Qu, qu*.

Name____________________

Qu qu	1. quail Qu qu	2. quilt Qu qu
3. quarter Qu qu	4. key	5. question mark Qu qu
6. balloon	7. quiet Qu qu	8. worm

Say the name of each picture. • If the name begins with the same sound as *queen*, write *Qu,qu* on the line.

Introduce Initial /kw/*Qu,qu* 117

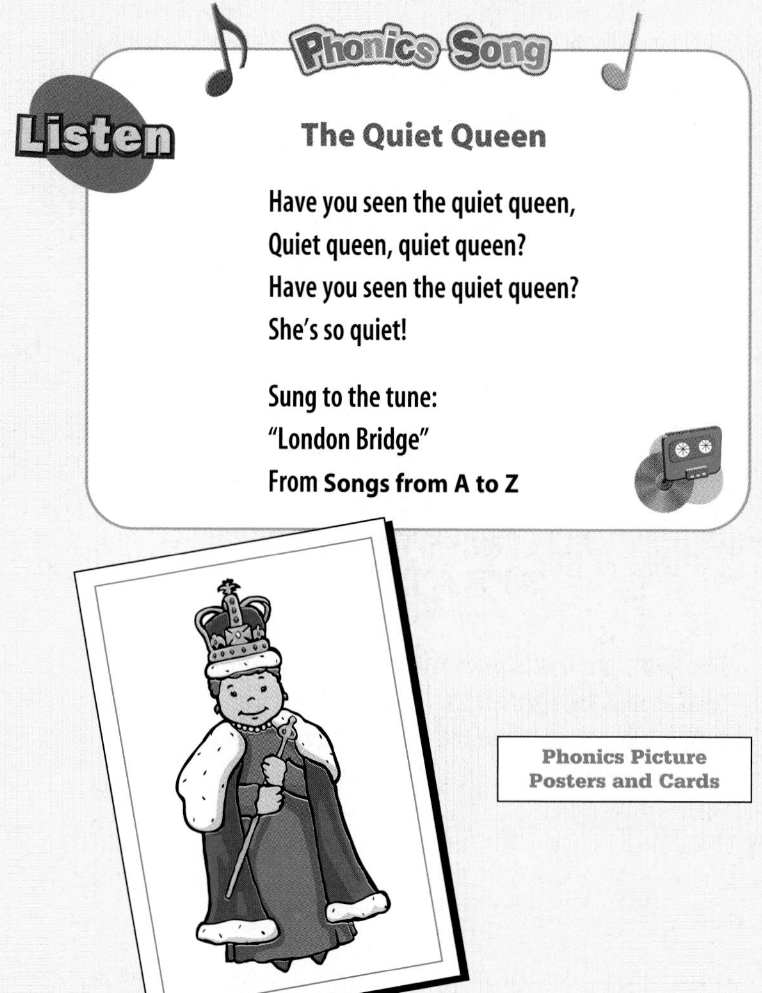

Phonics Song
Listen
The Quiet Queen
Have you seen the quiet queen,
Quiet queen, quiet queen?
Have you seen the quiet queen?
She's so quiet!
Sung to the tune:
"London Bridge"
From Songs from A to Z
Phonics Picture
Posters and Cards

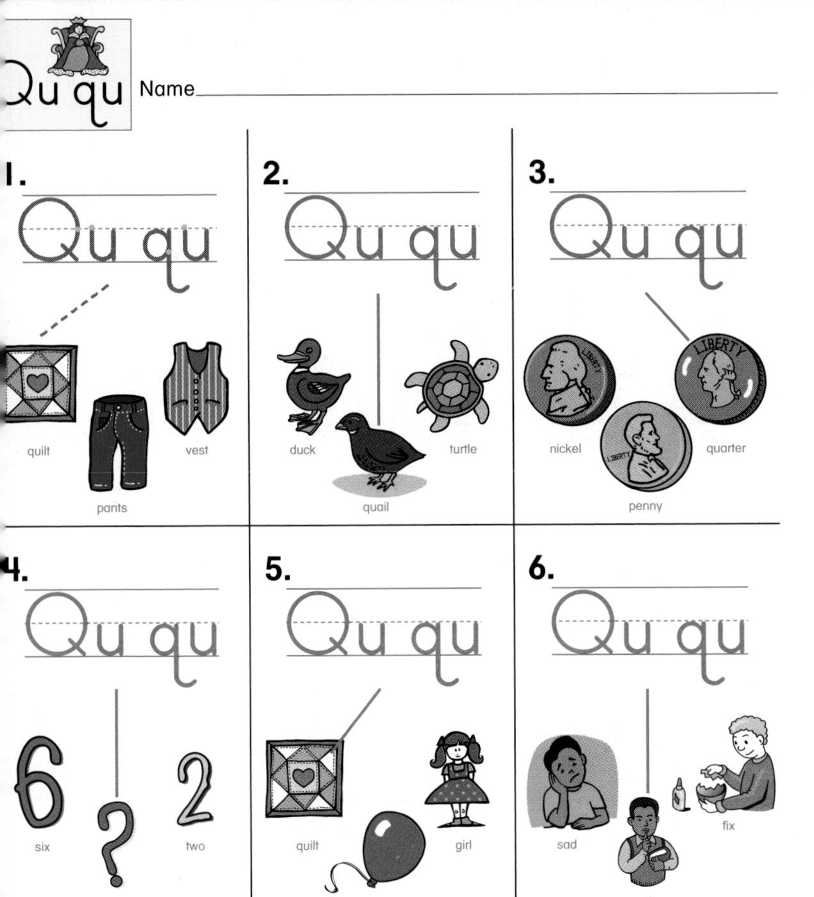
Qu qu Name

1. Qu qu

2. Qu qu

3. Qu qu

4. Qu qu

5. Qu qu

6. Qu qu

ite the letters *Qu,qu.* • Say the name of each picture. • Draw a line from *Qu,qu* each picture whose name has the same beginning sound as *queen.*

Review

Initial /kw/*Qu, qu*

OBJECTIVES

Children will identify initial /kw/*Qu, qu*.

PREPARE

PHONOLOGICAL AWARENESS Say the word *queen* and have children think of rhyming words such as *mean*, *bean*, *green*, *seen* and so on.

Listen

Whisper these words and ask children to place their finger on their lips as if to say "quiet" when they hear /kw/: *quick*, *fast*, *quack*, *quilt*, *quake*, *race*. *Phonemic Awareness*

TEACH

IDENTIFY INITIAL /kw/*Qu, qu* Write *Qu*, *qu* at the top of a sheet of chart paper. Remind children that the letters *Qu*, *qu* stand for the sound /kw/. Write the following grid of words on the chalkboard and have volunteers say /kw/ and circle the words that begin with *qu*:

net	quiet	dog	quack
quilt	quart	saw	quick
ant	queen	mop	ink

PRACTICE

COMPLETE THE PUPIL PAGE Read the directions aloud and help children identify the pictures. After working through the first item together, have children work on their own.

ASSESS/CLOSE

IDENTIFY AND USE INITIAL /kw/*Qu, qu* Use page 118 to assess children's progress with initial /kw/*Qu, qu*. Have children draw a picture of an object that begins with /qu/ and write *Qu*, *qu* under it.

TEACHING TIP

MANAGEMENT You may want to have children practice writing *Qu* and *qu* in small groups with handwriting models. If children confuse lowercase *q* and lowercase *g*, have them practice writing both letters.

ALTERNATE TEACHING STRATEGY

Children will create a paper quilt by writing the letters *Qu* or *qu*, and drawing a picture that begins with /kw/ on a square piece of drawing paper. Place their squares on a bulletin board to make a patchwork quilt. Then point to each picture and have a volunteer name it.

▶ **Visual/Kinesthetic**

Review

/ks/x, /kw/qu

Children will identify /ks/*x*, and /kw/*qu* in words.

PREPARE

PHONOLOGICAL AWARENESS Say the sentence *Fox had a box.* Have children name the words that rhyme. Repeat with the sentence *The Queen was rarely seen.*

Read aloud the following sentences and have children blend the sounds together to answer your questions: *People chop wood with an /a/ /ks/. What do people use to chop wood?* (an ax) *A duck says /kw/ /a/ /k/. What does a duck say?* (quack) *Phonemic Awareness*

TEACH

REVIEW /ks/*x*, /kw/*qu* Draw three letter boxes and write the letters *x* and *qu* on the chalkboard. Then say *quick* and ask children whether they hear /ks/ or /kw/ in this word. Have a volunteer circle the letter or letters that stand for the sound /kw/. Ask another volunteer to write the letters *qu* in a box to show where he or she hears the sound—at the beginning, in the middle, or at the end of the word. Repeat with other words, for example: *quit, mix, box.*

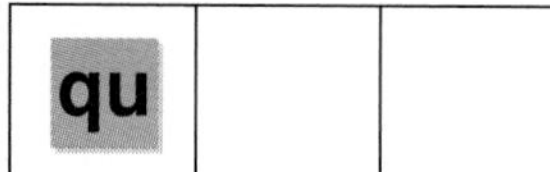

PRACTICE

COMPLETE THE PUPIL PAGE Read the directions aloud and complete the first item with children.

ASSESS/CLOSE

IDENTIFY AND USE /ks/*x*, /kw/*qu* Use page 119 to assess children's progress with /ks/*x*, /kw/*qu*.

Name____________________

1. qu — web, quail
2. x — ox, bell
3. x — mask, mix
4. qu — queen, girl
5. x — ax, hook
6. qu — vase, quilt

Trace the letter or letters. Say the sound they stand for. • Say the names of the pictures. • Draw a line from the letter or letters to the picture whose name has the same sound the letter or letters stand for.

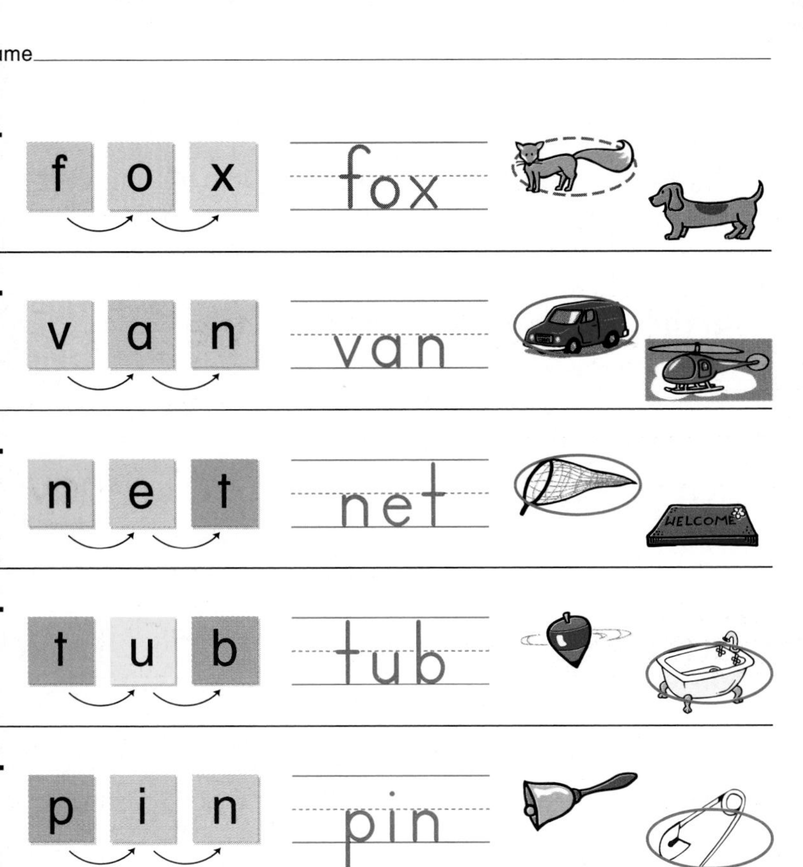

rst, blend the sounds and say the word. • Next, write the word. • Last, draw a cle around the picture that goes with the word.

20 Blending with Short *a, i, o, u,* and *e*

ALTERNATE TEACHING STRATEGY

ESL Show children these words: *cat, pup, hen, fox, duck, pig, dog, bug, rat, kid, bat, hog, ox.* Blend sounds to read the words aloud together. Display pictures of the animals and discuss them; then invite children to pantomime each animal as you point to its name.

▶ **Visual/Kinesthetic**

Blending with Short *a, i, o, u, e*

TESTED OBJECTIVES

Children will blend and read short *a, i, o, u* and *e* CVC words.

PREPARE

Write the following letters on the chalkboard: *a, e, i, o, r, x, ck, qu, b, t, m, n, d, u.* As you say a sound for these letters, have volunteers circle the appropriate letter or letters.

TEACH

MODEL AND GUIDE PRACTICE Place the *e* letter card from the Word Building Manipulative Cards on the chalkboard ledge and say /e/. Have children say the sound /e/.

- Place the *x* letter card next to the *e* letter card.
- Blend the sounds /e/ and /ks/ together and have children repeat the sounds after you.
- Place the *R* letter card before the *e* letter card.
- Blend the sounds /r/, /e/, /ks/ together to read *Rex*. Have children repeat the word *Rex* after you.

USE THE WORD IN CONTEXT Use *Rex* in a sentence to reinforce meaning: *Tyrannosaurus Rex was a huge dinosaur.*

REPEAT THE PROCEDURE Use these words to continue modeling and guided practice: *box, ten, quack, mix, mud.*

PRACTICE

COMPLETE THE PUPIL PAGE Read the directions aloud. Then help children blend the sounds and say each word.

ASSESS/CLOSE

BLEND AND READ WORDS Use page 120 to assess children's skill in blending with short *a, i, o, u,* and *e.*

Introduce

High-Frequency Words: *said, have, we*

OBJECTIVES

Children will identify and read the high-frequency words *said, have,* and *we*.

PREPARE

LISTEN TO WORDS Ask children to listen for the words *have, said,* and *we* in the sentences you read. Tell children to clap when they hear the words. Say the word before you read each sentence aloud:

have *My sister and I have a pet pig.*
said *Mom said there is a pet show.*
we *We took our pig to the show.*

TEACH

IDENTIFY THE WORDS Display the High-Frequency Word Cards *said, have, we* from the back of the Pupil's Edition on the chalkboard ledge. Point to each word and read it aloud. Distribute word cards and invite volunteers to match their cards to the ones on the ledge. Then write the sentences from the Prepare section on the chalkboard. As you read each sentence aloud, ask children to hold up the card for *said, have,* or *we* when they hear the word.

PRACTICE

COMPLETE THE PUPIL PAGE After reading the directions to children, make sure they understand that they are to circle more than one word in each row.

ASSESS/CLOSE

REVIEW THE PAGE Use page 121 to assess children's recognition of the words *said, have,* and *we*. You may wish to have volunteers say a sentence with one of the words.

Name____________________

1.	we	said	we	have	we
2.	said	have	said	we	said
3.	have	have	said	we	have
4.	said	said	we	said	have
5.	we	we	said	we	have

Read the first word in each row. • Circle the words in the row that are the same.

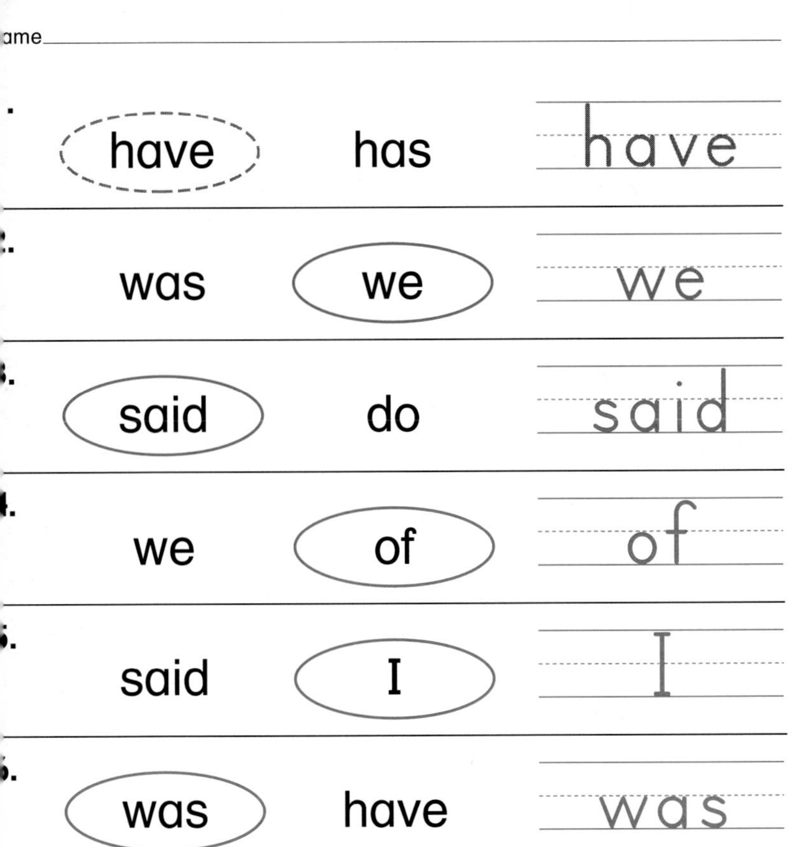
ame________________

.	have (circled)	has	have
.	was	we (circled)	we
.	said (circled)	do	said
.	we	of (circled)	of
.	said	I (circled)	I
.	was (circled)	have	was

sten to the word. • Circle the word you hear. • Then write the word.

McGraw-Hill School Division

22 Review High-Frequency Words

ALTERNATE TEACHING STRATEGY

Distribute a high-frequency word card to each child. Say a word and have children with that word come up to the front of the room and hold up their cards. Continue until all the words are identified. Then have children exchange their cards with classmates to get different words. Repeat the activity.

▶ **Auditory/Visual**

Review

High-Frequency Words

Children will identify and read the high-frequency words *said, have, we, of, I,* and *was*.

PREPARE

LISTEN TO WORDS Have children listen to the following sentences and clap when they hear the words you name:
was, of *Our pig was the winner of the show.*
we *We were really surprised!*
I *I gave our pig a hug.*
said, have *Dad said that we have a great pig.*

TEACH

IDENTIFY THE WORDS Write the sentences from the Prepare section on the chalkboard and read them aloud once. Then reread the sentences and invite volunteers to circle the high-frequency words you name. Arrange children in pairs and distribute a set of High-Frequency Word Cards from the back of the Pupil's Edition to each pair. Hold up each word card, one at a time, and have children say the word and hold up their matching card.

PRACTICE

COMPLETE THE PUPIL PAGE Read the directions aloud. Then say the following words for children to circle and write: (1) *have*; (2) *we*; (3) *said*; (4) *of*; (5) *I*; (6) *was*.

ASSESS/CLOSE

REVIEW THE PAGE Use page 122 to assess children's recognition of the words *of, I, was, said, have,* and *we*. You may wish to have children say a sentence using one or more of the High-Frequency Words.

Develop

Phonological Awareness

Blend Syllables

Teach After reading the poem, clap the syllables in the first line. Emphasize the two syllables in the word *jel-ly*. Tell children the word *jelly* has two word parts.

Practice Tell children you will say some word parts and they are to put the word parts together. Then tell children they have to guess what all of the words have in common. Say the syllables for the following words: yel-low, or-ange, red, pur-ple, green. Have children guess what the words have in common. (They are all colors.) Then repeat with other categories of words, such as food or sports.

Jim and Jan and Me

**Jim likes grape jelly,
Jan likes strawberry jam.
Jim drinks from his blue jug.
Jan uses her yellow cup.
Do Jim and Jan ever agree?
Oh, yes! They both love me
Their little brown pup!**

Identify Beginning Sounds

MATERIALS
- **Phonics Picture Posters**
  jar, yo-yo
- **Beanbag**

Teach Display the Phonics Picture Poster for *jar*. Tell children the word jar begins with the sound /j/. Say other words beginning with /j/ and have children say the /j/ sound after each word: *jam, jelly, June, jump*. Display the Phonics Picture Poster for *yo-yo*. Say the word *yo-yo* and the beginning sound /y/. Say other words beginning with /y/: *yellow, yawn, yam.*

Practice Children sit in a circle. Ask a question such as the following and toss the beanbag to a child to answer. Say: *Do* jelly *and* jam *sound the same at the beginning? What sound do you hear at the beginning of* yarn? *Which word begins with /j/–bump/jump?* Repeat until all children have had a turn.

Blend Sounds

Phonemic Awareness

MATERIALS

- Phonics Picture Posters

  cat, pig, hen, fox

Teach Display Phonics Picture Posters for *cat*, *pig*, *hen*, and *box*. Say "/k/-/a/-/t/." Have children blend the sounds to say the word. Then have them point to the picture that matches the word. Repeat for the other pictures.

Practice Play *"Do As I Say."* Give children directions to follow in a sentence in which one word is separated into sounds. Children blend the word as they follow the direction. For example, say: *Put your finger on your* /n/ /ō/ /z/. Reach and touch your /t/-/ō/-/z/.

Segment Sounds

Phonemic Awareness

MATERIALS

- Blocks

Teach Display three blocks. Then say the word *jam* and the individual sounds /j/-/a/-/m/. Move a block into a row for each sound. Repeat, tapping a block in order for each of the sounds, /j/-/a/-/m/. Say: *"The word* jam *has three sounds: /j/-/a/-/m/."* Have children repeat the sounds and the word with you.

Practice Give three blocks to each child. Children listen as you say a three-sound word and then segment the sounds, using a block to stand for each sound. Check understanding by having a child say the sounds for the class. Use such words as: *hum, wet, jig, yet, bog*.

Introduce

Initial /j/Jj

Children will identify initial /j/*Jj* and form the letters *Jj*.

PREPARE

PHONOLOGICAL AWARENESS Say the following words and ask the children to identify the rhyming words: *jelly*, *jar*, *far*, *belly*.

While singing the song "Jenna's Jars," hold up the Phonics Picture Poster for *jar*. Have the children jump when they hear a word that begins with /j/. *Phonemic Awareness*

TEACH

IDENTIFY INITIAL /j/*Jj* Write *Jj* on the chalkboard and tell children that the letters *Jj* stand for the sound /j/. Have children point to *Jj* and say /j/. Provide newspaper headlines and have children find, cut out, and paste examples of the letters *Jj* on construction paper. Children then draw pictures of things that begin with /j/ near the letters *Jj*. Invite children to identify their pictures.

FORM *Jj* Review how to write *J* and *j*, pointing out that the capital *J* has a top line, and the lowercase *j* has a top dot. Have children trace their Handwriting Models in the back of the Pupil's Edition.

PRACTICE

COMPLETE THE PUPIL PAGE Before children begin, read the directions aloud and help them identify the pictures.

ASSESS/CLOSE

IDENTIFY AND USE INITIAL /j/*Jj* Use page 123 to assess children's recognition of initial /j/*Jj*. Have children answer this riddle: *I begin with /j/. I fly high and fast. What am I?* (jet)

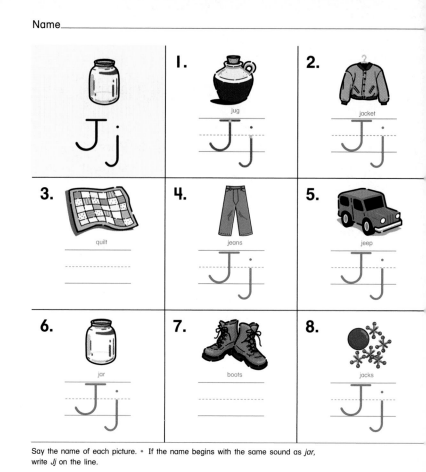

Name

Jj	1. jug Jj	2. jacket Jj
3. quilt	4. jeans Jj	5. jeep Jj
6. jar Jj	7. boots	8. jacks Jj

Say the name of each picture. • If the name begins with the same sound as *jar*, write *Jj* on the line.

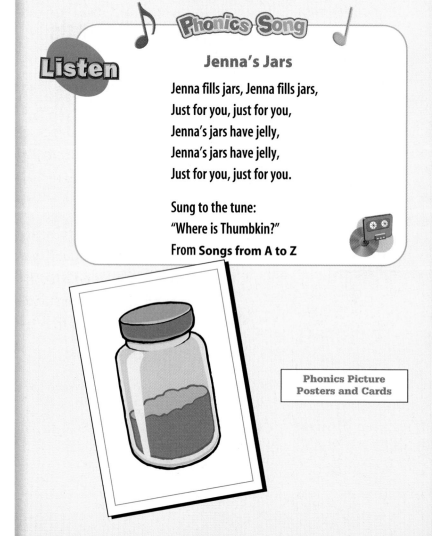

Introduce Initial /j/*Jj* 123

Listen
Phonics Song
Jenna's Jars
Jenna fills jars, Jenna fills jars,
Just for you, just for you,
Jenna's jars have jelly,
Jenna's jars have jelly,
Just for you, just for you.
Sung to the tune:
"Where is Thumbkin?"
From Songs from A to Z

Phonics Picture Posters and Cards

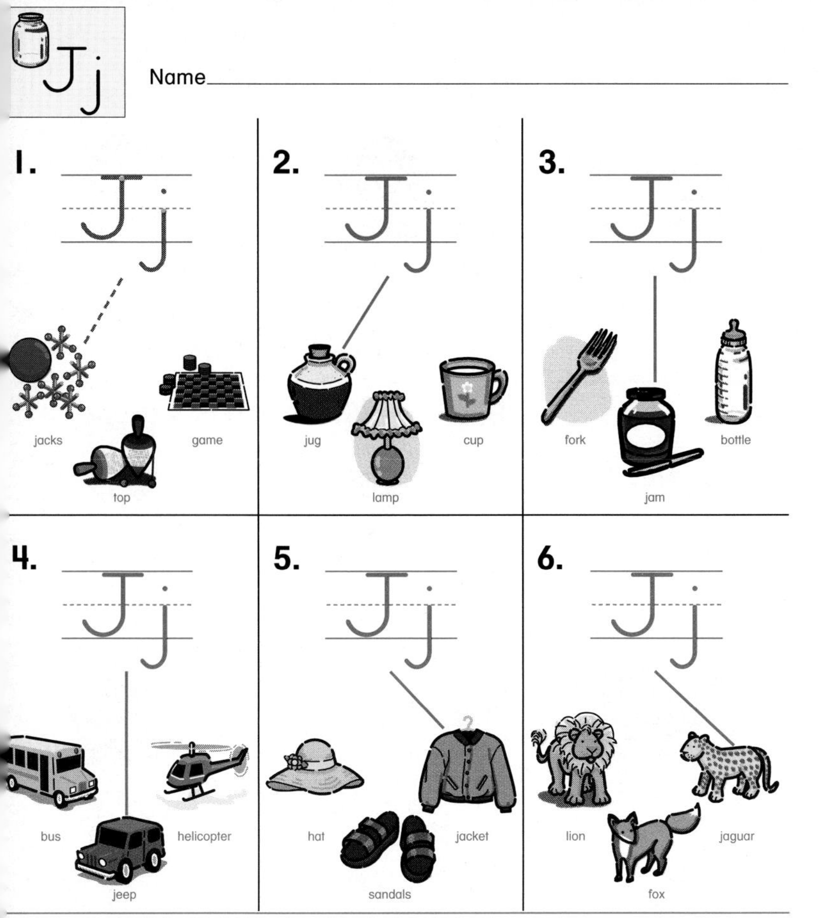

Jj Name

1. Jj
jacks game top

2. Jj
jug cup lamp

3. Jj
fork bottle jam

4. Jj
bus helicopter jeep

5. Jj
hat jacket sandals

6. Jj
lion jaguar fox

McGraw-Hill School Division

'rite the letters *Jj*. • Say the name of each picture. • Draw a line from *Jj* to each cture whose name has the same beginning sound as *jar*.

24 Review Initial /j/Jj

Review

Initial /j/Jj

OBJECTIVES

Children will identify initial /j/*Jj*.

PREPARE

PHONOLOGICAL AWARENESS Say the following pairs of words and ask the children to clap the syllable and say which word is longer: *jelly/jam; Jennifer/Joseph; jar/jingle; jacket/jeep*.

While singing the song "Jenna's Jars," hold up the Phonics Picture Poster for *jar*. Then have children think of words that begin with the /j/ sound. *Phonemic Awareness*

TEACH

IDENTIFY INITIAL /j/*Jj* Remind children that the letters *Jj* stand for the sound /j/. On the chalkboard, write the words *jam, jelly, jug*. Have children circle the beginning letter of each word and say /j/. Distribute the letter card *Jj* from the Word Building Manipulative Cards and invite children to take a walk around the classroom, looking for objects that begin with /j/. Tell children to place their letter cards by the objects they find. (Examples: jar, jacket, toy jet, jump rope, jacks.)

PRACTICE

COMPLETE THE PUPIL PAGE Read the directions aloud and help children name the pictures. Have children work on their own, then check their answers.

ASSESS/CLOSE

IDENTIFY AND USE INITIAL /j/*Jj* Use page 124 to assess children's progress with initial /j/*Jj*. Have children point to one of the *Jj* objects in the classroom, say its name and write *Jj*.

TEACHING TIP

MANAGEMENT For the Teach activity on page 123, find headlines with the letter *j* ahead of time. You may want to have children do this activity in small groups. For the Teach activity on page 124, place objects beginning with /j/*j* in various parts of the classroom.

ALTERNATE TEACHING STRATEGY

Have children complete the sentences with words beginning with /j/*j*. Read the following sentences aloud, having children say the missing word: *I flew across the country in a ____.* (jet) *For breakfast Tanya had toast and ____.* (jam) *My brother's name is ____.* (answer will vary) Have children make up their own incomplete sentences for classmates to complete.

▶ **Linguistic/Auditory**

Introduce

Initial /y/*Yy*

OBJECTIVES

Children will identify initial /y/*Yy* and form the letters *Yy*.

PREPARE

PHONOLOGICAL AWARENESS Read "Yoko's Yo-yo" aloud and have children clap out the syllables of *yesterday*, *Yoko* and *yes*. Then have children tell which word is longest and shortest.

Listen

While singing the song, "Yoko's Yo-yo," hold up the Phonics Picture Poster for *yo-yo*. Have the children whisper *yes* each time they hear the /y/ sound at the beginning of a word. *Phonemic Awareness*

TEACH

IDENTIFY INITIAL /y/*Yy* Draw a yo-yo (a circle) on the chalkboard and write *Yy* in the center. Tell children that the letters *Yy* stand for the sound /y/ like the beginning sound of *yo-yo*. Write these words around the yo-yo: *yes*, *yell*, *van*, *yak*, *you*, *jam*, *your*. Have children say each word with you. Invite volunteers to draw a line from each word that begins with /y/*Yy* to the yo-yo.

FORM *Yy* Some children may need to review how to write *Y* and *y*. Have children practice writing *Y* and *y* on paper using the Word Building Manipulative Cards as reference.

PRACTICE

COMPLETE THE PUPIL PAGE Read the directions aloud, name the pictures, and do the first item with children.

ASSESS/CLOSE

IDENTIFY AND USE INITIAL /y/*Yy* Use page 125 to assess children's knowledge of initial /y/*Yy*. Have children say a word that begins with /y/ and write *Yy*.

Name__________

Yy	1. yak Yy	2. jar
3. yam Yy	4. yawn Yy	5. vest
6. buttons	7. yellow Yy	8. yard Yy

Say the name of each picture. • If the name begins with the same sound as *yo-yo*, write *Yy* on the line.

Introduce Initial /y/*Yy* 125

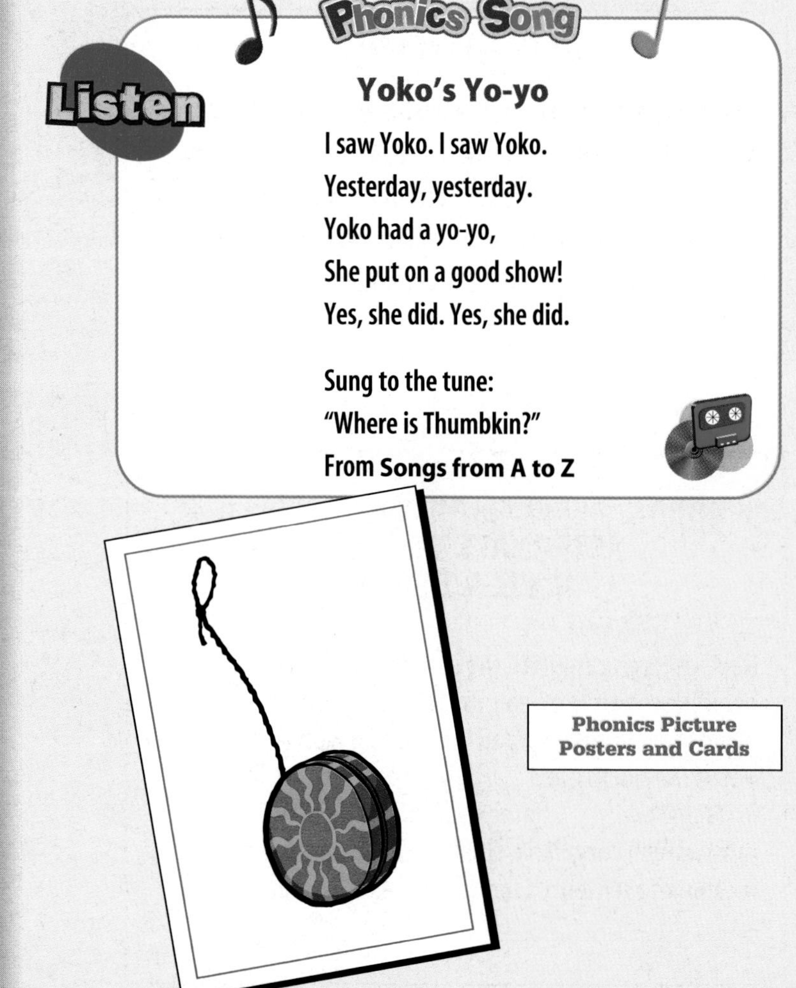

Phonics Song
Listen
Yoko's Yo-yo
I saw Yoko. I saw Yoko.
Yesterday, yesterday.
Yoko had a yo-yo,
She put on a good show!
Yes, she did. Yes, she did.
Sung to the tune:
"Where is Thumbkin?"
From Songs from A to Z

Phonics Picture Posters and Cards

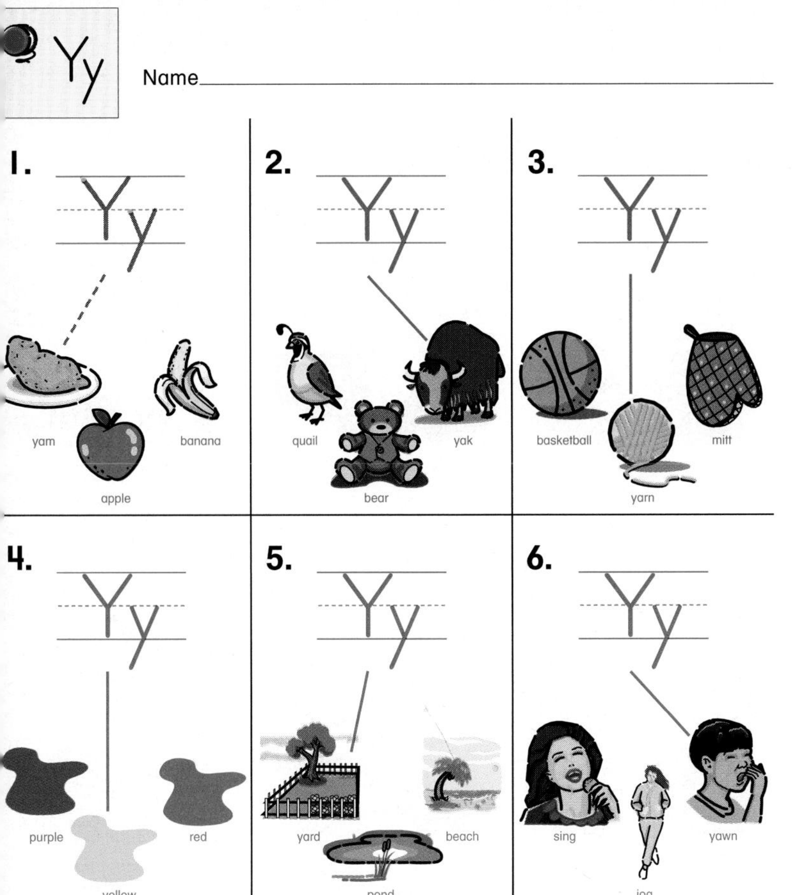

Review

Initial /y/*Yy*

TESTED OBJECTIVES

Children will identify initial /y/*Yy*.

PREPARE

PHONOLOGICAL AWARENESS Write the words *yesterday*, *yam*, and *year* on the chalkboard. Then say the words aloud in random order, having children clap out the syllables in each. Tell children that words with more syllables are usually longer when written out than words with less syllables. Invite children to use this information to point to the word which they think is *yesterday*.

Listen

Say the following pairs of words and ask children to nod *yes* if both words begin with /y/: *yo-yo, yum*; *yes, yell*; *yam, pig*; *yet, wall*; *yarn, year*. Phonemic Awareness

TEACH

IDENTIFY INITIAL /y/*Yy* Write *Yy* and the Phonics Song *Yoko's Yo-Yo* from page 125 on chart paper. Remind children that the letters *Yy* stand for the sound /y/. Invite volunteers to circle *Yy* when it appears at the beginning of a word while the class says /y/. Reread the rhyme aloud and have children read the words beginning with /y/*Yy* with you.

PRACTICE

COMPLETE THE PUPIL PAGE Read the directions aloud and help children identify the pictures. After completing the first item together, have children work independently.

ASSESS/CLOSE

IDENTIFY AND USE INITIAL /y/*Yy* Use page 126 to assess children's progress with initial /y/*Yy*. Have children name a color that begins with /y/*Yy*. (yellow)

LANGUAGE SUPPORT

ESL Children from other cultures may be unfamiliar with some of the items pictured on pages 125 and 126, such as yo-yo, yak, and yam. If possible, show children a yo-yo and explain that it's a toy; show them a yam and explain that it's a vegetable. Explain that a yak is a very large animal.

ALTERNATE TEACHING STRATEGY

Play a version of "Musical Chairs" with children. Arrange chairs in a row, one chair per child. Say a list of words, some of which begin with /y/. Have children walk around the chairs until they hear a word that begins with /y/. When they hear a *y* word, they have to find a seat.

▶ Musical/Auditory

Review

/j/j, /y/y

Children will identify /j/j and /y/y in words.

PREPARE

PHONOLOGICAL AWARENESS Say the following sentence and have children clap and count the number of syllables: *A young yellow yak juggled yams, jelly, and jam.*

Read these sentences aloud and have children blend the sounds together to answer your questions: */J/ /i/ /m/ won the race. Who won the race?* (Jim) *I heard the puppy /y/ /i/ /p/. What did the puppy do?* (yip) *Phonemic Awareness*

TEACH

REVIEW /j/j, /y/y Distribute the *j* and *y* letter cards from the Word Building Manipulative Cards. Then draw three letter boxes on the chalkboard and say the word *yet.* Ask children whether they hear /j/ or /y/ in this word. Have children hold up the letter that stands for the sound /y/. Invite a volunteer place the *y* letter card in a box to show where he or she hears the sound—at the beginning, in the middle, or at the end of the word. Repeat with other words, for example: *yes, job, jet.*

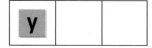

PRACTICE

COMPLETE THE PUPIL PAGE Read the directions aloud and guide children through each step.

ASSESS/CLOSE

IDENTIFY AND USE /j/j, /y/y Use page 127 to assess children's progress with /j/j, /y/y. Have children draw a picture of an item that begins with /j/ or /y/ and label it with *j* or *y.*

Name________________

1. y — elephant, yak
2. j — jeep, motorcycle
3. y — yam, watermelon
4. j — gate, jug
5. j — jacket, kite
6. y — card, yarn

Trace the letter. • Say the sound it stands for. • Say the names of the pictures. • Draw a line from the letter to the picture whose name has the same sound as the letter.

Review /j/j, /y/y 127

ame

j u g jug

h o p hop

k i ck kick

j e t jet

y a m yam

McGraw-Hill School Division

irst, blend the sounds and say the word. • Next, write the word. • Last, draw a rcle around the picture that goes with the word.

28 Blending with Short *a, i, o, u,* and *e*

Blending with Short *a, i, o, u, e*

TESTED OBJECTIVES

Children will blend and read short *a, i, o, u,* and *e* CVC words.

PREPARE

Display the *a, e, g, i, j, o, p, y, ck, d* letter cards from the Word Building Manipulative Cards. As you say the sound for each of these letters, have volunteers remove the appropriate card.

TEACH

MODEL AND GUIDE PRACTICE Place the *i* letter card on the chalkboard ledge and say /i/. Have children say /i/.

- Place the *g* letter card next to the *i* letter card.
- Blend the sounds /i/ and /g/ together and have children repeat the sounds after you.
- Place the *j* letter card before the *i* letter card.
- Blend the sounds /j/, /i/, /g/ together to read *jig*. Have children repeat the word *jig* after you.

USE THE WORD IN CONTEXT Use *jig* in a sentence to reinforce its meaning, for example: *Can you dance a jig?*

REPEAT THE PROCEDURE Use the following words to continue modeling and guided practice: *peg, jog, Jack, yap, duck.*

PRACTICE

COMPLETE THE PUPIL PAGE Read the directions aloud and encourage children to blend the sounds and say each word. Help children name the pictures.

ASSESS/CLOSE

BLEND AND READ WORDS Use page 128 to assess children's skill in blending with short a, i, o, u, and e.

ALTERNATE TEACHING STRATEGY

Write these words on the chalkboard: *jig, jog, yip, yum*. Have children blend sounds of the letters together to read each word aloud. Then provide context for these words by using them in sentences and using pantomime and sound effects. Have children act out the words as you point to them in random order.

▶ **Linguistic/Kinesthetic**

Read the Story

OBJECTIVES

Children will use their knowledge of phonics and decoding and high-frequency words to read.

Jack was a big red fox.

2

Van was a quick duck.

3

BEFORE READING

PREVIEW Have children look at the cover of *Van Can Win*. Invite volunteers to tell what is happening on the cover. Read the title aloud and talk about what the title means. Invite children to take a **picture walk** through pages 2 and 3 and tell what is happening. Write the high-frequency words (I, was, have, of, said) on the chalkboard and read them aloud to the children. Invite children to find the high-frequency words in the story.

MAKE PREDICTIONS Have children use the pictures to predict what and who the story is about. What do children think will happen? Write their predictions on the chalkboard.

Van can run and run.

4

Jack said, "We have fun."

5

DURING READING

READING SUGGESTIONS Point out the quotation marks on page 5. Remind children that quotation marks show the words a character is saying. Encourage the children to look through the story to find other pages where quotation marks are used. If necessary, remind the children to continue tracking what they read with their finger.

TEACHING TIP

MANAGEMENT Help children put together their own take-home story. Give the following directions to the children. Demonstrate as needed.

To put book together,
Tear out the story page.
Cut along the dotted line.
Fold each section on the fold line.

Van said, "A lot of fun!"

6

Van said, "I can win!"

7

"If you do not run, I can win!"

8

CENTER Activity

Cross Curricular: Language Arts/Art

WRITE AN ENDING Have children work in pairs to extend the story. Have children draw a picture and write a description of what happens after Jack the fox realizes he has been double-crossed. Encourage children to consider many different possible endings to the story before they begin their picture and caption. Display children's completed pictures as a mural in the center.

▶ **Linguistic/Visual**

Read the Story

AFTER READING

RETURN TO PREDICTIONS Encourage children to discuss whether their predictions matched what happened in the story. Talk about whether or not the story ended as children thought it would.

RETELL THE STORY Invite the children to retell the story in their own words. Encourage children to use the illustrations to help them.

STORY QUESTIONS Ask the following questions about the story.

- *What is Jack the fox doing when Van says he can win and starts running?* (tying his shoes) *Literal/Story Details*
- *Why does Van start running before Jack is ready?* (Because he wants to win.) ***Inferential/Cause and Effect***
- *What can Jack do to make sure Van doesn't start early the next time?* (Answers vary.) *Critical/Make Inferences*

Introduce

Numbers

Children will identify numbers from 1 to 5.

PREPARE

INTRODUCE NUMBERS Tell children numbers can be found everywhere, such as on a classroom door or a building. Discuss with children other places where numbers can be found, such as on telephones, food packages, rulers, etc. Ask children if they know their telephone numbers or their street address. Then tell children they will learn about the numbers 1-5 today.

TEACH

IDENTIFY NUMBERS Draw one circle on the board and tell children that it is a picture of one circle. Write the number 1 on the board. Read the number and have children repeat after you. Repeat with numbers 2 through 5.

PRACTICE

COMPLETE THE PUPIL PAGE Before children begin, read the directions aloud. Guide children to count the number of counters they see and draw that number of circles in the spaces provided. Tell children to write the number on the line.

ASSESS/CLOSE

REVIEW THE PAGE Use page 131 to assess children's ability to recognize numbers from 1 to 5 and to count quantities from 1 to 5. Say a number from 1 to 5. Have children draw that number of circles and write the number.

Name____________________

1. 3

2. 1

3. 5

4. 4

5. 2

Count the number of counters. • Then draw the same number of counters in the boxes. • Write the number.

Beginning Reading Concepts: *Numbers* 131

ALTERNATE TEACHING STRATEGY

ESL APPROPRIATE Give each child five craft sticks and 15 dried beans. Have them glue one bean on the first stick. Repeat process with two, three, four, and five beans. After the sticks dry, announce a number. Have children hold up the corresponding stick and say the number.

▶ **Kinesthetic/Auditory**

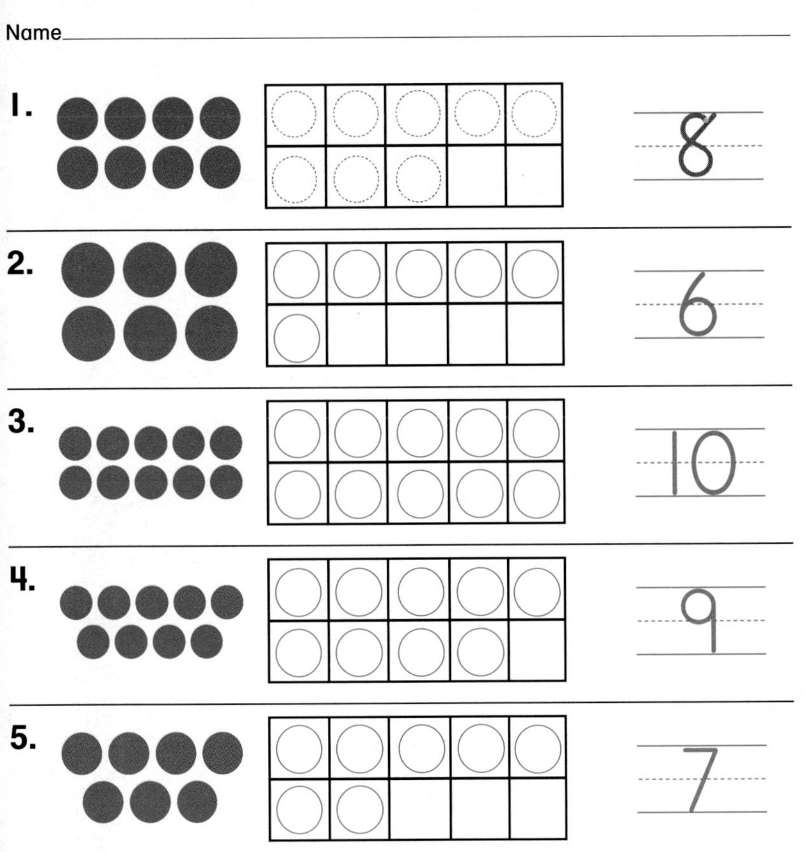

Name____________________

1. 8

2. 6

3. 10

4. 9

5. 7

Count the number of counters. • Then draw the same number of counters in the boxes. • Write the number.

McGraw-Hill School Division

132 Beginning Reading Concepts: *Numbers*

Introduce

Numbers

Children will identify numbers from 6 to 10.

PREPARE

REVIEW NUMBERS 1-5 Hold up cards for number 1-5, one at a time. Have children say the number and hold up the same number of fingers. Tell children they will learn the numbers 6-10 today.

TEACH

IDENTIFY NUMBERS 6-10 Invite six volunteers to stand before the class. Invite children to count the number of volunteers with you. Write the number on the board. Ask another volunteer to join the group. Count the children again, and write the number. Repeat until there are ten volunteers in the group.

Draw six circles on the board and count them. Have children repeat after you. Write the number 6 on the board. Read the number and ask children to repeat after you. Repeat with numbers 7 through 10.

PRACTICE

COMPLETE THE PUPIL PAGE Before children begin, read the directions aloud. Remind children to count the number of counters they see and draw that number of circles in the spaces provided. Tell children to write the number on the line beside the circles.

ASSESS/CLOSE

REVIEW THE PAGE Use page 132 to assess children's ability to recognize numbers from 6 to 10. Say a number from 6 to 10. Have children draw the corresponding number of circles and write the number.

ALTERNATE TEACHING STRATEGY

ESL APPROPRIATE Give each child five brown construction paper circles. Tell children to draw six "chocolate chips" on one "cookie." Have them repeat the process with seven, eight, nine, and ten "chocolate chips." Announce a number and have children hold up the corresponding "cookie" circle.

▶ Spatial/Visual

Develop

Phonological Awareness

Blend Onsets and Rimes

Teach After reading the poem, tell children the sounds /f/ and /un/ make the word *fun*. Then say: /b/ and /un/ make *bun*. Have children repeat the sounds and word with you.

Practice Call several children to the front of the room and privately assign each a beginning sound. Then choose a child to be a rime, such as /an/. This child stands next to the first child and they say their sounds and then blend their word. For example: /r/-/an/: *ran*. Repeat with different pairs of children and the words *pan, hat, wet, pet, pin*.

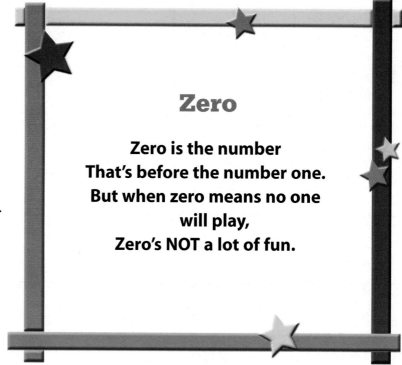

Zero

Zero is the number
That's before the number one.
But when zero means no one
will play,
Zero's NOT a lot of fun.

Identify Beginning Sounds

Phonemic Awareness

MATERIALS

- **Phonics Picture Poster** *zebra*

Teach Display the Phonics Picture Poster for *zebra*. Tell children the word zebra begins with the /z/ sound. Ask: *"What number word begins with /z/?"* (zero). Have children say the beginning sound in the following words: *water, zither, summer, yellow, jibberish, zillion, zoo, zigzag*.

Practice Play *"Zip Your Lip."* A volunteer says a word that may or may not begin with /z/. If the word begins with something other than /z/, the class gives that beginning sound. If the word begins with /z/, the class responds, *"Zip Your Lip"*; then another child takes a turn.

Blend Sounds

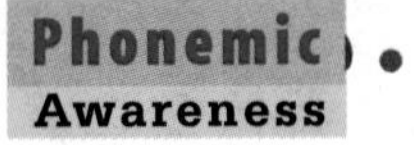

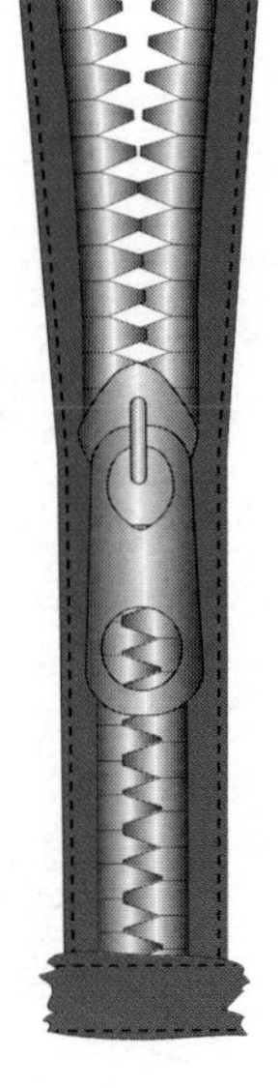

Teach Recall with children how to put sounds together to say words: /z/-/i/-/p/, *zip*; /v/-/a/-/n/, *van*. Lead children to blend the following words with you: *bag, dim, hot, jug, web*.

Practice Have children stand in groups of three and number themselves. Whisper a sound in each child's ear. For example : child # 1 is /z/, # 2 is /i/, # 3 is /p/. Children say the sounds in order and then all three say the word aloud: *zip*. Continue with other children and the following words: *zoom, zig, yes, jam, zap, Jack, joke*.

Segment Sounds

Phonemic Awareness

MATERIALS
- Word Building Boxes from Word Building Manipulative Cards
- Counters

Teach Display the Word Building Boxes with three sections. Say the word *web* and count and say the individual sounds: *web: first sound* /w/, *second sound* /e/, *third sound* /b/. *The word web has three sounds.* Then tell children you will put a counter in the box that shows the /b/ sound. Place a counter in the third box. Then repeat the sounds /w/-/e/-/b/ as you point to each box.

Practice Distribute one copy of the Word Building Boxes and one counter to each pair of children. Give a word and have pairs work together to say the separate sounds and count them. Ask: *How many sounds in the word? Where do you hear the ___ sound?"* Use the following two- and three-sound words: *at, zip, yes, by, up, zoom, sock, zig, quit, zoo*.

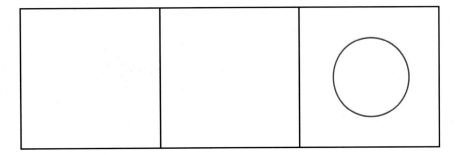

Introduce

Initial /z/Zz

Children will identify initial /z/*Zz* and form the letters *Zz*.

PREPARE

PHONOLOGICAL AWARENESS Say the following pairs of words and have children clap the number of syllables in each word and say which word is longer: *zero/zip; zoo/zebra; zig/zipper, Zachary/Zoe*.

As you sing the song "Zack's Zebra," hold up the Phonics Picture Poster for *zebra*. Have the children clap each time they hear the /z/ sound at the beginning of a word. *Phonemic Awareness*

TEACH

IDENTIFY INITIAL /z/Zz Distribute the *Zz* letter card from the Word Building Manipulative Cards. Tell children that the letters *Zz* stand for /z/. Have children point to their cards and say /z/. Draw a grid with 9 boxes and write a word in each box: *zero, zip, go, zoo, hot, zebra, nest, zipper, egg*. Place the grid on a table and read the words aloud. Have volunteers put the *Zz* letter cards on words with initial /z/*Zz*.

FORM *Zz* Some children may need to review how to write *Z* and *z*. Have children trace *Zz* using the Handwriting Models in the back of the Pupil's Edition.

PRACTICE

COMPLETE THE PUPIL PAGE Read the directions aloud and identify the pictures with children.

ASSESS/CLOSE

IDENTIFY AND USE INITIAL /z/Zz Use page 133 to assess children's recognition of initial /z/*Zz*.

Name________________

Zz

1. zero — Zz
2. horse

3. zipper — Zz
4. ruler

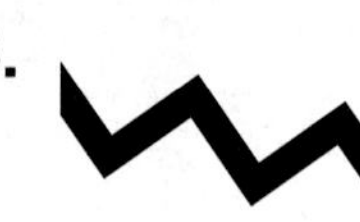

5. zigzag — Zz

6. zip — Zz
7. zoo — Zz

8. train

Say the name of each picture. • If the name begins with the same sound as *zebra*, write *Zz* on the line.

Introduce Initial /z/*Zz* 133

Listen

Phonics Song

Zack's Zebra

Zack's toy zebra zoomed past me,
Did you see? Did you see?
Zack's toy zebra zoomed past me,
What a zebra!

Sung to the tune:
"London Bridge"
From **Songs from A to Z**

Phonics Picture Posters and Cards

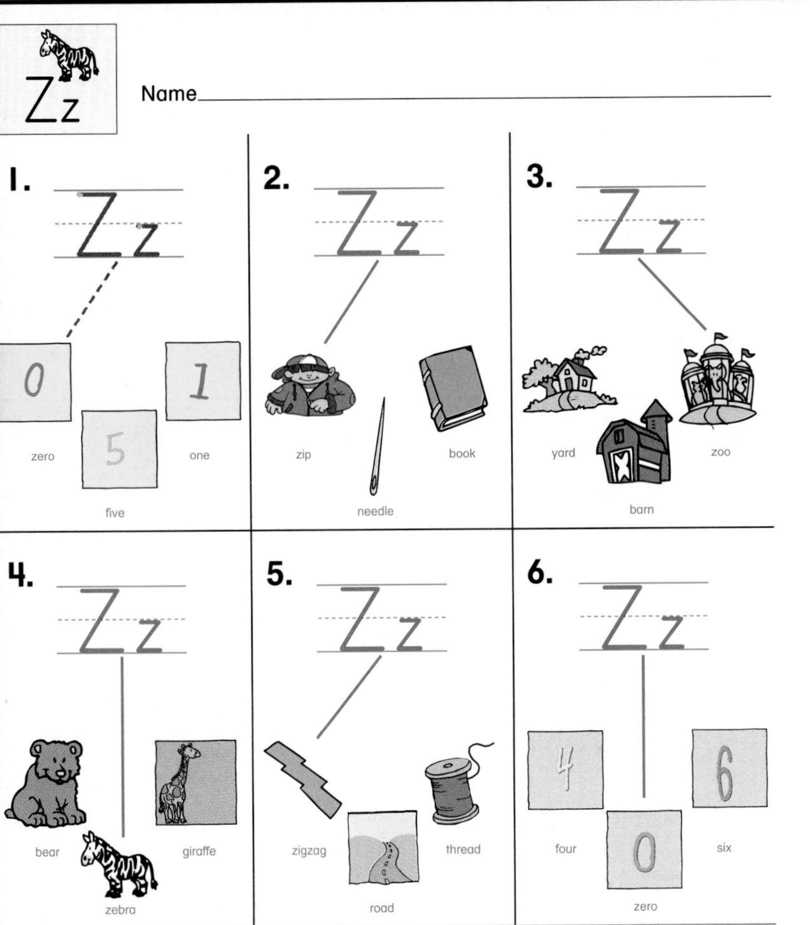
Zz Name________________

1. Zz — zero, five, one
2. Zz — zip, needle, book
3. Zz — yard, barn, zoo
4. Zz — bear, zebra, giraffe
5. Zz — zigzag, road, thread
6. Zz — four, zero, six

Write the letters *Zz*. • Say the name of each picture. • Draw a line from *Zz* to each picture whose name has the same beginning sound as *zebra*.

McGraw-Hill School Division

134 Review Initial /z/Zz

Review

Initial /z/Zz

Children will identify initial /z/Zz.

PREPARE

PHONOLOGICAL AWARENESS Tell children the words *zoo* and *shoe* rhyme because they have the same ending sound. Have volunteers say other words that rhyme with *zoo* such as: *two, you, blue, new, view, do* and so on.

Review singing the song "Zack's Zebra," while holding up the Phonics Picture Poster for *zebra*. Have children whisper the word *zip* when they hear a word beginning with the /z/ sound. *Phonemic Awareness*

TEACH

IDENTIFY INITIAL /z/Zz Write *Zz* on the chalkboard and draw a large zigzag line under it. Review that the letters *Zz* stand for /z/. Write *zero* on a part of the line and ask children what sound it begins with. Have children suggest other words that begin with /z/Zz. Add their suggestions to the line and have volunteers circle the letters *Zz* and say /z/.

PRACTICE

COMPLETE THE PUPIL PAGE Help children with the directions, pictures, and first item. Encourage children to complete the page on their own.

ASSESS/CLOSE

IDENTIFY AND USE INITIAL /z/Zz Use page 134 to assess children's progress with initial /z/Zz. Ask children to name an animal whose name begins with /z/. Have them write the letter that stands for /z/.

TEACHING TIP

INSTRUCTIONAL Have children make tactile letters by gluing beans or dried pasta on index cards with the letters *Zz* written on them. Then have the children trace the letter *Zz* when they hear /z/ as you say the following list of words: *zoo, dog, zipper, sat, night, zebra.*

ALTERNATE TEACHING STRATEGY

Create a zigzag path on the floor with masking tape. Have children, in turn, walk down the path when they supply a word that begins with *z*. You may wish to brainstorm a list of words with children prior to the activity.

▶ **Linguistic/Kinesthetic**

Review

Sound/Symbol Relationships

OBJECTIVES

Children will identify /y/y, /a/a, /d/d, /k/k, /s/s, /i/i, /t/t, /k/c, /f/f, /e/e, and /o/o in words .

PREPARE

PHONOLOGICAL AWARENESS Say *cat* and *hid* and encourage children to name words that rhyme with each word.

Then say the following sentences and ask children to raise a hand when they hear a word with the sound you say:

initial /y/ *Do you want to go to the park?*
initial /k/ *I have a new kite.*
initial /s/ *My sister will help me fly it.*

Phonemic Awareness

TEACH

REVIEW SOUND/SYMBOL RELATIONSHIPS Distribute the *e, o, y, a, d, k, s, i, t, c, f* letter cards from the Word Building Manipulative Cards. Say the following words and have children identify the beginning and ending sounds: *fit, dot, kit, cat, yet, sad*. For each word, have one volunteer hold up the letter card that stands for the beginning sound. Have another volunteer hold up the letter card that stands for the ending sound. Have children say the words with you as you point to the beginning and ending sounds.

PRACTICE

COMPLETE THE PUPIL PAGE Before children begin, read the directions aloud. Complete the page with children.

ASSESS/CLOSE

IDENTIFY AND USE *y, a, d, k, s, i, t, c, f, e, o* Use page 135 to assess children's progress.

Name____________________

1. yard — y __ d	**2.** ax — a __ x
3. cot — c __ t	**4.** fan — f __ n
5. soap — s __ p	**6.** map — m __ p

Say the picture name. • Write the letters that stand for the beginning and ending sounds in each picture name.

Name________________________________

1. | b | u | g |

2. | l | i | p |

3. | r | o | ck |

4. | t | u | b |

Say the picture name. • Write the letters that stand for the beginning, middle and ending sounds in the boxes. • Then read the word.

136 Phonics Review

LANGUAGE SUPPORT

Display the letter cards *o*, *r*, *u*, *g*, *p*, *m*, *ck*, *g* and *b* on the chalkboard ledge. Then write the word ending *ug* on an index card. As you say each of the following words, have children pick and place the letter that stands for the beginning sound in front of *ug*: *rug*, *mug*, *pug*, *bug*. Point to each letter as the children read the words with you.

Review

Sound/Symbol Relationships

Children will identify /o/*o*, /r/*r*, /u/*u*, /p/*p*, /m/*m*, /k/*ck*, /g/*g*, and /b/*b* in words.

PREPARE

PHONOLOGICAL AWARENESS Say the following words and encourage children to name words that rhyme with them: *rug*, *pop*.

Say the following sentences and have children blend the sounds together to answer your questions:
/B/ /o/ /b/ told a story. Who told a story? (Bob)
Pam found a red /r/ /o/ /k/. What did Pam find? (a rock)
The /m/ /o/ /p/ is wet. What is wet? (the mop)

Phonemic Awareness

TEACH

REVIEW SOUND/SYMBOL RELATIONSHIPS Draw three letter boxes on the chalkboard and distribute the *o*, *r*, *u*, *p*, *m*, *ck*, *g*, *b* letter cards. Say the following words and have children identify the beginning, middle, and ending sounds. Ask children to hold up the letter that stands for each sound. Invite volunteers to place letter cards in the correct boxes to show where they hear the sound. Say: *mop*, *gum*, *rob*, *mug*, *buck*, *rock*.

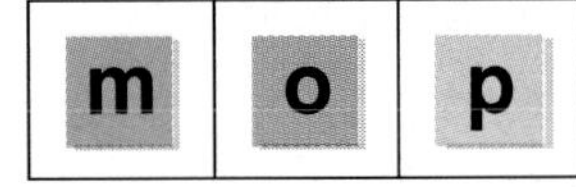

PRACTICE

COMPLETE THE PUPIL PAGE Read the directions aloud. Complete the page with children.

ASSESS/CLOSE

IDENTIFY AND USE *o*, *r*, *u*, *p*, *m*, *ck*, *g*, *b* Use page 136 to assess children's progress.

Review

Sound/Symbol Relationships

Children will identify /e/e, /w/w, /v/v, /ks/x, /kw/qu, /j/j, /n/n, /z/z, /o/o, /a/a, and /i/i in words .

PREPARE

PHONOLOGICAL AWARENESS Read this sentence aloud: *At the zoo, I saw an elephant, a fox, a zebra, and a quail.* Ask: *Which words name animals?*

Say the following sentences and have children blend the sounds together to answer your questions:

/J/ /e/ /n/ drew a picture. Who drew a picture? (Jen)
/T/ /e/ /ks/ is a rancher. Who is a rancher? (Tex)
Max hopes to /w/ /i/ /n/. What does Max hope to do? (win)

Phonemic Awareness

TEACH

REVIEW SOUND/SYMBOL RELATIONSHIPS Distribute the *a, o, i, t, g, f, e, w, v, x, qu, j, n, z* letter cards and draw three letter boxes on the chalkboard. Say these words and ask children to hold up the letters that stand for the beginning, middle, and ending sounds: *vet, win, zag, Jan, quit, fox.* Invite volunteers to place letter cards in the boxes to show where they hear the sound.

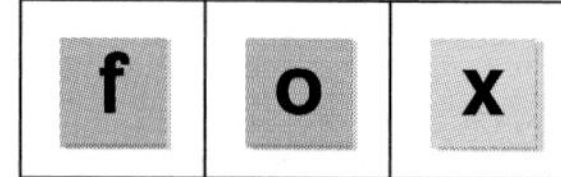

PRACTICE

COMPLETE THE PUPIL PAGE Before children begin, read the directions aloud. Complete the page with children.

ASSESS/CLOSE

IDENTIFY AND USE *e, w, v, x, qu, j, n, z, o, a, i* Use page 137 to assess children's progress.

Name

1. egg — e g
2. wax — w x
3. jet — j t
4. van — v n
5. zip — z p
6. queen — qu n

Say the picture name. • Write the letters that stand for the beginning and ending sounds in each picture name.

Phonics Review 137

Name

1. 
web
(e) a

w e b

2. 
fox
i (o)
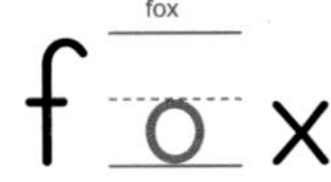
f o x

3. 
duck
o (u)

d u ck

4. 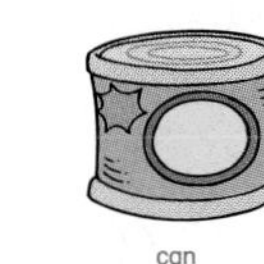
can
(a) i

c a n

5. 
six
e (i)
s i x

6. 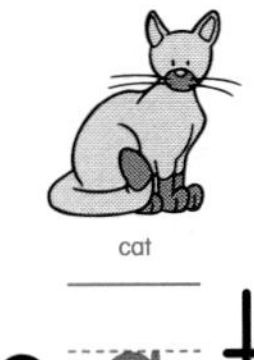
cat
(a) i
c a t

McGraw-Hill School Division

Say the picture name. • Circle the missing letter. • Then write the letter. Read the word.

138 Blending with Short *a, i, o, u,* and *e*

Blending with Short *a, i, o, u, e*

TESTED OBJECTIVES

Children will blend and read short *a, i, o, u* and *e* CVC words.

PREPARE

Write *a, i, o, u,* and *e* on the chalkboard. As you say each vowel sound, have volunteers circle the letter that stands for the sound.

TEACH

MODEL AND GUIDE PRACTICE Place the *a* letter card on the chalkboard ledge and say /a/. Have children say /a/.

- Place the *m* letter card next to the *a* letter card.
- Blend the sounds /a/ and /m/ together and have children repeat the word *am* after you.
- Place the *j* letter card before the *a* letter card.
- Blend the sounds /j/, /a/, /m/ together to read *jam*. Have children repeat the word *jam* after you.

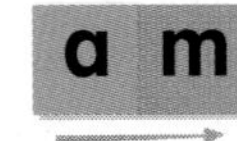
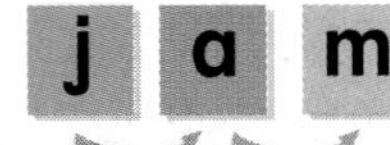

USE THE WORD IN CONTEXT Use *jam* in a sentence to reinforce its meaning, for example: *I like jam on toast.*

REPEAT THE PROCEDURE Use these words to continue modeling and guided practice: *kit, box, cup, led, sack.*

PRACTICE

COMPLETE THE PUPIL PAGE Read the directions aloud and help children name the pictures. Complete the page with children, guiding them to blend the sounds and say each word.

ASSESS/CLOSE

BLEND AND READ WORDS Use page 138 to assess children's progress.

ALTERNATE TEACHING STRATEGY

Have children repeat each short *a, e, i, o, u* word you write on the chalkboard, blending to read aloud such words as: *mix, jet, tick, quit, lap, sock, box, hum*. Invite volunteers to write their own short vowel words on the chalkboard for others to read aloud.

▶ **Linguistic/Auditory**

Introduce

High-Frequency Words: *she, my, me*

OBJECTIVES

Children will identify and read the high-frequency words *she, my,* and *me.*

PREPARE

LISTEN TO WORDS Read aloud the following sentences and have children listen for the words *she, my,* or *me.* Ask children to raise their right hand when they hear the words.

she, me—*She looks just like me.*
she, my—*She is my sister.*
she, me—*She is the same age as me.*
she, my—*She is my twin.*

TEACH

IDENTIFY THE WORDS Distribute High-Frequency Word Cards *she, my, me* from the back of the Pupil's Edition and write the words on the chalkboard. Read each word aloud and have children hold up the matching word card. Then arrange children in pairs and invite partners to play a matching game. When a child turns up matching words, he or she reads the word aloud and keeps the cards.

PRACTICE

COMPLETE THE PUPIL PAGE Read the directions aloud and remind children that they are to circle more than one word in each row.

ASSESS/CLOSE

REVIEW THE PAGE Use page 139 to assess children's recognition of the words *she, my,* and *me.* Have children write and illustrate a phrase using *she, my,* or *me.*

Name____________________

1.	me	she	(me)	my	(me)
2.	she	my	me	(she)	(she)
3.	my	me	(my)	she	(my)
4.	she	(she)	my	(she)	me
5.	my	(my)	me	she	(my)

Read the first word in each row. • Circle the words in the row that are the same.

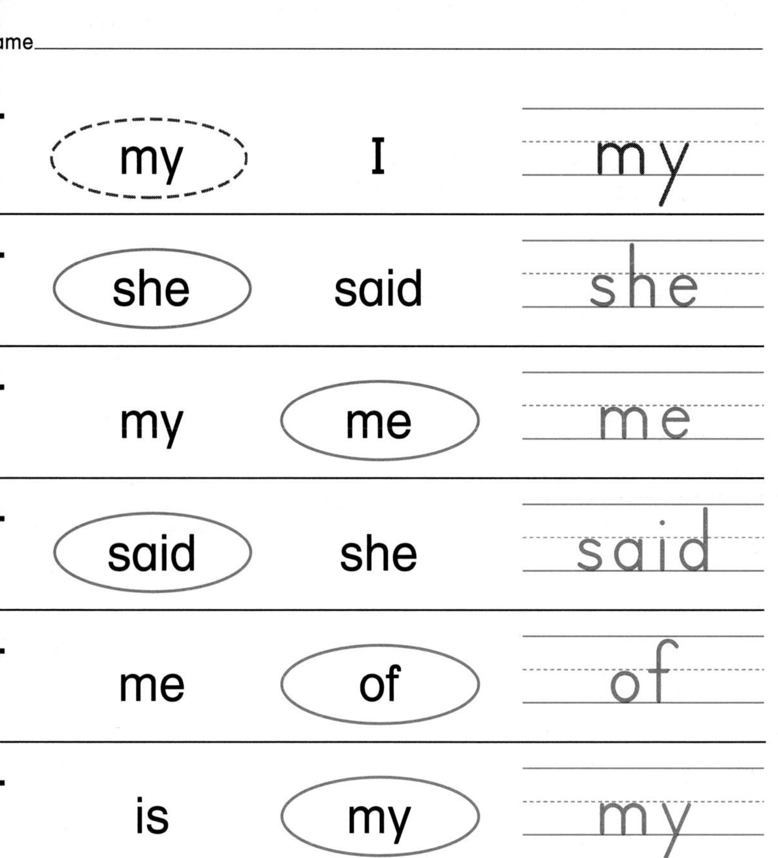

ame

.	my	I	my
.	she	said	she
.	my	me	me
.	said	she	said
.	me	of	of
.	is	my	my

sten to the word. • Circle the word you hear. • Then write the word.

McGraw-Hill School Division

40 Review High-Frequency Words

Review

High-Frequency Words

OBJECTIVES

Children will identify and read the high-frequency words *of, I, said, is, she, my,* and *me*.

PREPARE

LISTEN TO WORDS Slowly read aloud the following sentences. Ask children to tap with a pencil when they hear the words you name.

my, me—*My friend gave me a book.*

I, of—*I have a lot of books.*

she, said, is—*She said that is good.*

TEACH

IDENTIFY THE WORDS Have children work in small groups. Write the sentences from the Prepare section on several sheets of chart paper. Give each group the sentences and word cards. Display and read the sentences aloud, circling each high-frequency word. Invite volunteers to hold up matching word cards as you read. Then have group members take turns reading the high-frequency words and matching word cards to the sentences as you reread them.

PRACTICE

COMPLETE THE PUPIL PAGE Read the directions aloud. Tell children to listen to, circle, and write the words you say: (1) *my*; (2) *she*; (3) *me*; (4) *said*; (5) *of*; (6) *my*.

ASSESS/CLOSE

REVIEW THE PAGE Use page 140 to assess children's recognition of the words *of*, *I*, *said*, *is*, *she*, *my*, and *me*.

ALTERNATE TEACHING STRATEGY

Give each child a blank sentence strip. Assign a high-frequency word to each child. Then ask children to write a sentence using that word. Invite volunteers to show and read their sentences aloud. Have others point out the high-frequency word. Display children's sentences on a bulletin board.

▶ **Linguistic**

Develop

Phonological Awareness

Blend Onsets and Rimes

Teach Read the poem. Say the onset and rime for big: /b/-/ig/ and have children blend the sounds to say the word. Have children blend other beginning sounds with /ig/ to make rhyming words: /j/-/ig/; /w/-/ig/; /f/-/ig/.

Practice Have children sit in a circle. Say an onset and rime and blend them, such as /m/-/an/ *man*. Give a new onset. Children take turns blending the onsets and rime /an/, and make new words. Repeat with other ending sounds, such as _in, _up, _en.

A big brown hen and a yellow duck
Were talking yesterday.
But all I heard was "Yak! Yak! Yak!"
From the big brown hen and
the yellow duck.

Blend Sounds

Phonemic Awareness

MATERIALS

- Ruler

Teach Say the sounds /g/-/a/-/p/, elongating the sounds. Then shorten the sounds as you say them together: *gap*. Have children repeat the sounds and word with you: /g/-/a/-/p/: *gap*. Repeat blending sounds with the children for words such as: *bib*, *hack*, *lot*, *fed*, *tap*, *mom*.

Practice Divide children into three groups and have one child in each group stand. Use a ruler to 'conduct' the children as they blend a word. Assign beginning, middle, and ending sounds to the three children. Point to each to say the first, second, and third sounds separately. Increase the speed of the separate sounds until the children blend the word smoothly. Repeat with another child from each group and a new word.

Segment Sounds

Phonemic Awareness

MATERIALS

- Word Building Boxes from Word Building Manipulative Cards
- Counters

Teach Use the Word Building Boxes to point out the three sounds in the word /b/-/a/-/g/. Then ask: *what sound is last, what sound is first, what sound is in the middle?* As children respond to your questions, move a marker into the appropriate box. Say the sounds and blend them back into a word.

Practice Distribute Word Building Boxes and counters to each child. Say the following three-sound words: *sack, box, quit, zoom, yam, jog, hop, can*. Have children say the individual sounds in the word as they point to the boxes. Then ask children to place a counter in the box that shows either the beginning, middle, or ending sound.

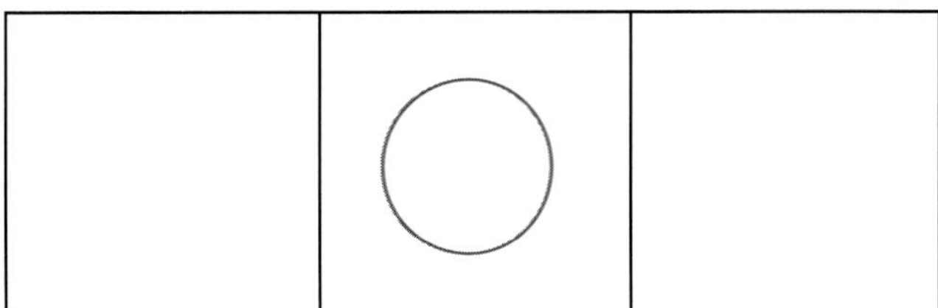

Substitute Sounds

Phonemic Awareness

MATERIALS

- Word Building Boxes from Word Building Cards
- counters

Teach Display a Word Building Box with three sections. Say these sounds: /k/-/a/-/p/, putting a counter in each box for each sound. Remove the first counter and say: *If I change the /k/ to /t/, what word do I have?* (tap) Continue to demonstrate substituting sounds in the beginning and ending position. Use these words: *box/fox; tan/tap; tag/bag; sat/bat; sick/sip; sock/rock*

Practice Call three children to stand at the front of the class. Assign each a sound such as /m/-/u/-/d/. Have the class say each sound in order and blend the word *mud*. Then assign a volunteer to replace the first child and say a new sound such as /b/. Have the new sounds repeated and blended: /b/-/u/-/d/, *bud*. Continue with other words.

Cumulative

Review

OBJECTIVES

Children will review sound/symbol relationships.

PREPARE

PHONOLOGICAL AWARENESS Say the words *do*, *you*, and *jet*. Ask a volunteer to say the two words that rhyme. Then have children name other words that rhyme with *do*.

Read aloud the following sentences and have children blend the sounds together to answer your questions:

A duck says /kw/ /a/ /k/. What does a duck say? (quack)
A cricket has /s/ /i/ /x/ legs. How many legs does a cricket have? (six)
The /j/ /e/ /t/ is noisy. What is noisy? (the jet)
I ate a baked /y/ /a/ /m/. What did I eat? (a yam)
The family rode in a /v/ /a/ /n/. What did the family ride in? (a van)

Phonemic Awareness

TEACH

REVIEW SOUND/SYMBOL RELATIONSHIPS Put the letter cards *d*, *j*, *qu*, *v*, *w*, *x*, *y* and *z* in a large jar or paper bag. Invite a volunteer to pick a letter out of the jar and say a word that begins or ends with that letter sound. Write each word on the chalkboard and have children read it aloud with you.

PRACTICE

COMPLETE THE PUPIL PAGE Read the directions aloud and help children identify the pictures. Complete the first item together and guide children through the page as needed.

ASSESS/CLOSE

IDENTIFY AND USE *d, j, qu, v, w, x, y, z* Use page 141 to assess children's progress. You may wish to say a word that begins with one of the letter sounds and have children say the name of the letter it begins with.

Name____________________

1. n — wagon — ____ n
2. t — towel — t ____
3. z — zoo — z ____
4. j — jeep — j ____
5. m — drum — ____ m
6. a — astronaut — a ____

Look at the letter. • Say each picture name. • Write the letter on the first line if you hear the sound for the letter at the beginning of the word. • Write the letter on the second line if you hear the sound at the end of the word.

Cumulative Review: Phonics 14

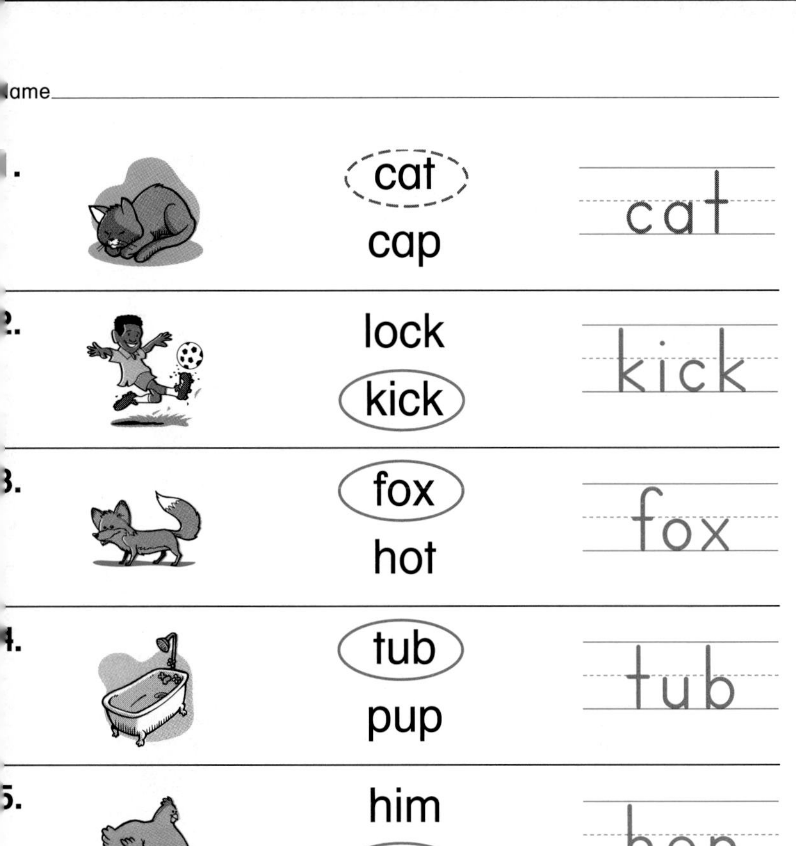
Name

1.	cat / cap	cat
2.	lock / kick	kick
3.	fox / hot	fox
4.	tub / pup	tub
5.	him / hen	hen

Read the words. • Circle the word that names the picture. • Then write the word.

Cumulative

Review

Children will review /k/c, *ck*; /h/h, /l/l, /m/m, /p/p, /t/t, /u/u; and read CVC words.

PREPARE

PHONOLOGICAL AWARENESS Say the following sets of words and have children identify the rhyming words in each set: *tack, ball, sack; ham, pat, Tam; up, hot, cot.*

Say each of the following sentences. Have children listen for the word with the sound in the initial, medial, or final position. Invite children to wave when they hear that sound.

initial /p/ *Jim wore black pants and a red shirt.*
final /k/ *Jack had a coat with many pockets.*
medial /u/ *Bud always wears white shoes.*

Phonemic Awareness

TEACH

PHONICS AND DECODING Write the words *luck, tap, cup, hut, mop, hat,* and *him* on index cards and place them in a hat. Invite volunteers to choose a word, display a card, and read the word aloud. If children have difficulty, use the letter cards from the Word Building Manipulative Cards to model blending.

PRACTICE

COMPLETE THE PUPIL PAGE Before children begin, read the directions aloud and help them identify the pictures. Complete the first item with children. Then have children finish the page on their own.

ASSESS/CLOSE

IDENTIFY AND USE *c, ck, h, l, m, p, t, u* Use page 142 to assess children's progress.

ALTERNATE TEACHING STRATEGY

Pair native English speakers with children learning English as a second language. Give each pair the letter cards *c, ck, h, l, m, p, t, u, a* and *b*. Have children build and read CVC words using the letter cards. Children can take turns writing down each new word. Then have pairs read the list of words they built.

▶ **Kinesthetic/Interpersonal**

Cumulative

Review

BJECTIVES

Children will review /a/a, /e/e, /o/o, /b/b, /f/f, /g/g, /n/n, /s/s, and read CVC words.

PREPARE

PHONOLOGICAL AWARENESS Say the following sets of words and have children identify the rhyming words: *big, ball, pig; win, fin, ham; sat, web, Jeb.*

Read aloud the following sentences and have children blend the sounds together to answer these questions:

/B/ /e/ /n/ bought some fruit. Who bought the fruit? (Ben)
He put it in a /b/ /a/ /g/. What did he put it in? (a bag)
Ben ate a /f/ /i/ /g/. What did Ben eat? (a fig)

Phonemic Awareness

TEACH

PHONICS AND DECODING Review the sounds these letters stand for: *a, e, i, o, b, f, g, n, s*. Tell children that you will say a word and then invite three volunteers to spell the word by placing the letter cards from the Word Building Manipulative Cards in correct order on the chalkboard ledge. For example, say *fan*, emphasizing the sound each letter stands for. Call on a child to choose the letter that stands for /f/ and place it on the chalkboard ledge. Call on another child to show the middle sound, and so on. Repeat with *beg, sob, tug, get, fin*.

PRACTICE

COMPLETE THE PUPIL PAGE Read the directions aloud and help children identify the pictures.

ASSESS/CLOSE

IDENTIFY AND USE *a, e, o, b, f, g, n, s* Use page 143 to assess children's progress.

Name__________

1. (u) a — s u n
2. (b) — b ed
3. j (g) — pi g
4. (o) a — s o ck
5. f (w) — w eb
6. (n) w — ca n

Say the picture name. • Circle the missing letter. • Then write the letter. • Read the word.

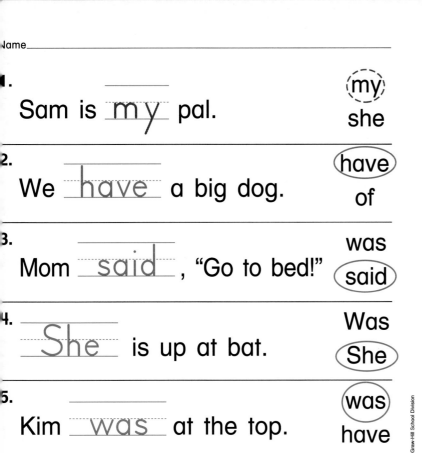

Name____________________

1. Sam is my pal. — (my) / she

2. We have a big dog. — (have) / of

3. Mom said, "Go to bed!" — was / (said)

4. She is up at bat. — Was / (She)

5. Kim was at the top. — (was) / have

Read the sentence. • Then circle the word that completes the sentence. • Write the word on the line.

144 Cumulative Review: High-Frequency Words

Cumulative
Review

OBJECTIVES

Children will identify and read the high-frequency words *my, she, have, of, was, said.*

PREPARE

LISTEN TO WORDS Read aloud each sentence and ask children to hold up a pencil when they hear the word you name.

my *Rosa is my little sister.*
of *Rosa drew a picture of me.*
said *I said that it looked just like me.*
was *Rosa was pleased that I liked it.*
she *She gave me the picture.*
have *Now I have the picture by my bed.*

TEACH

IDENTIFY THE WORDS Write *my, she, have, of, was,* and *said* on the chalkboard and read the words aloud. Reread the words, out of order, and invite volunteers to find and circle each word. Arrange children in pairs and distribute the High-Frequency Word Cards from the back of the Pupil's Edition to each pair. Write the sentences from the Prepare section on the chalkboard and read them aloud. Have children hold up each word card when they hear the circled word in the sentences read aloud.

PRACTICE

COMPLETE THE PUPIL PAGE Read the directions aloud and complete the first item with children.

ASSESS/CLOSE

REVIEW THE PAGE Use page 144 to assess children's progress with the words *my, she, have, of, was, said.* You may also wish to have volunteers hold up a word card and say a sentence using that word.

LANGUAGE SUPPORT

Play a matching game with children. Provide two sets of high-frequency word cards. Mix up the cards and place them face down in rows on a table. Each child then turns over two cards. If they match, the child says the word, uses it in a sentence, and then keeps the cards. If the cards do not match, they are turned face down again and the next child takes a turn.

Cumulative

Review

Children will identify and read the high-frequency words *you, and, is, has, are, we, the, that.*

PREPARE

LISTEN TO WORDS Read aloud the following sentences and have children tap a foot when they hear the words you name.

you *Have you ever seen a kangaroo?*
and, the *My dad and I saw kangaroos at the zoo.*
has *A kangaroo has long back legs.*
are *Its back legs are good for jumping.*
we *We saw a baby kangaroo.*
is *A baby kangaroo is called a joey.*
that *That baby was really small.*

TEACH

IDENTIFY THE WORDS Write the words *you, and, is, has, are, we, the* and *that* across the chalkboard. Leave enough space under them for word cards. Display the High-Frequency Word Cards from the back of the Pupil's Edition along the chalkboard ledge. Read each word aloud and have volunteers place the correct word card under each word printed on the chalkboard. Write the sentences from the Prepare section and read them aloud. Name each high-frequency word and invite children to circle it in the sentences.

PRACTICE

COMPLETE THE PUPIL PAGE Before children begin, read the directions aloud and complete the first item together.

ASSESS/CLOSE

REVIEW THE PAGE Use page 145 to assess children's progress with the words *you, has, and, is, has, are, we, the, that.*

Name ________

1. Can you fix it? — (you) / has
2. Sid and Tam are wet. — was / (and)
3. Pam has a red hat. — is / (has)
4. We can go! — Are / (We)
5. That is a big cat! — The / (That)

Read the sentence. • Then circle the word that finishes the sentence. • Write the word on the line.

Name

1. I have a pet. — (I) he

2. Pop said we can go. — (go) a

3. Can I run with you? — go (with)

4. He can pack the box. — (He) Go

5. The pig is in mud. — (is) to

Read the sentence. • Then circle the word that completes the sentence. • Write the word on the line.

ALTERNATE TEACHING STRATEGY

Display the word cards for the high-frequency words you wish to review. Hold up each card and have children read the word aloud. Then name a high-frequency word and invite a volunteer to use it in a sentence. Write the sentence on chart paper. When all the words have been used in sentences, cover each high-frequency word with a piece of paper. Then read a sentence with the children and invite a volunteer to choose the correct word card to complete it.

▶ **Linguistic/Logical**

Cumulative Review

TESTED OBJECTIVES

Children will identify and read the high-frequency words *I, he, go, a, with, is, to*.

PREPARE

LISTEN TO WORDS Slowly read each sentence aloud and have children clap when they hear the words you name.

I, to *I like to watch my brother play soccer.*
he, is, a *I think he is a good player.*
go, with *I go to games with my sister.*

TEACH

IDENTIFY THE WORDS Display the High-Frequency Word Cards from the back of the Pupil's Edition *I, he, go, a, with, is,* and *to* on the chalkboard ledge. Read each word aloud, out of order, and invite volunteers to point to the word card that names the word. Then write the sentences from the Prepare section on the chalkboard and distribute word cards to partners. As you read the sentences aloud, ask children to hold up word cards when they hear the circled words in the sentences.

PRACTICE

COMPLETE THE PUPIL PAGE After reading the directions aloud, complete the first item with children. Then have children finish the other items on their own.

ASSESS/CLOSE

REVIEW THE PAGE Use page 146 to assess children's progress with the words *I, he, go, a, with, is, to*. Challenge children to brainstorm an oral sentence containing *I, go,* and *with*.

Read the Story

Children will use their knowledge of phonics and decoding and high-frequency words to read.

I have a red bug.

2

My fun bug is Dot.

3

BEFORE READING

The Red Bug

PREVIEW Discuss with children what is happening in the picture on the cover and pages 2-4 of the story. Invite volunteers to read aloud the title, *The Red Bug*. Ask children to identify the red bug. Write the high-frequency words (*she*, *my*, *me*) on the chalkboard. Point to each one and read aloud. Invite children to search through the story for these high-frequency words.

MAKE PREDICTIONS Ask children to tell who this story is about. Encourage children to predict what these story characters will do. Record children's predictions on the chalkboard.

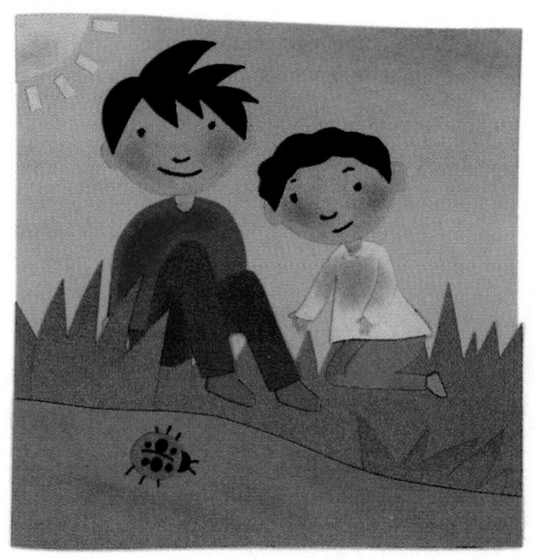

She can sit in the sun.

4

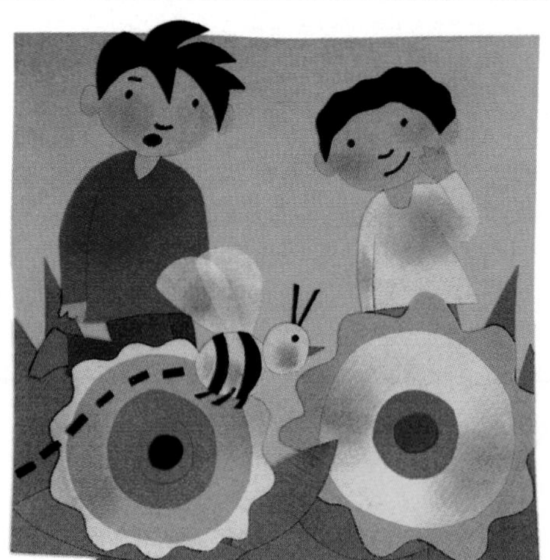

That big bug is Buzz.

5

DURING READING

READING SUGGESTIONS Remind children to use the pictures as they read to help them better understand what is happening. The pictures can also help read new words, such as *leg* on page 4. Invite children to find the exclamation points and quotation marks in the story. (page 6 and 7) Remind them of the meaning of these marks in a story. Have children track the print with a finger as they read.

TEACHING TIP

MANAGEMENT Help children put together their own take-home story. Give the following directions to the children. Demonstrate as needed.

To put the book together,
Tear out the story page.
Cut along the dotted line.
Fold each section on the fold line.

Big Buzz is not fun!

6

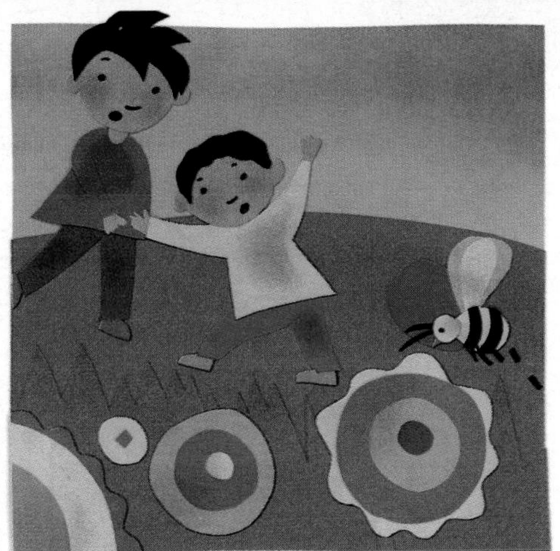

"Quick, Dan! Run to me!"

7

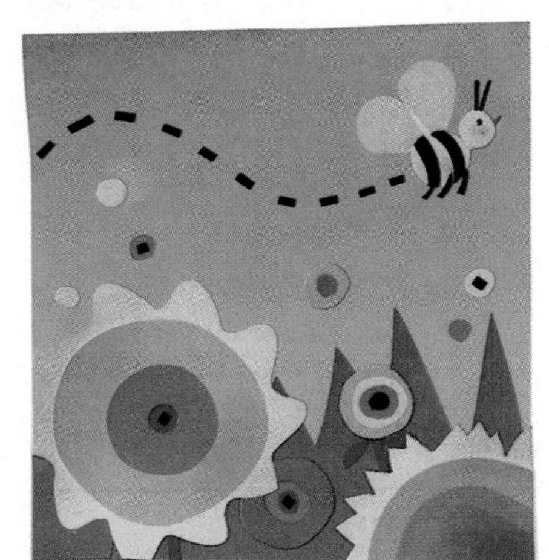

Buzz is not a fun bug.

8

Read the Story

AFTER READING

RETURN TO PREDICTIONS Read aloud the children's predictions from the chalkboard. Help children compare how close their predictions were to what actually happened in the story. Did children correctly predict the story's ending?

RETELL THE STORY Invite the children to retell the story in their own words. Encourage children to relate one sentence each about the beginning, middle and end of the story.

STORY QUESTIONS Ask the following questions about the story.

- *What is the ladybug crawling on in beginning of the story?* (on a leaf) ***Literal/Story Details***
- *Why does Zack want his brother, Dan to stay away from the big bug, Buzz?* (Because he is afraid Buzz will hurt Dan.) ***Inferential/Use Illustrations***
- *Why is it all right for the boys to be near a lady-bug?* (Because ladybugs do not harm people.) ***Critical Thinking/Make Inferences***

Cross Curricular: Language Arts

INTERVIEW THE CHARACTERS Arrange children in groups of four. Have group members role-play Zack, his Mom, and his brother, Dan, being interviewed by a TV reporter. Tell reporters to ask each character one question. Have children conduct their interviews in front of the class.

▶ **Auditory/Interpersonal**

Cumulative Review

OBJECTIVES

Children will identify colors, shapes, and left and right.

PREPARE

REVIEW COLORS, SHAPES AND LEFT-TO-RIGHT Review the colors and shapes by showing children *red*, *blue*, *yellow*, *orange*, *green*, and *purple* construction paper. Review a *circle*, *square*, *rectangle* and *triangle*, naming them as you draw them on the board. Tell children the circle is on the left and the triangle is on the right.

TEACH

INDENTIFY COLORS, SHAPES AND LEFT-TO-RIGHT Tell children that you will show them shapes that have different colors. In the top pocket of the pocket chart, place a blue square, yellow triangle, orange rectangle, green circle, and a purple square. Invite children to name in order the color and shape of each in the top pocket of the chart, beginning with the first shape to the left. Change the order of the shapes and repeat.

PRACTICE

COMPLETE THE PUPIL PAGE Before children begin, read the directions aloud. Help children name the pictures, emphasizing the color and shape where appropriate. Remind children to draw a line from each object to the place where it belongs.

ASSESS/CLOSE

REVIEW THE PAGE Use page 149 to assess children's recognition of colors and shapes and understanding of left-to-right. Have children name the color and shape of an object and the place where it belongs.

Name____________________

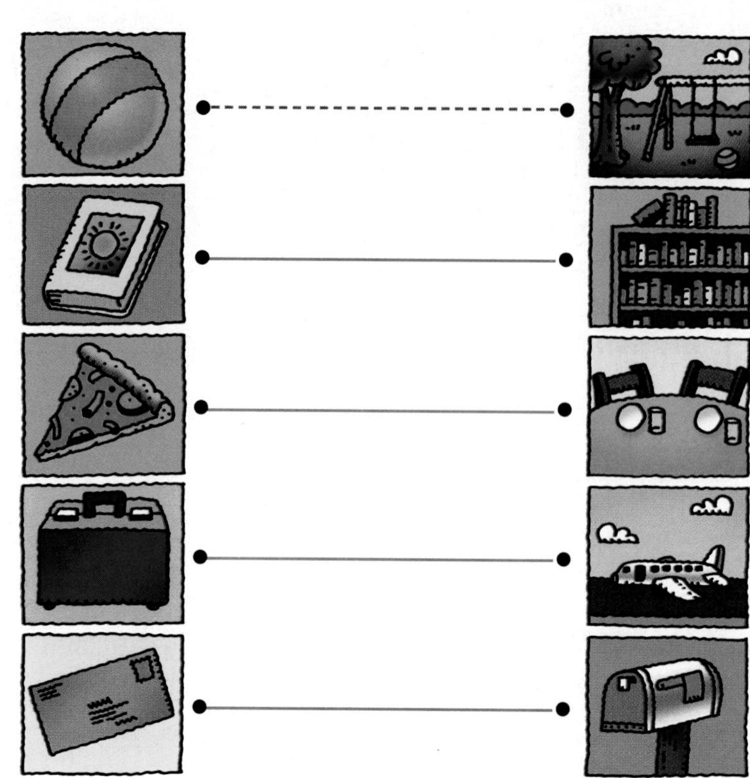

Name each color and shape. Draw a line from left to right to connect each object with the place it belongs.

Beginning Reading Concepts: *Cumulative Review* 149

TEACHING TIP

INSTRUCTIONAL Draw a *red circle*, *blue square*, *yellow triangle*, *orange rectangle*, *green circle*, and *purple square* in a column along the left side of a piece of chart paper. Then draw the same items in a different order on the right side. Invite a volunteer to draw a line from the shape on the left to the matching shape on the right and say the color and name of the shape. Repeat with the remaining shapes.

Name________________________________

Draw a line from top to bottom to connect each flower with a flower pot. Count the flowers. Circle the two groups of flowers that have the same number.

150 Beginning Reading Concepts: *Cumulative Review*

Cumulative Review

OBJECTIVES

Children will identify categories, numbers, and top to bottom.

PREPARE

REVIEW CATEGORIES, NUMBERS AND TOP-TO-BOTTOM Write the numbers 1 through 10 in a column on the board. Ask children to recite the numbers from top to bottom. Tell children that the numerals 1-10 can be put in the same group because they are all numbers.

TEACH

IDENTIFY CATEGORIES, NUMBERS AND TOP-TO-BOTTOM Draw three circles on the chalkboard. In the first circle, draw 4 hearts of different sizes. In the second circle draw 3 happy faces of different colors. In the third circle, draw 2 stars of different sizes. Tell children that you have put the shapes in categories or groups. Count how many objects are in each group then have children repeat after you. Write the number of object at the bottom of the chalkboard, below each group. Ask volunteers to draw a line from the circle of objects at the top and connect it to the number at the bottom.

PRACTICE

COMPLETE THE PUPIL PAGE Before children begin, read the directions aloud. Tell children to draw a line to connect each flower to the correct flowerpot below. Have children circle the two groups that have the same number of flowers.

ASSESS/CLOSE

REVIEW THE PAGE Use page 150 to assess children's ability to count, identify categories, and demonstrate top-to-bottom.

ALTERNATE TEACHING STRATEGY

ESL APPROPRIATE Give small groups of children some multicolored linking cubes. Invite children to sort the cubes by color and create separate-colored towers. Tell them to count the number of cubes in each tower, encouraging them to count from the top to the bottom.

▶ **Interpersonal/Kinesthetic**

Writing

Write messages from left-to-right and from top-to-bottom.

PREPARE

Discuss with children the different stories they have read. Which one was their favorite? Why?

TEACH

WRITE A CLASS MESSAGE Work with children to write a message about the decodable stories they have read. Brainstorm with children a list of things that they want to tell about the stories.

Ask each child to dictate one sentence about the stories. As you write each sentence, model:

- beginning on the left side of the paper.
- writing left-to-right, leaving a space between words.
- beginning a new line under the last line written to reinforce the concept of writing top-to-bottom.

Reread the message with children. Be sure to track each word you read, emphasizing the directionality left-to-right and top-to-bottom.

PRACTICE

COMPLETE THE PUPIL PAGE Have children write a message to a family member or friend. Remind children to write their message from left-to-right and from top-to-bottom.

ASSESS/CLOSE

REVIEW THE PAGE Review children's writing. Note their spelling of high-frequency words as well as decodable words they have learned in previous lessons.

Name ______________________________

Write a message to a friend or family member. • Remember to write from left-to-right and from top-to-bottom.

Name

Write a message to a friend or family member. • Remember to write from left-to-right and from top-to-bottom.

is

the

see

he

with

has

and

go

a

that

for

you

to

are

do

we

have

said

of

was

I

my

she

me